THE PRICE

THE PRICE

Nyla Chantry

VANTAGE PRESS
New York

FIRST EDITION

Copyright © 1998 by Nyla Chantry

Published by Vantage Press, Inc.
516 West 34th Street, New York, New York 10001

Manufactured in the United States of America
ISBN: 0-533-12662-2

Library of Congress Catalog Card No.: 97-91402

0 9 8 7 6 5 4 3 2 1

To my mother, Pearl Elizabeth Tooley Creviston, for her insight in writing and keeping a personal diary and poems. For her willingness to keep important documents, including letters, all of which helped me piece together this story based on the lives of my relatives, I thank her.

The Price

For every action there is an equal and opposite reaction, or so the scientist will say, but I propose another truth: with every deed there comes a price. This price can be positive or negative depending on the deed. When the price is positive and comes to you for a good deed, all who are around you share in the gifts of the payment, whether they be money, happiness, or even unnoticed blessings. But when the price is negative and you are the one required to pay for bad actions or decisions, all too often the ones you care about most are forced to pay with you, the innocent as well as the guilty. Sometimes this negative price is so great, the consequences so grievous, that one can only get through the pain by hanging onto the outstretched fingers of God and praying for his loving mercy.

For every action there is a reaction; with every deed there comes a price.

CONTENTS

PREFACE

The Price is part fiction. The medium of fiction was used so that the individual impact and the personal dimensions of this family could be explored. In another sense, this book is not fictional. It tells the real story of what happened to the main people of the story.

Using both fiction and actual facts presented some interesting challenges in the writing process. The fictional people and events are intermingled with the real people, places, dates, and events, so from time to time it is hard to tell what is history and what is not.

Sometimes fictional license had to be used in order to add dimension where little was known of the real facts. It is hoped that adding fiction to fact provided interest to the reader.

The character list at the beginning of this novel only includes the real people written about here; all others are fictional characters. It is the writer's desire that the living relatives of these people mentioned will not be offended by the style or description of characters written about in this book. Please accept the author's apology if anything offensive has been penned.

ACTUAL PEOPLE OF NOTE IN THIS NOVEL

(All other characters not listed are fictional.)

The Knowles Family

John Knowles (father)
Susan Knowles (mother)
Mabel Alice (daughter), born 1881
Claramead Myrtle (daughter),
    born 1885
Albert (son), born 1888
John Junior (son), born 1889
Clarence (adopted son of John)
Richard Martin

The Tooley Family

Obediah Anathias Tooley (father),
    born 1869
Claramead Myrtle Knowles Tooley
    (mother), born 1885
Pearl Elizabeth (daughter), born
    1905
Helen Agnes (daughter), born 1907
Roy Freeman (son), born 1909
Earl Eugene (son), born 1911

Lawmen

Sheriff Homer Remer
Judge Raymond Woods

The Broughtons

Nat Broughton, born 1869
Claramead Myrtle Knowles
    Tooley Broughton

Lewiston Children's Home

Samuel B. Chase
Mrs. Williams
Mr. and Mrs. Howland
Mr. and Mrs. Waters

Laura Waters
Miss Quiggley
Miss Savage
Hazel, Elizabeth, and Viola
Reverend Covington

Foster Families and Concerned Folk

Mrs. Sleighter (Roy)
John and Lottie Lewis (Earl and
    Helen)
Lyons family of Lewiston bank
    president (Helen)

Mrs. Bethmann (Helen)
Susan Jett (Pearl)
Katherine Wallace
Carrol, Lou, and Alice Lilly (Pearl)

Diary Entries

All people (as well as dates, places, and events) are real.

Utah People

Merlin Taylor
Herb Creviston
Fredrick Hoffman

Others

Marie Tooley
Harry Duncan Broughton
Stancy Broughton
W. J. Costello, attorney

Moscow, Idaho, People

Lyons Family (Pearl)

Otto and Helen Lyons (father and
  mother)
Adam, Joseph, Jacob, and Donald
  Morgan (four sons)

Mr. and Mrs. Creetmore (Pearl)

Yearout Family (Pearl)

Charles (father and preacher)
Lillie (mother and nurse)
Floyd (son)
Paul (son)

Lee Family (Pearl)

William Lee, attorney and judge
Madeline Lee (wife)
William (Billy, son)
Richard (son)
Mary Madeline (daughter)
Baby daughter
Miss Talbot (part-time child-care
  worker)
Mr. and Mrs. Thomas Shields
  (Madeline's Brother and his
  wife)
Mrs. Willis, daughter Belle, and
  baby Phyllis

Judge Forney
Mrs. Forney (sickly wife)
Mrs. Harrison (Mrs. Forney's
  mother)

Hylton Family

Uncle Hirum (father)
Aunt Belle (mother)
Ruby (daughter)
Jewel (son)

George Jensen
Doris Penwell
Ione Penwell
Mary Green

THE PRICE

YOUTH AND DREAMS

"Myrtle, come in now!" Mother shouted to the girl reading a book under the oak tree. "You need to do your chores and finish your school lessons before supper."

She was christened Claramead Myrtle Knowles, the second child of John and Susan Knowles. The first one, also a girl, was Mabel Alice, born four years before Claramead, in 1881. After Myrtle, two boys, Albert in 1888 and the next year John Junior in 1889, joined the family.

The fourteen-year-old girl obediently closed her book of poetry and pondered the tasks that lay ahead. Her thoughts went back to three years ago, when her job was to get up before the sun and help her mother or father with milking the two cows that provided milk, not only for the family but also to sell. It was nice in the summertime watching the sun spread its rays to light up the hills and meadows of Barron County, Wisconsin, where they lived. The winter, however, was a different story. When the ground was frozen all around and the air frigid cold the task of milking was unpleasant for both man and beast. The bags of the cows were always full. Chilled fingers grabbing already-cold udders could bring a reaction of flying buckets, stool and occupant being displaced into unfriendly parts of the milking stalls. Myrtle had been more than happy to relinquish this occupation to her brothers as soon as they were old enough. Now her place of work was in the kitchen with her mother and older sister.

It was Myrtle's responsibility to take the cream that had been skimmed off the top of the milk, place it in the big churn, and make it into butter. It took a couple of hours to complete the task, but that gave the young girl time to dream, to ponder what her new pampered life would be like when "Prince Charming" came to rescue her from this life of slavery. He would be tall and very handsome and take her to his beautiful white house on the top of a hill where she could look out of her windows on the beautiful gardens stretching from the front walk as far as the eye could see. It was such a wonderful dream, but it would have to wait for a few more years. Right now she had chores to do.

She was almost to the back door when she heard the loud talking coming from the normally quiet kitchen. Myrtle paused to listen to her mother and sister arguing. Harsh words were being spoken by both. The sobbing sounds coming from Myrtle's happy sister clued Myrtle in that the topic was very serious.

1

"We will not discuss this further," were the words of her mother. "If you think I am unreasonable just wait until you tell you father and see what he has to say about the Martin bunch."

As soon as Myrtle entered the kitchen door the conversation ended. She was curious to know what was going on. But by the tone of voices and the glaring looks she thought better of asking any questions at least for the time being. Everyone worked in silence that afternoon. With the sour mood permeating the room, it wasn't even a good atmosphere for daydreaming.

The dark, cruel words Myrtle had heard earlier paled in comparison to the ones bouncing around at the dinner table when Mabel announced that she and Richard Martin wanted to marry. Father had all kinds of reasons and accusations about why Mabel should not get mixed up with the Martins; they were dishonest, cheats, and all his dealings with them had been bad. He cited example after example of the Martins' mischief and philandering, but Mabel was in love and nothing else mattered. As the ugly words continued to be exchanged, Myrtle slipped away from the table and off to her bedroom, where she covered her head with a pillow. She had never seen her father so angry and her mother so devastated before, and it really worried her.

Mabel came into their shared bedroom a few minutes later with tears streaming down her face and the outline of a handprint welting in crimson on her right cheek.

"I'm eighteen years old, and by law I can make my own decisions," were her last words to her parents before she slammed the bedroom door. "I've worked hard for this family since I was seven years old, and now it's my turn to be with the man I love," she added tearfully in tones only Myrtle could hear.

"Won't father give you his blessing?" inquired the young girl.

"Blessing? Are you kidding? He thinks the whole Martin family is a bunch of charlatans and swindlers. He claims they are all good-for-nothings and is appalled at my judgment for seeing otherwise. He's wrong, Myrtle. Richard is so wonderful and we love each other so much. I don't know why Father is so unreasonable."

"You're in love. Oh, Mabel, that's *so-o-o*. . .romantic!" exclaimed the ardent-minded girl. "I want to know every detail about you and Richard," Myrtle insisted.

Mabel brushed away her tears as she began to tell her younger sister the feelings only a girl in love can know.

2

"Oh, Myrtle, Richard is so handsome and sweet. He tells me all the wonderful things we will do when we move to Minnesota on his grandfather's place."

"Minnesota?" questioned Myrtle. "Does Father know you're going to Minnesota?"

"Yes, he knows. I think that is the real reason he is mad about the whole thing. He won't be able to boss me around anymore," Mabel retorted in an unreasonable manner. She crawled under the covers and pulled them tight around her head. "Mother won't have me around either to do all her work."

"Did you say all those things to Mother and Father?" Myrtle inquired with surprise.

"I sure did," Mabel bravely replied. "I meant every word. You wait and see. Mother will be sorry she laid her hand to my face. I'll show her." Mabel acted strong and in control, but under her bedcovers she cried and shook for at least an hour.

Myrtle lay in the dark room going over in her mind the scenario that had been acted out that evening. There was a sick feeling in her stomach as she realized her nice, secure family could be torn apart by Mabel falling in love. When you found the man of your dreams, it was supposed to be the most exciting time of one's life. A girl dreams of the perfect romance and her family being happy and supportive. Myrtle felt so sorry for poor Mabel. She deserved a better dream, not this nightmare she was going through. Myrtle closed her eyes in an effort to bring on sleep. Maybe everything would be better in the morning.

At the break of dawn Myrtle woke to unfamiliar rustling sounds. Mabel was up and quietly gathering items of clothing from drawers and closets. The old trunk normally stored under the bed was now on top, opened, and receiving the bounty in a hurried manner.

"What are you doing?" the younger sister asked as she rubbed the sleep from her eyes.

"Sh-h-h!" was Mabel's reply. "I don't want anyone to know I'm up yet." She quickly finished her task and slipped the full trunk back under the bed.

The sick feeling returned to the pit of Myrtle's stomach as she realized what the impact of her sister's actions meant. Just then, the wake-up bell from the kitchen rang, heralding all to rise and be about their daily tasks.

"What are you going to do, Mabel?" she asked her sister.

"I don't know yet, but I'm meeting Richard today. I'll decide after we talk," she replied. "Don't you dare tell Mother or Father about the trunk. You have to promise me," she pleaded.

Myrtle agreed reluctantly, even though she didn't like what might happen as a result of her silence.

Everyone sat quietly at the breakfast table. No one wanted to comment on the angry feelings existing about Mabel and her beau. The usual happy words and morning greetings had been smothered by the thick cloud of resentment hovering around the kitchen.

Mabel stirred the food around her plate but couldn't seem to put any of it into her mouth. She soon arose from her chair and started her milk chores as if she was anxious to get them finished. Sorrow hung heavy on Myrtle as she thought of the full trunk under the bed. She wanted to scream this knowledge so everyone would be aware of how serious Mabel was about being with Richard. Yet Myrtle had vowed her silence, and she hoped she would be strong-willed enough to keep her promise. The tears welling up in her eyes were about to give her anxiety away, so Myrtle, too, left the table without eating. She went to find her notepad and pen. She took the writing items from her drawer and sat down to write her sister a message.

Dear Mabel,

I know you are hurting inside and angry, but if you leave home without Mother and Father's blessing, just remember, when all the hurt is gone, you have a family who loves you, especially me. Please don't forget me. Write when you get settled.

Your loving sister,
Myrtle

Myrtle folded the note and tucked it inside the trunk, hoping her sister would find it and be willing to respond. Myrtle had a bad feeling as she left the house for school that she might not see her sister again for a long time.

After her chores were finished, Mabel left the house and returned a few hours later with Richard and his wagon. The two of them loaded the trunk into the wagon, and Mabel left that day with tears in her eyes. The brief scratching on the paper read:

Family, I'm sorry, don't hate me. I love you,

Mabel

The family was not the same after Mabel left. Everyday living was more solemn. Mother had to work harder, and there didn't seem to be time for fun. Myrtle tried to pick up the slack with the milk procedures and keep up her studies as well, but her schoolwork had to be put away if Mother needed extra help with the milk.

It was almost eight months after Mabel had left home that Myrtle received a letter from her big sister. Inside was a picture of a very slender Mabel and her handsome husband, Richard. The letter read:

Feb. 11, 1901
Dear Myrtle,

I found your note and believe me, I have not forgotten any of my family and especially not you. I think about you more than you might suppose.

Richard and I were married a few months ago. This is our wedding picture. It wasn't the grand wedding I had always dreamed of, but it will have to do.

The Martin place here in Atkin, Minnesota, is not exactly as we had hoped. It's OK, I guess. Richard's brother Eli and his wife Mona are living here also. His brother Daniel is coming next month. One big happy family (Ha Ha). The brothers are planning some business venture and Richard promises we will soon be rich enough to get a place of our own. I sure hope so because this group living is not always easy.

Myrtle, tell everyone I love them and I'm sorry I was so "pigheaded" when I left. Please ask them to forgive me.

Love
Mabel

Myrtle studied the picture for a long time and held the letter to her bosom. Her mother, knowing who the letter was from, knocked at the bedroom door and asked permission to enter and read the long-awaited news. What the two of them shared that March afternoon would be a memory that Myrtle would remember for the rest of her life.

5

Myrtle corresponded with her sister all summer, and her mother finally gave in and wrote a letter to her married daughter in August. In a return letter from Mabel in September 1901 Mabel expressed her gratitude for her family's forgiveness and a hope that she would be able to come and visit the following spring. This, however, was the last letter Myrtle received for a long time, even though she continued to write in hopes of receiving an answer.

It was April 1902 when Myrtle got word there was a package for her at the train station and hurried to retrieve it. Inside were her letters dated back from September of the previous year with a note attached stating: "No Occupants At This Address." She was confused by what she received. All sorts of thoughts entered her mind as to the meaning of the package. Mabel hadn't mentioned she was moving, and if she did leave that address, why had she just stopped writing? This just did not make sense to the young girl. By the first week in May, the questions began to get answers.

MOTH HOLES IN THE DRESS

Graduation, a time Myrtle had looked forward to for many years. Now she would be able to find herself a teaching position and do what she loved most: help others learn. There were so many things to be arranged, selecting just the right fabric for her graduation dress, fittings at the Taylor shop, trying on shoes, selecting a hat, the list seemed to go on and on. If only Mabel were here to help her, they could have such fun.

The day finally arrived when Father had agreed to take her to the town of Greenville, where more stores were available, to make the important selections. Myrtle went from shop to shop looking at everything before making any choices. She felt so grown-up and important as each shopkeeper made a big fuss over their merchandise and her good taste in purchases.

Myrtle had just finished at the milliner shop and was perusing the businesses up and down Second Street when she caught a glimpse of a man at the blacksmith shop across the street. He resembled her brother-in-law, Richard Martin. Her heart almost skipped a beat as she anticipated finding her sister with him or close by. Myrtle hurried toward him and called out his name. The man stepped backward and seemed to disappear into the shadows of the stable, like a mirage in the desert. She quickly crossed the street. As she stepped inside the doorway, Myrtle was met by a person who stretched out his arm, abruptly halting her forward motion.

"Well, hello, little lady. Did you run across the street just to see me?" the man asked with a menacing tone of voice.

Myrtle was startled. Her emotions turned to fear and then anger as the man took his hand from the doorway and slid it around her waist. He then grabbed her other hand and pretended to dance with her as she struggled to pull away.

The man was of medium height and build. He had sandy brown hair and a large scar that extended from above his left eyebrow to his ear. The smells of his clothing and body were those of a person who had been on horseback for several days without the convenience of a place to bathe. He laughed sportingly. "Playing hard to get?" he teased the unwilling girl.

The blacksmith watched the man's actions but said nothing as the perspiration rolled from his stiffened forehead and down onto his chest.

"Excuse me, sir!" Myrtle called to the blacksmith. "I thought I saw Richard Martin come in this shop a few minutes ago. Do either of you know him?"

The man with the scar, still trying to be cute, made a fool of himself answering for the blacksmith. "Now what would you want with someone called Richard when you could get lucky and have me? I'm sure I could do anything better than the other guy you're looking for. Do you want to see?" He puckered his lips and leaned down for a kiss.

The smithy turned and gave Myrtle a firm, straight-in-the-eye look as he answered, "No. You better leave now, lady."

Myrtle could sense something was very wrong and immediately turned and got out into the sunlight and the fresh air of the street.

Inside the blacksmith shop, the hammer was released from the gun that had been pointed at the smithy. A voice from the shadows spoke almost in a whisper.

"OK. Now get back to work and finish fixing the broken shoe."

"Who was the good-looking girl?" the man with the scar asked of his partner, who had been hiding in the shadows.

He cleared his throat and went to the doorway to make sure the girl was nowhere around before he answered, "That my friend, was my sister-in-law."

"Well, I hope for our sake she doesn't go straight to the sheriff and get the posse on us again," the scar-faced man responded.

"She won't," the man answered confidently. "I'm sure she doesn't suspect that anything is wrong." Richard Martin went back inside to make sure the blacksmith was working rapidly to replace the broken horseshoe.

Myrtle went quickly to the general store, where she knew her father would be loading supplies. She had been frightened by the scar-faced man and a little confused by the actions of the blacksmith. She wanted to blurt out her experience to her father as soon as she saw him, but he was busy making conversation with Mr. McDaniel. She waited until they were on their way back home to tell her father what had happened.

After hearing of his daughter's strange experience, John Knowles sat quietly for several minutes before responding.

"Myrtle," he finally said, "I'm going to ask you to refrain from telling your mother this story. Anything to do with the Martins right now will just upset her more than she already is. She has been having terrible dreams lately, and this will just add more grief to her already-tormented soul."

"Are these dreams about Mabel?" the young girl questioned.

"Yes, and they have been terrifying her. So you can understand why we must not mention possible sightings. It would just upset her," he replied.

"I wouldn't want to do anything to distress Mother," Myrtle commented "I'll do my best to keep the incident to myself." She sat quietly and pondered on the events that had happened and tried to put the bad experience behind her.

The next morning, as Myrtle was finishing the breakfast dishes to make room for the milk processing, she saw three men on horseback coming up the road toward the house. She recognized Sheriff Baker as one of the three, but the other two riders were strangers. It seemed the whole family noticed the visitors at the same time, as they came from their various tasks and congregated around the three horsemen.

"Mornin,' John," Sheriff Baker greeted as he dismounted from his Appaloosa. The other two men stayed atop their horses surveying each person and the surroundings. They seemed to be looking for someone or something. One of the strangers was a short, portly man who fidgeted a lot in his saddle. He appeared to be nervous and kept his hand near his handgun holstered by his side. The other man was taller and sat very rigid in his saddle. He was dressed from head to toe in black. Even his eyes were piercing black as they studied each person on the ground below him.

Sheriff Baker had known the Knowles family for at least twenty years, so it was normal they would engage in a little small talk before getting down to the real reason for the visit. But light conversation was not on the portly man's agenda, and he interrupted abruptly.

"We're looking for Richard Martin and Vernon Hudson. Have any of you seen them around here lately?" the rude man questioned.

The color drained from John's face as he stepped toward the two men and firmly stated, "No."

"Well, we know your daughter Mabel had been married to Martin. So we figured he would be back hiding in these parts," the portly man added.

"What do you mean, *had been* married to Richard?" Mother tensely questioned.

"When a person lives with criminals they are bound to get caught in the cross fire, and—" the short man blurted out before he was stopped by the sheriff.

"Hold on here, Mr. Lungrun," the sheriff cautioned. "John, Susan, I'm afraid we have some bad news to tell you. Maybe it would be better if we go inside where you can sit down," he suggested.

Susan Knowles grabbed the porch railing as her knees began to buckle in anticipation of the news she was about to hear. Albert went to her aid as John moved to the other side of the horsemen.

"Has something happened to my daughter?" John questioned the men with panic in his voice.

"I'm afraid so, John. Let's go inside," the sheriff pleaded with the anxious father.

The other two men dismounted from their horses and were introduced to the family as United States marshals. Everyone went into the house, and the visitors were invited to sit around the big kitchen table with John and Susan Knowles before the details of the bad news were shared. The boys were asked to go outside and tend to the horses. Myrtle was told to go to her room, but she was too curious to obey. She hovered behind the slightly opened kitchen door to listen to what was being said.

In silence, the younger sister listened, as tears rolled down her face, to the terrible fate that had taken her sister Mabel's life. It seemed Richard, Eli, and Daniel Martin had hooked up with their two cousins Gary and Vernon Hudson and engaged in a series of bank robberies in and around Atkin, Minnesota. As law enforcement officers closed in around Grandpa Martin's farmhouse, a gun battle ensued. Two officers were killed outside before the others were able to storm the house and get inside. When they did, there were several people dead. The people were later identified by Daniel Martin, the only survivor. He was wounded so badly he died a week later, however. The dead were Grandpa Martin; Richard's brother Eli; Eli's wife, Mona; Gary Hudson, his cousin; and Mabel. Richard Martin and his cousin Vernon Hudson had been able to escape through the root cellar while all the shooting was going on. Vernon had been grazed by a bullet on his left temple from his ear to his eye and would be carrying a deep scar for the rest of his life. He would be easy to identify, was the report. The dying man gave the information freely because he was angry the two men had left without at least taking the innocent women with them. They had simply left the women in the house to die.

Myrtle's heart leaped with the knowledge that she *had* seen Richard Martin and the other man with the scar at the blacksmith's shop after all. No wonder Richard had not wanted her to see him. That coward had caused her sister to be sucked into his lifestyle and then left her in the house to be killed. For the first time in her life, Myrtle felt hatred for another person. She wanted to lash out at something to ease the pain.

Mother sat very still while the men explained the circumstances surrounding her oldest daughter's death. Without saying a word, she got up from her chair and went to her bedroom. She went to a chest at the foot of her bed and opened it. Inside were memories of the past tucked away neatly. Down near the bottom was a little white wool christening dress that had been worn by Mabel when she was just a few weeks old. The grieving mother clutched the tiny dress to her bosom and went back to the kitchen where the men were talking. She began speaking as if it were another time. She did not seem to notice anyone in the room. She held the little dress up to the light that filtered through the window. Mother began to shake and brush the material frantically.

The men at the table stopped their conversation, and all eyes turned to the motions of this mother holding the small baby dress.

"Oh no, oh no!" Mother exclaimed in a state of panic. "How could this have happened? I took such care to protect it. Look. Look. Moth holes. I have to fix it. Where is my sewing box?" She moved in haste to a cabinet by the pantry where the box containing the needle and thread was kept. All the while she was talking out loud but seemed oblivious to the presence of anyone in the room. After she hurriedly grabbed the needle from the container she accidentally pushed its sharp point into her right finger. The prick caused a large drop of red blood to come rushing out and fall on the precious white dress. It was the sight of the blood on her baby's dress that started the tears to erupt from her eyes. Mother finally began to outwardly wail and sob for the loss of her daughter.

John moved to comfort his wife, but no amount of trying could give the woman solace. The visitors stood up and told the grieving family they were going to leave. Myrtle entered the kitchen and followed the marshals onto the porch, then closed the door behind them.

"Mr. Baker," the young girl said, "I'm pretty sure I saw Richard Martin and that Vernon guy yesterday."

The three men stopped and listened intently as Myrtle retold her experience at the Greenville blacksmith shop.

"Why didn't you say something about this earlier?" the man in black inquired.

"My father asked me not to speak of the Martins in front of my mother because it would just upset her. As you saw for yourselves, he was right," Myrtle explained.

"You better not be making up a story like this just to send us on a wild goose chase or you will be in some big trouble, young lady. Mark my words," the rude portly marshal announced.

Myrtle stiffened her body and looked the man straight in the eye. "I beg your pardon, sir. I do not lie. You go to Greenville and ask the blacksmith on Second Street. He can verify my story. Now good day!"

Myrtle turned and left the men standing on the porch. Her safe and secure dreams of youth shattered by Mabel's death, Myrtle retreated into the house to mourn with her devastated family.

QUICKSAND NIGHTMARE

Susan was never the same after the news of Mabel's horrible fate but had spells of living in the past and treating her grown children as if they were toddlers again. She couldn't stand it when they were out of her sight as she was afraid they might be in danger. At the dinner table she would want to cut food for them in fear they might cut themselves with the utensils or choke on a piece of food that was too large. The boys, John Junior and Albert, now in their early teens, were not very patient with their mother and would make small mocking gestures behind her back. Myrtle, however, was very concerned and would scold the youths for their disrespect.

It was the times Susan's mind was in reality that were hardest for the family. She had a strong desire for revenge against her son-in-law. She would plead for John to go with her and look for Richard Martin and make him pay for what he had done to her sweet Mabel. John would try in every way he could to make her understand the marshals would find the two men and make them pay, also explaining that he couldn't just up and leave their home and animals and go scouting around the country looking for those criminals. The cows needed milking, and their customers depended on the fresh milk they delivered. These explanations were only momentary pacifiers. Susan would be quiet for a short time and then start all over with the same concerns.

The doctor would stop by each week to check on Susan's condition and leave her a new supply of medication. Yet she didn't seem to improve. The boys had to take turns staying home from school to help Myrtle with the milk chores because her mother was not mentally capable of working the way she had in the past.

Myrtle felt cheated; her dreams of becoming a teacher were being bogged down in the "quicksand" of milk and cream. She had no time for herself as she tried to keep up with the milking, cleaning, cooking, and other responsibilities placed upon her since her mothers' illness began.

One Thursday afternoon in the early spring of 1903 Myrtle took off her apron and decided it was time she took a break and got out in the fresh air. John Junior and Albert had taken their fishing poles and hiked about two miles from the farm to their favorite fishing hole. Mother was taking her regular afternoon nap, which seemed to be brought on by the medicine the doctor left each week. Myrtle knew an apricot tree near the Harrisons' place was full of ripening fruit and needed to be relieved of a basketful of bounty. She would have just enough time for a relaxing stroll before Father returned from work and wanted his dinner.

The sun was warm and every bird seemed to be singing its happiest songs just for her benefit. Her daydreams were pleasant as she admired every new blade of bright green grass and examined the colors of the different flowers along the path. One would not imagine life had become less than happy for Myrtle as she casually walked her way home. It wasn't until she smelled the smoke in the air that she came back to reality. She searched the sky for the direction from which the recognizable odor was coming. The sky that had been azure blue when she left the house was beginning to blacken and fill with soot and ash. Terror filled her being as she realized the smoke was coming from the direction of her house. She released the full basket of fruit from her hand and ran toward the source of the smoke. As Myrtle crested the hill she could see the cow stalls were completely engulfed in flames.

"The poor cows!" she exclaimed as she continued toward the fire. "How could this have happened?"

What had been terror at the sight of the fire turned to horror as Myrtle got closer to the burning stalls. She saw her mother coming from the inferno. Her skirt was on fire and her uncovered skin burnt and charred.

Returning from work, John had also seen the smoke. He whipped the team to race toward home. He arrived just in time to see his wife running from the stalls. His daughter grabbed her and pulled her to the ground. Myrtle rolled her mother in the dirt to extinguish the flames burning her clothing. Father jumped from his moving wagon and raced to give his courageous daughter assistance.

The burnt clothing was pulled from Susan's body, but the wounds on her skin were deep and open. John cradled his beloved in his arms and told her he loved her.

She opened her eyes and spoke.

"Promise me, John, you will get those men that killed our Mabel. Promise me," Susan uttered as she grabbed John's shirt with her blackened hand.

"I promise, sweetheart," John responded.

"We can go now to find Richard and punish him for taking our Mabel away from us. The cows said it was allright to leave tomorrow," Susan whispered her final words. She closed her eyes and gave up the ghost, in her husband's tender arms.

Myrtle cried out in an apologetic manner, "I'm so sorry, daddy! It's my fault for leaving her alone. I thought she was sleeping and it would be all right." She buried her head in her hands and wept along with her father for the women each of them loved.

The cows perished in the fire along with all the buckets, churns, and separators. There would be no more milking chores for the Knowles family. Mother had eliminated that part of their lives with one devastating swing of the burning torch.

The next days after the fire brought a close family even closer. The jobs of removing charred rubble and preparing for a funeral kept heartsick bodies busy. The work was accomplished mostly in silence. It didn't take a lot of talking to fulfill the unity and purpose in the tasks.

After everything was cleaned up and Mother properly laid to rest, the reality of what this loss meant for the family set in. A big slice of their daily routine had been taken away. Whether to rebuild or replace the loss had to be weighed.

Myrtle contemplated what the impact of not having milk chores to do each day could mean for her future. Perhaps now she could pursue the teaching career she had dreamed about. On the other hand, how could she even think about leaving her father and brothers? They would need her now more than ever before. She would have to forget her dreams for the time being and take care of the family needs first.

It was several weeks before the family members could look at one another without tears coming to the surface and even longer before laughter returned to the house. John Junior and Albert were now free to attend school each day. It was hard for young teenage boys to stay gloomy for long. Myrtle was glad happiness was being experienced again by the boys. It gave her something to look forward to when her brothers came home in the afternoons. Albert would tease John Junior about how the girls made eyes at him, so John Junior would joke back about the teacher who gave Albert special attention.

Life was beginning to get back to normal at the Knowles home when Father came with disturbing news. Myrtle could tell right away something was terribly wrong. He didn't even come into the house after work but went straight to Mother's grave site. He sat for about an hour to meditate at his deceased wife's resting place. It was nearly pitch-black outside when he finally came into the house. The boys had already gone to their rooms to do their homework. Myrtle was still up, trying to be patient and wait for her father.

15

His face was grim and drawn when he entered the kitchen. Myrtle could tell he needed to get something off his mind.

"Get your brothers in here, Myrtle. I need to discuss something with everyone present," Father instructed.

The obedient daughter did what her father had asked. When everyone was gathered around the table, Father laid out the situation.

"I stopped to see Sheriff Baker today," Father began. "It seems Richard Martin and Vernon Hudson bought two tickets on a train for northwestern Montana. The two U.S. marshals that came here tracked them as far as Fargo, North Dakota. They allegedly got on the train headed for Montana."

"What's going to happen now?" John Junior questioned.

"Well, the marshals have notified the authorities in Montana. However, Sheriff Baker didn't sound very positive about those two ever being brought to justice out in that wild country," Father explained.

"If I were older I'd go to Montana and look for those crooks myself," Albert announced.

"Can't something else be done? The men can't get away with those injustices without some sort of punishment," Myrtle retorted haughtily.

"You're right," Father added. "I have been doing some thinking." He paused before making the next statement. "I think we need to make some changes in our lives. Some big changes. What would each of you think about leaving Wisconsin and heading out west?" He paused again to get a reaction from his children.

"Go on, daddy," Myrtle encouraged. "I would like to hear your ideas." Albert and John Junior each nodded their approval of Father's continuing.

"I have been thinking about going somewhere like northwestern Montana. People have told me there are many opportunities for making a living on the new frontier. I could make shoes and boots or farm. Myrtle, you could have a chance to teach school. You boys could learn a number of skills such as lumbering, mining, or building. The possibilities are endless." Father paused again before continuing. "I'm sure your mother would approve."

Myrtle listened with mixed emotions as her father painted the picture of a new beginning in an untamed land. "Daddy, could you really leave this place where we were all born and raised? Especially now that Mother is buried here?" she questioned.

16

"Myrtle, I could do it if all of you would come with me," he replied. "I made a promise to your mother, and I feel I need to do what I can to keep the promise. If it means going to Montana or wherever to bring Martin to justice, then that is what I want to do. I know you are old enough to live on your own, Myrtle, but you are my strength right now. I'm asking you to come with me. Besides, these boys need a woman around to keep them in line. Please think about it," he pleaded.

Everyone was quiet as they contemplated what they were being asked to do. Myrtle was unsure if she really wanted to pull up roots and go to the unknown. However, with her brothers' enthusiasm and her father's need for her, she agreed to go with the family.

"One more thing," Father added. "There will be a lot of preparation to be done here before we can leave. *But*," he emphasized in a very serious tone, "we must not tell *anyone* our destination is Montana. Or that we will be looking for Martin. There are too many folks around here who might share the information with the wrong people. It's good to have the element of surprise on your side if you want to catch a *rat*. If anyone should ask where we are going, tell them we're going to California to make a fresh start," he concluded.

Each one took a silent vow that he or she would follow John's counsel and keep the real purpose of the move a secret.

There was not a lot of sleep for anyone at the Knowles house that night. Each family member lay awake to contemplate this new chapter of adventure they were about to embark on.

THE SNOW PRINCESS

The fresh blanket of snow made the back alleyway of Tooley's Tavern look clean and uncluttered. It hid the crates of empty liquor bottles and glazed the rooftops of the small town, like white frosting on cakes.

Obe's thoughts went back to other snow scenes. Ones that were colder, so cold everyone stayed inside huddled around stroked fires to keep from freezing. Five years in Alaska looking for gold now seemed like a dream. A fallen dream that had started with hopes of finding the "mother lode" and becoming rich. Rich enough to buy a ranch with horses and cattle. Then perhaps he would marry, if the right woman came his way.

Winters in Fairbanks, Alaska, had been cold, but so were the women. The few gals Obe had met were hard of heart. They were only looking for wealth, like the men. *Why else would females be in such a hard-to-survive-in place?* Obe had thought many times. Oh, a man could have a woman be nice to him if he had gold in his pouch. When it ran out, however, so did the woman. She would be off looking for another purse to empty. Obe blamed his youth for being vulnerable to sweet-talkin' gals. He had given up months of backbreaking work for a few days of "dancing with ice," as he called it. When the clouding snowflakes melted from in front of his eyes, he could see Alaskan women were not the kind he was looking for. He had been swindled, robbed, and flimflammed out of all the dust he had panned. These experiences had made his once-soft nature strong and tough. He had learned some hard lessons about trust. He vowed he would not be cheated out of what was rightfully his again.

Obe's luck had not been all bad in the frozen tundra land. A saloon keeper by the name of Nat Broughton had taken him in when he was down and out. Nat had taught him the things necessary to run his own place. He also helped Obe get a small stake together, enough money to start his own saloon here in Thompson Falls, Montana. Obe and Nat had become good friends and hoped to someday be partners in a really fancy nightclub.

Born September 15, 1869, in Glencoe, Minnesota, Obediah Anathias Tooley, a name he shared with his father, had often wished the title was given to one of his eleven siblings. His brothers James and Charles were constantly trying to keep Obe out of fights in his youth, due to the teasing received about his name. The tauntings generated by older boys at school about Obe's strange-sounding handle seemed to be the reason for most of the scraps. Obediah would often show up at home all scuffed up and dusty. In spite of it, he was always willing to go back the next day. His father was patient with Obe and seldom got angry about his defending his name. Obediah Senior could relate to the challenge because of similar childhood memories.

Obe had always wanted to someday be rich. He also wanted adventure in his life. He had heard tales of men prospecting for gold and silver, also of some who had struck it rich in faraway places. Obe had spent his early manhood following the newly discovered strikes. He shipped out on a freighter to China. After that he went to Australia, but he never found the rich metals others had told of.

Obe had learned a man like him was never fully dressed if he didn't have a gun strapped on. He carried a concealed handgun in a half-breed shoulder holster under his coat. He had spent many hours in practice and knew how to use the piece well.

He had also learned the ways of a gambler and was very good at dealing cards to his advantage. Obe Tooley had won and lost more money by the time he was thirty than most men would do in a lifetime.

The recollections of his youth seemed so long ago. Here it was January 1904, and the soft, fluffy snow beneath his feet encouraged Obe to take a deep breath of clean, crisp air. As the sun broke through the cloudy gray sky, a golden beam of brightness was placed on the path in front of him. The sudden glare caused him to quickly react, closing his eyes to protect them from the bright rays. When he regained the focus back to his eyes from the quick white blindness, he saw a young woman coming out the back door of the small schoolhouse at the end of the alleyway. She took the broom she was carrying and swept the new snow from the top of the wood box.

Obe had never seen her before. He figured she must be the new schoolteacher some of the people who frequented his tavern had spoken of. They claimed she had arrived from Wisconsin with her father and brothers about three months previous. They had settled at the old Miller place, about two miles up Sugar Loaf Canyon.

In Obe's mind she seemed too young to be a teacher. Why, some of the mountain girls were bigger than this one, he thought. She was tall enough; about five feet and four inches was his estimate. She seemed so slender to him. She didn't look to weigh more than a hundred pounds, if that. The sunbeams that were fighting their way through the wispy clouds brought out the golden red hues in her auburn hair. It was pulled at the sides and hung partway down her back.

When all the snow was off the wood box, Myrtle opened it to retrieve a few sticks to add to the fire in the schoolhouse stove. She had only lifted the lid partway when an explosion of black fur and claws sprang forth in her direction. The quick movement and glaring yellow eyes of the beast brought her instant panic. She screamed and jumped back almost simultaneously. With this movement, her feet slipped on the icy ground. For one fleeting second Myrtle was airborne before disappearing into a snowy bed of whiteness.

The big black cat that had been placed in the box earlier in the day by a mischievous student had successfully played its role in the practical joke intended for Miss Knowles.

Myrtle instantly tried to regain her vertical position. However, the snow was cold and heavy as it clung to her wool dress, preventing success on the first try. She wiped the icy powder from her lids and lashes and opened her eyes. She was able to focus in time to see the big hand and strong-looking arm reach down, as if from heaven, to give her assistance.

Obe Tooley, the rough-cut saloon keeper, felt like a gallant prince of the North as he lifted this lovely snow princess out of the white dungeon that held her captive.

"Are you hurt?" the prince inquired of the maiden, as he brushed the snow from her dress.

"I don't think so," the princess replied as she fought the rosy blush from coming to her face in vain. "I must have been quite a sight flopping around like a beheaded chicken in the snow."

"Not at all," Obe responded. "What I saw was more like a lovely swan trying to take flight."

With his description they both broke into laughter, as the warm sun began to liquefy the hardness of the ice around them.

"Can I help you with your wood?" Obe asked.

"Thank you," she replied as she lifted the lid on the box.

Obe loaded his arms with the seasoned pine. With the young woman leading the way, he made his way into the schoolroom, to the potbelly stove. After stoking the fire with tinder and a log, he turned to the woman and stated, "By the way, I'm Obe Tooley, and you are?" He extended his right hand for a shake.

"I'm Myrtle," she stammered a bit, "uh—Myrtle Knowles."

"Nice to meet ya, Myrtle," he replied as their hands met for a shake. "Anything else I can do for you before I go?" Maybe clean the blackboard, or pound the erasers?" he teasingly inquired.

"No, thank you," she answered as she chuckled slightly. Myrtle then motioned towards the door, playing her role of schoolteacher with a naughty student. "You need to go home now to your wife," she added.

"Looking at you, I can see why some men might get married. As for me, I don't have a wife yet," Obe stated.

Myrtle was pleasantly surprised. The gentleman looked to be in his midthirties, an age at which most of the men she knew were married and had families.

"I'll keep my eye out for varmints or critters to bring around to see you," Obe playfully stated.

"You leave your pets at home, mister, but you're welcome to come and visit any time after school hours," she suggested.

Obe caught himself blushing a little as he tipped his hat to leave the lovely schoolteacher. He stepped out into the crisp, cold air once again; this time he didn't seem to notice the chill. The temperature was the same as before he met Myrtle, but somehow there now was a certain warmth he couldn't quite explain.

MISSION IN THE CANYON

The few weeks following the meeting of Myrtle and Obe were full of anticipation and unfamiliar excitement. Obe used every feeble excuse he could come up with to visit the teacher. She conveniently made herself available for the visits. Myrtle was the sweetest, most innocent creature Obe had been around for many years. He could make her laugh with his subtle humor, and she amazed him with her youthful wisdom.

Myrtle stayed in town most of the winter months. With all the snow, traveling up the canyon road to where her father and brothers were living was often a hardship and sometimes even impossible.

There were always rooms available at Aunt Betty's Boarding House, located a few doors down the street from Tooley's Tavern. Myrtle stayed there when she couldn't get home and back. Now that she had met Obe, she was happy to stay in town. She enjoyed all the attention she was receiving from him. Even if there was more than fifteen years' difference in their ages, she was intrigued with this western character. Not only did Myrtle enjoy staying in town; she began to hope winter would last longer than normal as an excuse to be with Obe.

Obe had made arrangements with Betty to have supper at her boarding house whenever he wanted. In exchange, he gave her discounted prices on "spirits," as she called them. He also made sure she had her own private bottle. It seemed Obe was showing up for meals much more often now that he had met the pretty teacher.

As the weeks went by, Myrtle and Obe were becoming simply "giddy." They were acting like a couple falling in love. It was obvious to anyone paying attention that the two of them were becoming more than just friends.

One evening after supper at Betty's, Obe invited everyone at the table over to the tavern for a late-night party. It had been a particularly warm day, and it felt like spring might come early to Thompson Falls.

"Drinks on the house tonight, my friends!" Obe shouted, and everyone in the saloon took advantage of the owners's hospitality.

Myrtle had never tasted this kind of alcoholic beverage. She liked the way the liquor made her feel. She danced freely, without her normal inhibitions, as the drinks caused her to be light-headed and giggly.

The piano man played all the old favorites: "Oh, Susannah," "She'll Be Coming round the Mountain," and "I Dream of Jeannie with the Light Brown Hair."

As the last song was playing, Obe asked Myrtle to dance. While holding her close, he whispered in her ear. "I don't dream of Jeannie; I dream of Myrtle with the dark auburn hair."

He wanted to look in the eyes to get an approving glance, but Myrtle, being unsophisticated in the expressions of romance, could only look down and blush. "I would like you to meet my family someday soon," were the only words the shy Myrtle could say.

Obe took this remark as a positive sign of acceptance. His heart seemed to pound wildly inside his chest as they finished the dance in silence.

It was two weeks before a wagon could travel the narrow muddy road up Sugar Loaf Canyon. Myrtle had made preparations and collected supplies. She figured the men at home would be low on several items. She had made arrangements with Aunt Betty to provide a full two days' worth of her cows' milk, in exchange for Myrtle making a large batch of the special Dutch cheese her mother and grandmother had taught her to make. Betty was delighted at the prospects of having the cheese, and Myrtle was excited to take the fresh milk to her brothers. She knew fresh cows' milk was one of the commodities her siblings missed most after leaving Wisconsin.

Myrtle had tried to tell Obe about her family without going into detail about the pain they had been through the last several years. She was not sure what her father would think about this man she was going to bring home, in light of her sister's tragedy. But Myrtle hoped her father would be open-minded and at least give Obe a chance to prove himself.

After all the supplies were loaded, Myrtle and Obe climbed aboard the wagon and started up the road leading to the canyon. All the way, Myrtle tried to coach Obe on what to say and do when meeting her father. She was so nervous her hands shook and her stomach was jittery. At one point, she thought she might be sick.

Obe didn't act the least bit nervous on the surface. He pretended to be calm and collected as he made small talk and teasing remarks to Myrtle. He had brought a new bottle of Old Crow in his coat pocket just in case he needed to calm anyone in this tense situation. The whiskey had always worked in the past for the tavern keeper. He had little doubt it would be different this time. He obviously had more confidence in the situation than Myrtle.

The winter months of December, January, and February had been particularly cold and snowy in this northwestern Montana place. The men who had been cooped up in the house together for days on end were ready for company. The three guys were so happy to see Myrtle and the fresh provisions she had brought that Obe could have been the devil himself and they still would have greeted him politely.

As Myrtle introduced Obe to her family, she tried to be very straight-forward and formal. John Senior watched his daughter closely as Obe told about himself and his traveling experiences. Myrtle's father could tell by the gleam and excitement in her countenance that this man was more than just a wagon driver to his daughter.

It was not known by Myrtle whether her father liked Obe because of his charm and wit or because he was so lonesome for company he would have liked anyone. Myrtle didn't really care about the reason. She was just happy her father and Obe took up with each other and seemed to become friends.

Obe took a real interest in the boots John and the boys were making and bought a pair that, he said, "fit like a glove." He even offered to take a few pairs to town and do advertising for them. The two men gabbed and drank all evening. Myrtle was much more relaxed and happy than she had been on the way up the canyon earlier in the day.

After supper, the schoolteacher set her brothers down and gave them each an assignment in the books she had brought with her. They in turn reported back on the other books they had studied during the time she was away. Myrtle was trying to keep them up to grade level with the home schooling they were doing. There would only be a few weeks more of bad weather; then the boys could go into town and attend regular school with the other students.

WHITE LACE AND GOLD BANDS

The next few visits between Obe and John were warm and cordial. By April, Obe felt confident enough to ask John's permission to marry his daughter.

Myrtle had gone down to the creek to find the watercress the boys reported was growing there. Obe seized the moment to be alone with her in the beauty of the mountains that spring afternoon. He saw her sitting on a large granite rock by the crystal-clear water. She looked so beautiful to him, he felt he was looking at a goddess. Myrtle had taken the combs out of her auburn hair and was running her fingers through it. She helped the strands flow softly in the gentle breeze as she perused the wonders of nature. Obe was mesmerized by her beauty and prayed in his heart she would agree to be his bride.

Myrtle had experienced a special "woman's intuition," the previous week, that Obe was preparing to propose marriage. When she saw him alone looking for her, she poised herself in anticipation of the question she hoped he would ask. With an almost "clairvoyant" ability, Myrtle questioned the man.

"You've been talking with Daddy, haven't you?"

"Yes," Obe replied. "We talked about the weather and boots—you know, the usual stuff."

"You know what I mean, silly," the anxious maiden retorted impatiently. "About us."

"Us?" he questioned as he made large motioning gestures with his arms. "You and me?"

Myrtle raised her right eyebrow and with her most stern teacher look glared at Obe. This expression made him chuckle, and he could no longer hold his poker face.

"Your father said if I would take hold of your left hand, like this," the awkward prince demonstrated the action, "then kneel on one knee, and nicely ask you to marry me, you would say yes. Is he right?"

"I've always lived by the commandment in the Good Book to honor thy father. If that is what my father said," the princess replied, "as a good daughter, I would have to obey."

Obe was speechless for the first time since he had seen Myrtle in the alleyway.

"Well," she stated, then motioned with her hands for him to speak. "Do you have something you want to ask me?"

Obe struggled within himself to find just the right amount of "syrup" to go along with the next few words. He had waited thirty-four years for this moment, and he wanted it to be perfect.

"Myrtle Knowles, you would make me the happiest and most honored man ever born if you would agree to be my wife." The words seemed to roll as gracefully off his masculine tongue as mud sliding down a mountaintop.

The statement was so common and predictable, but for Myrtle it was like the sweet sound of music to her delicate and receptive ears. She blushed, then responded.

"Yes, if we can get married soon?" she added.

Obe was surprised with the anxious girls' response and pleasantly answered, "Is May the first soon enough?"

May 1st, let's see." The young woman thought a moment before finishing her response. "That's three weeks away. OK, that's soon enough." Myrtle smiled and threw her dainty arms around Obe's neck. They shared their first long, sweet kiss.

EXPOSING THE SCAR

The first three months of marriage were like a dream come true for Myrtle. She and Obe had moved into a small four-room house. To the bride, it was her own castle. Not the big white one on the tall hill she had dreamed of as a young teenager. However, she presumed that one could come later in their lives.

While Obe was at the tavern in the afternoons and evenings, Myrtle would use the time alone to paint, sew, and decorate her domain. When everything was just as she wanted it to be, she would spent her time baking, cleaning, or curled up reading a book.

One extremely warm August night, Myrtle decided she didn't want to stay home alone. She walked to the tavern to visit with Obe. As usual, she entered through the rear door. She was about to step into the bar area when she saw something that brought terror to her soul. She quickly backed up into the shadows. She didn't want the man with the scar on his face standing at the bar to see her. Myrtle's heart, pounded wildly as she stared at one of the reasons her family had made the big move to Montana. Inside her mind, she wanted to jump into the room and scream accusations at him. But she knew she needed to be calm and not let him know she was there.

The scar-faced man was standing at the bar having a drink with two other fellows. Myrtle could only wait patiently in silence until Obe got close enough to hear her whispers.

"Obe, could you come here?" softly spoke the voice from the darkness.

Obe had not heard her come in but recognized his wife's voice immediately. "Myrtle?" he questioned.

A hand reached from the darkness, grabbed Obe's arm, and pulled him towards it. He could feel the trembling of her hand, the tenseness of her whole body, as she held onto him tightly.

"Honey! What's the matter?" Obe concernedly questioned.

Myrtle placed her fingers to his lips and pleaded softly for silence. "Please don't let on I'm here or say my name. I need to ask you some questions."

Seeing how troubled his wife was, Obe walked her outside into the alleyway. They could speak privately there.

"The man at your bar with the scar on his face, do you know him?" the trembling woman asked.

"He's been here a couple of times," Obe responded. "His friends call him Vern."

"Do you know where he lives?" was her second question.

Obe was getting very concerned about his wife's demeanor. He now wanted to know if she knew this man and what he had done to cause this kind of reaction.

"It's a long story. I'll tell you all the details when you come home. Right now, I need you to casually find out where this man lives before he leaves the saloon. Obe, be very careful. This Vern guy is wanted by the U.S. marshals. He could be dangerous. One more thing, he can't know that me or any of my family is here in Montana. That information could alert him, causing him to be on the run again," Myrtle added.

Obe was not the type to be sticking his nose into other people's business. However, in this case, he figured he had married into a mess, whatever it was. He would try to find out about the scarred man as his wife requested.

The tavern owner calmed himself as he returned to his customers. He started casually making conversation, as was normal for him to do. He worked his way around the bar talking to one patron and then another. When he got around to the party with the scar-faced man, he calmly inquired, "I've seen you gents in here before, haven't I? Do you live around these parts?"

The man with the scar remained silent, but one of his companions replied in a slurred and husky manner, "Hell, no! We don't live in this womanless town. I'm from Missoula, where the women are round-hipped and long-legged." He laughed at his own description, then raised his mug and boomed out loud enough for everyone in the room to hear, "A toast to sweet-assed women!"

Everyone laughed and raised their glasses in agreement with the lusty salute.

When the noise quieted down a bit, Obe continued his nonchalant inquiries "If you live in Missoula, what are you doing in this neck of the woods?"

The large man answered with the information the bar detective was looking for. "We're with Sweet Water Lumber, and we're loggin' up North Fork," the loud man replied, and then raised his mug for another salute. "A toast to the men of Sweet Water Lumber."

Several of the patrons raised their mugs to join in the toast.

The intoxicated man learned over the bar to ask Obe a question. "Are there any women for sale in this damned place?" The words were slurred as he asked.

"None right in town," was the barkeeper's answer. "About three-quarters of a mile up Pinewood Road there's a house on the right side with a sign that says: NATTY BLOOMS. Go see her."

The big man downed the remaining beer in his mug, slid off his stool, and staggered out the door. The other two men just looked at each other and snickered.

"It's a good thing there's a woman around here. Ole Tucker seems to have an *extra*-healthy drive, if you know what I mean," the man with the scarred face commented, then nudged his friend's shoulder, and they both broke into laughter.

"You fellows have a good time tonight and come back again," Obe cordially remarked before moving on to another side of the room.

It was late before Obe was able to close the saloon and go home. He somehow knew Myrtle would be waiting up for him. He was right. She was sitting in the almost-dark room, wrapped in a blanket and crying. The flickering light of the single candle gave the house a lonesome glow as Obe sat down on the small sofa by his bride.

Myrtle spent the next few hours telling her husband all about the tragic deaths of her sister and mother and how the man with the scar fit into the whole scenario. She was now afraid of her own safety if Vernon Hudson or Richard Martin got wind of her presence in Montana. They would know she could identify them and might try to harm her. The shaking wife asked her husband to help get Vernon behind bars without letting him know she was the one who had spotted him.

"We'll go talk to Sheriff Gardener in the morning and see how the law wants to handle the matter. I'm sure putting Hudson behind bars will be as easy as shootin' ducks in a rain barrel." Obe tried to make light of the situation to easy his wife's fears. "Come on, young lady. Let's get a little sleep before the sun comes up." Obe covered her up. He held her close until the trembling stopped and he could tell she was asleep. As he lay next to his lovely princess and studied the new lines in her brow, he realized the responsibilities of being married were more complicated than he had anticipated.

It took Myrtle almost an hour of searching through "Wanted" notification at the sheriff's office the next morning to find the one she was looking for. Her father had been told by the sheriff in Wisconsin that flyers had been sent to all the towns in Montana. They had descriptions of Martin and Hudson and the crimes they had committed.

Wanted

For crimes of: BANK HOLD-UPS, ROBBERIES AND THE MURDER OF TWO FEDERAL LAW ENFORCEMENT OFFICERS

$100.00 Reward for Either

RICHARD A. MARTIN: Age 24 approximately 180 lbs, 6'1" tall, black hair, green eyes, mustache, no visible marks or scars.

VERNON L. HUDSON: Age 30 approximately 165 lbs., 5'10" tall, light brown hair and brown eyes. Believed to have a large scar on the left side of his face from the eyebrow to the ear.

Both men are wanted in connection with crimes committed in Minnesota, but are believed to be relocating somewhere in northwestern Montana. There is a $100.00 reward offered for the capture and conviction of each man.

After reading the flyer, Myrtle handed it to Sheriff Gardener. It soon became apparent why the Wanted posters were so stacked up and unorganized as the aging man searched through his pockets and around his desk for his misplaced spectacles. When his deputy, Wade Cody, finally located them, the sheriff slowly stumbled over each word as the deputy listened carefully. Both men had trouble deciphering the written words, the sheriff because of his poor eyesight and the deputy because he could not read.

"You know, I've seen a man around town with a scar like that," the eager deputy remarked.

"Vernon Hudson was in my saloon last night," Obe announced. "I know where you can find him."

"Before he tells you, I would ask a favor," Myrtle chimed in.

"A favor?" questioned the sheriff.

Myrtle then told the sheriff and his deputy part of the story she had told her husband the night before. She wanted to get her father and brothers involved in seeing this particular criminal captured.

Sheriff Gardener was very sympathetic to the pleading woman. He agreed to try to give her time to get her family in town before the arrest.

Obe then gave the lawmen the information about the fugitive's employment with Sweet Water Lumber. Obe also informed them that the men of the company came into his tavern every other Friday night, in conjunction with their paydays.

"Well, if he was in town last night, then it gives us about two weeks to get ready for the next time he shows up," the sheriff remarked. "It will give Wade here enough time to go down to Missoula and get the federal marshal. Being's he's wanted by them, they can come up here and help with the arrest."

"I'm going to inform my menfolk about the situation. I'm sure they will be coming in to introduce themselves to you before the end of the week. If Mr. Hudson does happen to come into town before your deputy or the marshal gets back to help, they could assist you," Myrtle stated with assured resolve. She was excited about ridding the family of this burden of justice hanging over them.

Obe hitched up the horse to the wagon so Myrtle could leave that day to alert her family of the discovery and the sheriff's plan. He knew she would more than likely stay in the canyon while the men were on the hunt as someone would need to care for the animals while the guys were away. He hated the thought of being away from his wife for even one day but knew this was a mission that needed resolving. Fairness in dealing with one another tends to make people flourish with contentment and happiness. Where injustice leads to feelings of bitterness and resentment, stubbornness will take over. Obe knew until Martin and Hudson were made to pay for their crimes Myrtle would never be at peace with life.

Myrtle arrived midafternoon with the news about the scarred man and what was going to happen with the lawmen. The tension in the house was high as John Senior and his two sons readied themselves for the long-anticipated journey.

Myrtle made each one promise to be careful and not do anything foolish or unlawful himself. She reminded them they were not a "lynch mob" but civilized citizens looking for justice, not vengeance.

The boys only half-listened to their sister's lecture. She followed one and then the other around the house as they gathered the necessary items to take with them. They loved their sister and knew she was right, even though each one had voiced actions they might do if they ever got their hands on the outlaws.

Father was quiet as he got his gear together. As he was putting his things in the wagon, he turned to his concerned daughter and reported,

"Girl, we are honorable men now. When we return home again, we will still be honorable men."

That statement brought peace to Myrtle's soul as she watched the three men leave the yard and go from her sight that late afternoon.

The long waiting and nervousness of the lawmen and their appointed posse came to an end the night the men of Sweet Water Lumber got their pay vouchers.

The employees came into town in one large wagon, whoopin' and yellin' all the way. The first stop was right in front of Tooley's Tavern, so each lumberjack could get a few drinks under his belt before moving on to other spots of rest and relaxation.

They entered the "waterin' hole," crowding each other as they made their entrance inside the doorway. One jack boomed out he was "thirsty as hell," and the others laughed and shouted for the barkeeper to bring on the drinks.

Obe willingly obliged, drawing drinks for each customer, all the time keeping his eyes searching for the man with the identifying mark. It wasn't until Obe took a full tray of brew to the large, round card table that he spotted Vernon Hudson seated there with five other men, starting up a game of poker.

After serving up the tray of drinks, Obe walked to the end of the bar closest to the door and signaled one of the two men sitting there. One of the men got up and quietly exited through the door, leaving the other one to be the waiting sentry.

Obe tried to keep calm as he served the next round. The adrenaline was rushing so rapidly through his veins he was sure someone would notice the liquid in the glasses shaking as he set the drinks in front of them.

Why is it taking so long for the sheriff to get in here? the nervous bartender thought to himself as he wiped the forming sweat beads from his forehead. Time seemed to be moving in slow motion. The long seconds ticked away at a snail's pace on the clock behind the bar.

"Hey! Barkeep! Bring us another round over here!" one of the jacks yelled, bringing the nervous man out of his apparent trance. "You look like you're sleepin' over there?" the jack added rudely.

Obe was just getting out fresh glasses when the lawmen came through the front doors of the saloon. The jovial noise ceased as eight men with drawn pistols and rifles entered and positioned themselves around the room.

"We're looking for a man named Vernon Hudson," were the words that broke the silence. The U.S. marshal eyed each man who was seated around the poker table.

"What do you want him for?" was the question asked by one of the jacks seated at the bar.

The marshal was stone-faced as he circled the table looking for his man. When he had him spotted, he answered the question that had just been posed.

"He's wanted for the murder of two federal marshals, abandonment of innocent women, and bank robbery," the unshaken lawman answered. "They say he is pretty easy to spot. He has a large scar on his left temple," the man of ice added as he stared Hudson straight in the eye, just waiting for the outlaw to make a move.

The scene quickly became very ugly as the desperate criminal retrieved a large knife from his boot in a futile attempt at a getaway. The first shot fired hit Hudson in the arm, and the second one hit him in the right side near the hip.

Most of the lumberjacks were stunned by the blood that was draining from their fellow worker's body. They either hid under furniture or tried to exit through the doors. A couple of stupid ones, however, drew weapons. Bullets began to fly around the inside of Obe's place of business. By the time the ceasefire had taken place, Obe's establishment had sustained considerable damage.

He felt sick as he viewed his losses. There were broken windows, mirrors, glasses, and liquor bottles lying in puddles of the liquid money on the bar and floor. The tavern owner was unable to verbally express his anger at the senseless destruction. All of it was caused by people with no apparent ability to use their brains in a dangerous situation.

Vernon Hudson was taken to the jailhouse, and the doctor was called in to dress the wounds. The two jacks who had drawn and started the senseless destruction were also arrested and locked up.

Obe was standing in the doorway of his wrecked saloon trying to assess the losses when John and the boys came to share the good news. They had been so involved in securing the prisoner they hadn't even given Obe's troubles any thought.

"The little weasel spilled his guts," were the first words out of Albert's mouth. "He said Richard Martin was up north in Sandpoint, Idaho, hid out in some whorehouse. Hudson hopes we get him."

33

"Yeah," John Junior chimed in, not wanting his brother to tell the whole story himself. "He said Richard took all the money and skipped out on him. He was fixin' to head up that way himself in a few weeks, find ole Martin, and get his money back," the younger boy explained.

John Senior tried to tone down his son's enthusiasm when he saw the damage Obe was looking at. "This is terrible, Obe," John said in an apologetic manner. "I feel responsible for you sustaining this amount of destruction to your source of income."

"It's not your fault, John. I guess a person has to expect this sort of thing when he has this kind of business. It still doesn't make cleaning it up, or the cost of repairs, any less hard." Obe admitted.

"Well, the boys and I will stay in town until we have your place repaired enough to open the doors for business again," John stated. "We will find a way to repay you for your sacrifice."

The price of justice had been felt by Vernon Hudson that day, through the sting of two bullet wounds. However, Obe Tooley also felt a string in the role he played in the fight for justice and likewise paid a price.

"BUTTERCUPS MAKE ME SMILE"

By the time Myrtle returned home from the canyon, the men had cleaned up the debris from the tavern. They had also boarded up the broken front window. They would have to wait several weeks, to replace such a rare commodity as a large glass window in this remote western region.

Myrtle had been sick the whole time she was at her father's house. Obe, however, was now in such a foul mood about the business, her homecoming was not at all what she had anticipated. She had looked forward to a wonderful happy reunion with her husband. Instead, a grumpy man with a bad attitude was the only one to meet her.

She tried to help her husband and be cheerful, but the constant nausea she felt prevented her from doing even simple tasks without being sick.

Myrtle finally went to the doctor to get help. When he explained to her that pregnant women often felt that way, her whole countenance changed. She could hardly wait to share the glad tidings with Obe and her family. A baby could be a spark of hope and rejuvenation of life for everyone, a new catalyst for bonding the living and the dead in a circle of love. Myrtle had waited for this time all of her life. As a child she had only pretended to play "mommy" with her toy dolls. Now the fantasy was becoming a reality. It was time to put away playthings. This baby growing inside her was real and would be born in the latter part of April.

Myrtle waited for what she thought was just the right moment to spring the news of new life to Obe. She hoped the information would be the "broom" needed to sweep away the gloom now being disseminated from her husband. The table was carefully set with her finest linens and sparkling dishes. Not grand ones, like the rich folks had, just the simple but elegant ones that had been her mother's and grandmother's before. Myrtle made sure the breakfast foods of fried ham and flapjacks were cooked the way Obe liked them. She then summoned him to the kitchen.

Obe first noticed the bright yellow buttercups. They were in a small vase in the center of the table.

"Flowers?" he remarked. "What's the occasion?"

"Eat your breakfast before it gets cold," she replied in an effort to change the subject until she was sure her man had a full stomach.

The smell of the ham made Myrtle nauseous. She struggled to keep down the contents of her own stomach and maintain her composure.

35

"Aren't you going to have some of this meat?" Obe inquired of his wife.

Myrtle took a deep breath and began to babble out the story. She told about the doctor, her sickness, and her pregnancy in a manner that made absolutely no sense to her husband across the table. When she realized the words she had planned to say were all mixed up and confusing, the expectant mother got so nervous, the contents of her stomach were beginning to rise. She managed to get to her feet and out to the back porch. Her breakfast immediately surfaced and was ejected from her slender body.

Obe was stunned by his wife's actions and followed her out the back door. "What is the matter with you?" he questioned his wife. "What did the doctor say?"

"I'm pregnant, Obe. We're going to have a baby," she answered when she gained control of her body.

He was speechless as he stared at his wife with a disbelieving look in his eyes. The ramifications of her words made Obe stiffen in selfish anger. He was not ready for the added burden of a child. A new wife and her family's problems of dutiful revenge were enough right now. The thoughts made him hostile and unwilling to think logically. He responded to Myrtle's announcement like a jealous spoiled child. "I'm not ready to have children right now. I have things I need to do before adding another mouth to feed here!" Obe shouted. The "I"'s seemed to blurt out of his mouth with no thought for anyone but himself. "I've got too many other things to think about. I'm not ready to take on the responsibilities of a baby. I've got work to do." With the last "I," Obe grabbed his hat and slammed the door behind him. He left Myrtle standing dumbfounded by herself in the kitchen.

Her first reaction to seeing the monster come out of what she thought was a mild-tempered man was fear and shock. Her body was stiff and shaking as her eyes filled with tears, which quickly spilled down her flushed cheeks. Obe had reacted like a toddler who didn't get his way. *He is not the man he's supposed to be,* Myrtle thought, *and he'll just have to get over it.*

It was late when Obe returned home that night, hiding something behind his back. He removed his hat and gently threw it across the room. This action was a gesture of apology, and he then waited for Myrtle's reaction.

"Well, you didn't shoot holes in my hat," he stated. "Is that a sign you'll let me come in?"

"Only if you're in a better mood now than when you threw your little fit and stomped out," was her reply.

Obe had had the whole day to logically think his situation through. He realized he had acted like a real jerk. Apologizing to anyone was an unpracticed skill for him. Yet he knew his bride certainly deserved an apology from him.

"Honey," the humbled man began. "I'm sorry I behaved so badly...." He paused to think of the words he had been rehearsing. He couldn't remember exactly the way he had practiced each sentence. "U-uh" he stammered. "Here; I brought you flowers." He brought his hand from behind his back to expose the small bouquet of bright yellow buttercups he was hiding.

"Maybe we should start this day over," the meek man suggested.

The sight of this new mild-mannered man and the flowers brought instant upturning to Myrtle's mouth.

"Buttercups make me smile. I don't know what it is about those darn flowers, but they cause me to smile every time." She giggled softly, trying to pretend it was the flowers and not the man who was making her so happy.

"So," he started and took a deep breath. "I hear we're going to have a baby. Tell me again what the doctor said."

A GEM FROM HEAVEN

By the time spring of 1905 came to Thompson Falls, the Tooleys were back on an even keel with their affairs. Richard Martin was nowhere to be found in Sandpoint, Idaho, as Hudson had reported he would be. He had been there before the authorities arrived, but it would just be a matter of time before they caught up with him, the sheriff had reported to Myrtle, as they now knew he was in the area.

Obe had his tavern back in good condition. His business was running as well as could be expected, with the constant threat of the temperance movement. Some folks were wanting to bring an end to the sale and transport of liquor in the United States.

Myrtle got over her "morning sickness," as it was called. She spent a lot of time making clothing and blankets for the anticipated arrival of the new baby. Obe was hoping for a boy, as many men do, but still was leery about the prospects of being a father. When a daughter arrived on April 22, 1905, he quickly changed his mind and decided a baby girl was better.

Love had never been felt so strongly by Myrtle as it did the moment the infant child was placed in her arms. A special bond seemed to instantly form between mother and daughter, a feeling nothing would ever be able to break. As the infant opened her eyes for the first time and looked at her mother, Myrtle felt a swelling in her heart and soul. She felt she had known this sweet spirit forever. It was if a friendship were being rekindled after a long separation. She held her daughter close to her face, kissed her delicate little cheek, and softly whispered, "I'll love you forever." Myrtle handed the newborn to Obe. "Well, Daddy what do you think we should name her?"

Obe carefully studied his girl before giving his answer. "She certainly is a precious little thing," he stated. "We could name her Jewel."

"Yes," agreed Myrtle. "She is precious. *Jewel* denotes something flashy or glittery, though. I want her to grow up with a deep inner beauty. Deep and lustrous so she will soak up light but send it back to everyone in a soft and inviting manner." She paused to reflect on her own thoughts before continuing. "Obe, could we name her Pearl? That's the kind of gem I want her to aspire to be."

He thought about what his wife had said for several moments, all the time looking at the small bundle in his arms. "Pearl. Yes, I think she is truly a pearl. A special gem sent from heaven. We'll name her Pearl Elizabeth.''

They both smiled and agreed this child was definitely worthy of such a regal name.

Many changes were made now that a baby was added to Obe's and Myrtle's lives. Myrtle was the doting mother, spending most of her waking hours caring for little Pearl. Obe, on the other hand, made a fuss over his little girl when out in public but at home he was tense and irritable with everything that was out of place because of the baby. As Pearl grew older and became mobile, Obe would fuss and worry that things might get damaged or broken with a toddler on the loose. Myrtle tried to stay patient with him. She knew it wasn't the baby that worried Obe but the bigger issues that made her husband nervous.

There was a struggle going on in the eastern United States since the early 1800s that was now starting to greatly affect the western states. It was the experiment of ''prohibition,'' the legal regulation of the manufacture, transportation, and sale of alcoholic beverages. This was what Obe Tooley was really worried about. Some of the folk, mostly women, were trying to influence the government to get rid of the bad elements encouraged by the presence of a saloon. They were pushing to make Sanders County dry.

The fact that Obe's tavern had just been renovated and looked nice on the outside had nothing to do with what the women desired. They wanted to clean up the town and get rid of the sale of liquor altogether. The cause had been spurred on by a member of the Women's Christian Temperance Union. She was traveling around to the churches in western Montana preaching the evils of alcohol. She claimed banning the use of all alcoholic beverages would solve the problems in their homes.

There had been enough women taking up the fight against liquor that a statute for new liquor licensing would be going before the voters in November. Obe had no idea how this might affect his ability to run his current business in Thompson Falls. He knew he needed to prepare for a possible move.

It was not welcome news for Obe when Myrtle announced she was again pregnant. The baby would arrive in February. *We certainly don't need another mouth to feed to add to our troubles,* was Obe's selfish thought. Myrtle tried to keep her feelings to herself. She didn't want to add to her husband's already-sour attitude. She loved her little Pearl so much, she was sure another baby would just mean double love.

THE PRICE OF DUTY

It was October of 1908. The trees were getting their new autumn colors when Myrtle's father came down from the canyon to talk to the sheriff. He had received word from the U.S. marshal, who was fairly sure he had Richard Martin spotted in Missoula but needed a positive identification in order to arrest the man.

John Senior had suffered a bout of pneumonia during the summer, and the illness had left his body quite weak. Both Albert and John Junior were still working with a lumber company and wouldn't be back from the timber site for another three weeks. Neither of them was available to help their father drive the team to Missoula.

John had come to see if Myrtle or Obe might go with him. With Myrtle pregnant again, it was decided Obe would be the one to go.

Obe was not thrilled about getting involved with arresting criminals again. But as it would be in another town and not at his saloon, he was willing to go. He also wanted to check out the towns to the south of Thompson Falls. He might have to relocate his business if the county went dry.

As the two men traveled south en route to Missoula, Obe stopped at the different small towns and inquired casually about their feelings toward prohibition. Most people he talked to reported that they were in favor of closing down the saloons and cleaning up their towns. By the time John and Obe reached their destination, Obe could tell moving south of Thompson Falls would not be a good thing.

When they entered the city limits of Missoula, Montana, one of the first things to catch Obe's eye was a large poster. It was an invitation to a political rally that was taking place the following day. One of the candidates running for governor of Montana would be arriving by train at 2:00 P.M. October 5, 1908. A parade would start at the train station and go to the center of Main Street. After the parade, the people would have the pleasure of hearing Mr. James B. Picket. He would explain why people should want to vote for him on Election Day.

Banners of red, white, and blue were already draped across the streets and storefronts in anticipation of the big event. Many people of this town liked what Mr. Picket said he would do if elected governor.

Obe was against all politicians. It didn't matter if the president himself came to town; Obe wasn't planning to vote anyway. *All they want to do is change things and figure a way to get more of the workingman's money,* was Obe's thought.

The two travelers were tired but stopped in to see the local sheriff before making sleeping arrangements. John and Obe were greeted with enthusiasm when they arrived at the lawman's office. The sheriff, his deputy, and a U.S. marshal were all there waiting for them. After all the introductions were made the marshal explained why they thought the man they were thinking of arresting was Richard Martin.

"When we arrived in Sandpoint, Idaho, where Mr. Hudson thought Martin was living, the whorehouse was in the process of being vacated by the women who worked there. We talked to them and asked where they were moving. We couldn't get straight answers out of anyone. As I began to track their movement over the next few months, the trail led me to a place just outside of town here called the Pleasure Palace," the marshal reported.

"We have been keeping an eye on the comings and goings of the people who work there. We're pretty sure a man who stays in the house is Richard Martin," the sheriff said.

"This man keeps a low profile, spending most of the time inside the house. The deputy here has set up a place at the top of a hill near the house where he can secretly view anyone entering or leaving the place. By using a telescope, he can even get a close look at faces. Our suspect always takes a morning stroll to and from the outhouse at the east side of the property. We can see his face clearly as he returns to the main house," the marshal added.

"We would like you two men to come with us early tomorrow morning and see if you can identify the man in question as Richard Martin," the sheriff requested. "If it is him, we plan to arrest him right then. Are you prepared to help, if necessary?"

"Believe me, sir, I would like nothing more than to see Martin arrested if it is him," John firmly stated. "We'll be here by six; count on it."

John and Obe left the sheriff's office and went to the nearest hotel. They each acquired a room. They wanted to get the trail dust off their bodies and clothing before finding a place to have supper.

The hotel they checked into was very modern. It had the luxury of hot and cold running water and a commode in each room. Obe had never stayed in a place as modern as this. He washed himself and some of his traveling clothes, then laid them on the balcony to dry in the late-afternoon sun. He watched the hustle and bustle of this large, spread-out town from his vantage point on the second-floor terrace. He wondered if he could ever be happy anywhere but in a small place like Thompson Falls. Myrtle had mentioned several times how much fun it was to be in a place with so much variety for making shopping choices. But she seemed happy to be in a small town, Obe thought.

Obe left his room to get John for supper but found his father-in-law very tired. John requested some food be brought to his room. He apologized to Obe for not going with him, but he felt he could use the rest in order to be up and ready before six the next morning.

Obe had no problem with exploring the city by himself. He was interested in finding a saloon to compare with his own. He inquired of a produce salesman in a market near the hotel. The man directed Obe to the closest saloon, two blocks to the east and one block north.

"Can't miss it," the salesman stated. "It's over near the railroad station."

The explorer studied each storefront as he walked by. He looked at each elaborate display set to lure in the impulsive shoppers. Obe caught sight of himself reflected in one of the windows and thought how dapper he looked in his suede coat and string tie. Myrtle had insisted he bring it to wear in the city.

As he rounded the corner by the train station, Obe spotted the SALOON sign he had been looking for. What he saw in small print at the bottom of the sign both surprised and delighted the man. The words spelled out: NAT BROUGHTON, OWNER AND PROPRIETOR.

Nat Broughton, Obe's old friend from Alaska! It had to be the same man, Obe thought. He studied the sign and then the front of the building. It was the grandest-looking saloon he had ever seen in these parts. The windows were etched with scroll designs. From outside a person could hardly see inside. The swinging doors were smooth wood with etched panes of glass in diamond shapes three rows down. Obe had only seen doors this fancy in magazine pictures. It would cost a pretty penny to replace all this glass, he thought.

As he walked through the swinging doors and looked around, Obe was amazed at the lavish decor everywhere. There were large wood moldings around the ceiling and pillars down the walls with fine filigree carvings. A big mirror hung behind the bar with a mural of scantly clad women of ancient Greece. They seemed to float around the walls and up to the ceiling. The walls were a soft smoky green with white moldings and pillars. The color added a nice contrast to the dark wine-covered cushions on large high-backed chairs that were arranged around the tables.

How different this place was from Nat's saloon in Fairbanks. That place had dark walls and plank wood floors. *He must have got hold of a lot of gold to buy all this,* Obe thought.

"What will you have?" the man behind the bar asked his customer without taking a good look at him.

"I'd like a Fairbanks special," Obe replied.

The barkeeper looked up and studied the face of the man who had made the request, then stated, "Only a few people knew about a Fairbanks special, and most of them are dead now. Why, Obe Tooley, you're a sight for sore eyes. You old son-of-a-gun." The man reached his hand across the bar to shake his friend's hand and exchange a warm greeting. "What are you doing in Missoula?" Nat questioned, but went on before receiving his answer. "Not opening another saloon down the street to steal all my customers I hope."

"Well, if I were to set up shop around here, I'd sure as hell make mine nicer than this old garbage heap you have here," Obe responded, with a tongue-in-cheek grin.

Both men laughed and slapped each other on the back in a gesture of friendship. They each had big stories to tell and talked for several hours. Most of the tales were upbeat and funny. But when the subject of politics and the potential abolishment of alcohol came up, the two men were worried about their businesses.

"Yes, my friend, times are changing. I've been under a lot of pressure to close down this fine place, but for a different reason. There is an investor with big money who has offered to buy me out. He wants this building I have renovated for another reason. The man wants to make this place into a dining and dancing club, like the rich folks back east have. I'm just waiting for the right price to be offered before I'll sell. Anyway, what else can an old sour dough like me do without a business to take care of?" Nat stated.

"I may not be so lucky," Obe responded. "If the people in my neck of the woods vote to make the area a dry county in November, I'll be forced to close down my place and move on."

The two saloon owners toasted to good luck, prosperity, and bad weather on voting day before parting company for the remainder of the night. Obe promised to stop back by the saloon before leaving town the next day.

The knock at the door jolted the sleeping man and he sat straight up in bed. His head was throbbing from the alcohol he had consumed only a few hours before. It took him some time to figure out just where he was and why. Obe very seldom drank enough liquor to cause a *hangover*. After all, his livelihood depended on selling the stuff, not drinking up the profits. So he had almost forgotten how bad a hangover felt.

He stumbled around the room trying to get dressed. He bumped into everything, it seemed, making thumps and clanks as he moved.

The noise coming from inside Obe's room caused John to be concerned. He was afraid his son-in-law might be hurt or sick. When Obe finally emerged from his room, John could immediately recognize the symptoms of intoxication.

By the time the lawmen were in their designated positions in the hills around the suspect's hideout, the sun was just starting to show its first rays at the top of the tallest mountains in the eastern sky.

The excitement of the manhunt had chased away any thoughts of a headache or tiredness from Obe's body. He was ready to take part in any action that might happen. He checked the gun he always carried in the shoulder holster, making sure it was loaded in case he had to use it.

With the scope in place, the deputy scanned the windows and doors of the house. He was looking for any signs of movement from the people inside. After what seemed hours of nervous waiting, a curtain was draped to one side and a woman with long blond hair gazed out. She appeared to be acting as a sentry, looking for outside movement.

Everyone outside held their positions in hope their presences would not be detected. Not even a blade of grass moved as the men also held their breath in silence.

A few seconds after the woman left the window, the back door opened. The man in question exited through the rear door and walked up the hill to the old outhouse. His face was not visible to the man operating the scope. It was almost fifteen minutes later when the suspect came out of the latrine.

John moved to the scope and waited for the man to come out of the shadows. He wanted to see the fellow in the sunny areas of the narrow path before making his identification.

"That's him!" the vengeful father stated, "I'd recognize the rotten scoundrel anywhere."

44

"Are you completely positive that's Richard Martin?" the sheriff interrogated John. "We don't want to arrest him if you aren't absolutely sure."

"I'm sure. If you want a sworn oath I'll give it to you, but that *is* Richard Martin," John stated without delay.

With the sure identification, the sheriff signaled the hidden posse. The lawmen moved in on the fugitive. They hoped to make a peaceful arrest so no one would be hurt.

Martin was startled by the sudden movement but was prepared for just such an occasion. Without warning or hesitation, the rogue pulled a pistol out from under his open shirt, dropped to the ground, and began firing at the deputies.

The sounds of shots pierced the silence of the calm autumn morning and sent chills down Obe's neck and back. He leaped for protection behind a large rock, pulled out his pistol, and cautiously moved to peek at the action. The next thing he heard was the screaming of women's voices. Obe looked toward the sound. Three women in sleepwear came from the house. They ran to the man who lay bleeding on the ground a few feet from the back door. The women were yelling obscenities at the sheriff and other men as they knelt down by the dying man.

John hurried to the scene and glared at Richard Martin, starring at the villain with all the hate he held for the man showing in his eyes. He had traveled many miles and sacrificed dearly to see this knave suffer for his crimes. John wanted Martin to know his former father-in-law had helped to bring him to justice.

Martin opened his eyes as he lay suffering from the wounds. He saw the man with hate in his eyes standing over him.

"You!" the dying man sputtered in amazement.

"Yes," John Knowles replied. "I finally tracked you down, Martin. Now maybe I'll be able to sleep nights, knowing my daughter's killer is rotting in the ground." With that statement the satisfied father turned and walked to his wagon.

Richard Martin died in the arms of the three weeping whores.

"A just ending for the unholy man," were the words of the U.S. marshal who had tracked Martin to this place.

John and Obe started back to town with the other lawmen. Before they had gone very far, John requested Obe pull off the trail and let the others go on ahead. John got out of the wagon and walked into a wooded area to be alone. He was afraid of being seen by anyone. His emotions began to surface in the form of shaking and tears. He sat on the ground in a small grove of trees and, for the first time in his adult life, cried out loud.

The memories surrounding this horrible incident came to John's mind. He grieved for everything concerning it. The promise he had made to his dying wife was now fulfilled. All the sacrifices made by his living children, to make this trek out west to avenge their sister and mother, were now ended. The burden had been lifted from his head, and he felt like a freed man. John Knowles had carried out his honorable duty and could now live the rest of his life in peace. The price of justice had been paid in full.

CRUSADERS FROM THE UNDERWORLD

It was afternoon by the time John and Obe got back to Missoula. They could hear the whistle of the train before they saw it crest the hill at the west end of town. The puffs of black smoke polluted the clear sky as the big black viper seemed to snake its way down the hill. Something about this scene sent a chill down Obe's back. It made a shudder go through his soul. With this kind of transportation branching throughout the West, it meant change. The kind of change the small-town fellow dreads. Too many people in one place, and fences.

As the train grew closer, the red, white, and blue banners were visible. The men could see this train was the one the political-minded people had been waiting for. Folks began to gather at the station as the engineer continued to sound the loud whistle.

John's team of horses became excited and nervous. They were frightened by the noise and commotion as the locomotive came to a screeching stop at the station, a few doors from Nat Broughton's saloon. Obe quieted the team, took them to the far side of Nat's building, and secured them to the hitching post.

Obe walked around to the front of the saloon, where he could see that a lot of folks were lined up on both sides of the street for about a block. A larger crowd of people had gathered near the front of a newly erected platform. They all seemed to be watching and waiting for someone, or something.

The two curious men stopped to watch as the train door opened. A short, robust man dressed in a white suit with a bright red vest and a blue stovepipe hat came out on the first step. He held up a trumpet and proceeded to blow a fanfare. With this, more people began coming out of houses and stores and merged towards the heralding sound.

At the conclusion of the bugling, the colorfully dressed man marched down the steps and called out in a loud voice: "Your candidate for the office of governor of the glorious state of Montana, the Honorable James B. Picket!"

The people began to applaud and cheer as Mr. Picket appeared at the top of the stairs. He was a medium-built man wearing a black suit and vest, with a gray-striped ascot at his neck. The black top hat matched his shiny black hair and handlebar mustache. He carried a black cane and walked with a slight limp as he made his way down the street and onto the stage.

Obe was so mesmerized by Mr. Picket's resemblance to what he imagined Old Scratch, the devil himself, would look like he didn't even notice the small band of women wearing dark gray dresses who were following behind the man.

The trumpeter continued blowing his horn until Picket and the six women in gray were all seated on the platform, where everyone below could see them. Then once again the heralding ceased and the robust man announced in a loud voice: "Ladies and gentlemen, the distinguished Mr. James B. Picket, the next governor of Montana."

The men and women on the stage led the applause and encouraged all the people gathered to join in.

When the politician began his speech, Obe slipped away from his father-in-law and took refuge in his old friend's place of business.

"What do you think of that fellow Mr. Picket?" Nat Broughton questioned his friend Obe as he came up to the bar.

"Kind of *spooky-lookin'* to me," Obe replied with a sneer. "Gives me the *shivers, in fact.*"

"I agree," Nat stated. "I've read some of his speeches in the newspaper, and he's not the kind of a guy us saloon owners want in office. He's pushing for statewide prohibition."

"No wonder the hair stood up on the back of my neck when the train rolled into town," Obe retorted.

As Mr. Picket's speech dragged on, some of Nat's regular customers began to slowly filter into the saloon. Everyone coming in seemed to have a general feeling of dislike for the ideas this candidate was expounding.

"This guy is crazy if he thinks I'm going to go along with his 'dry state' plan," an older gentlemen was heard to say.

"A man's got to have some form of recreation," commented another.

The grumblings and murmurings were being expressed throughout the large room as Nat's customers discussed the politician's message.

Obe went to the window to see where John had planted himself. He wanted to introduce his father-in-law to Nat before they headed back to Thompson Falls. Obe noticed as he scanned the crowd that most of the men had left the platform area. The women were now gathered closer to the stage. One of the women dressed in gray who had come with Picket was standing giving a speech. After she was finished speaking, she took a sign attached to a long stick and placed it upright in a holder at the front of the stage. Then another women in gray stood up to give her message. In between each talk, the other women onstage would shake tambourines, like a rattlesnake would shake its tail, warning of a strike.

John had spotted Obe and motioned for him to come out of the saloon. "Obe, you need to hear these gals. It's as if they are casting a spell over these womenfolk who are listening," John reported to his son-in-law.

Obe watched and listened as each gray-clad woman showed her fangs and spewed the venomous words over the crowd of ladies below. He walked a few steps to his left so he could read the signs the women were placing in the holders in front of the audience. Each one had a different statement about the evils of alcohol. JOIN THE ANTI-SALOON LEAGUE OF AMERICA, one stated. FREE YOUR HUSBANDS FROM THE BONDS OF LIQUOR ADDICTION, CLOSE DOWN THE EVIL SALOON, SAVE YOUR CHILDREN FROM THE LIQUOR MONSTER, and TEMPERANCE WILL KEEP YOUR HUSBANDS OUT OF HELL, the messages all were similar in nature and were having a marked effect on the ladies crowded around the stage.

As the last female rose to speak, Obe felt the presence of some evil force around the crowd. She was dressed in women's clothing, but she had the husky build of a man. Her dark hair was wound tight to her head, and her voice was deep and boomed over the air like thunder.

"Ladies, the time is now!" she growled out. "You must band together and stop the evil that has spread across this nation and into your very own homes. The rise of liquor consumption and its disastrous social consequences are taking over your lives. You must show courage and take back what is being stolen from you."

Obe was amazed as this snakelike creature continued to show her fangs and spit out poison to the unsuspecting prey, who listened intently.

Liquor is the root of all evil," the viper continued. "Think how different your life could be without this ugly demon in it. You would have more money for food, clothing, and even education if it wasn't being wasted in the saloons. Your husband would be sober and less irritable to you and the children. He would be home more where he belongs and could be much more productive. You, my fine citizens, need to rid your town of the saloons and take your husbands home with you. Even as our next governor was finishing his message this day your menfolk were leaving you here alone and going into that saloon over there."

The woman paused as she pointed her finger in the direction of Nat's place of business before continuing.

49

"Come, ladies. Join with the soldiers of the Anti-Saloon League of America. Together we can wipe out this alcoholic plague that is crippling our families."

The tambourines were being shaken and pounded like drums as the woman in gray marched down the stairs and into the female audience. The signs were pulled out of the holders and handed to willing crowd participants. The thunderous voice of the leader boomed out in a cry for vengeance. The snake had struck and the prey was wound tightly in its coils.

"Let us march together to take back our husbands. We can destroy the evil that keeps them in chains. Together we can conquer!" the leader instructed.

There defiantly was strength in numbers, as this newly formed army of women marched toward the building where Obe and John were standing. Obe became almost paralyzed as he realized what the ladies were about to do. It was like a nightmare he had no control over. All he could do was watch as a thrown rock went hurling through the air, just missing his head. The stone didn't miss Nat's beautiful front window, however, and both men ducked out of the way of the shattered falling glass.

With the first action, a rush of courage turned a marching army into an ugly mob. The band of women agitators stormed Nat's saloon screaming and yelling.

The occupants of the saloon were caught off guard. They had no idea that war had been declared on this business until the rock broke the window. Placards and sticks were used as weapons. The female soldiers broke mirrors, bottles, glasses, and anything else that got in the path of the weapons. They confronted their husbands and tried to drag them home. Some of the women grabbed hair, some ears, and others drove their men like cattle, hitting them with the sticks.

Nat tried to stop the destruction. He grabbed at swinging objects and yelled for people to get out, but his efforts were in vain. As he leaned over to get a club he kept behind the bar, someone hit him over the head with an ashtray and knocked him out cold.

It seemed forever before the sheriff and his deputies arrived at the scene to arrest the remaining women and take them off to the jail. But it wasn't in time to stop the intended destruction of the saloon that had been the League's target.

Obe felt so helpless. He couldn't remember ever having to face an army of housewives before. How could a man fight this kind of enemy?

The ladies weren't really evil but had been caught up in the passion of the spoken word. It was ugly for Obe to have viewed these sweet women shopping in the stores one minute and being moved to hate and destruction the next. A man couldn't draw his gun on a female with only a stick in her hand. *How was I supposed to fight a band of housewives?* he wondered.

After helping his friend to the doctor's office, Obe went back to Nat's broken saloon to secure anything left of value. Nat would need every penny and unbroken object in order to reopen his doors sometime in the near future.

John and Obe stayed in Missoula a couple of days extra before starting for home to make sure Nat was going to be OK.

"I think I'm going to get out of Montana," Nat confessed to his friend. "I hear Idaho might be a more friendly place."

Obe shook his head in agreement as he looked at his troubled friend. "Let's keep in touch, Nat," Obe requested of his friend. "Perhaps someday things will be better for both of us. Who knows? We might get that place we've talked about so much."

MOVING NORTH

The next few years brought many changes in the lives of the Knowleses and the Tooleys. Myrtle gave birth to her second child. This one was also a girl, and they named her Helen Agnes. She was born February 10, 1907, and was a cute little redhead.

Myrtle's father met a widow woman and married her in the spring of 1908. Albert, Myrtle's brother, was twenty years old at the time. He went north into Canada with a silver-mining company to work. John Senior and his new wife adopted a ten-year-old boy, by the name of Clarence, and proceeded to raise him as their own.

November elections of 1908 came, and the people voted to make Sanders County dry. Obe was forced to move his business elsewhere. He went to a small town just north of Thompson Falls, called Trout Creek, and again opened another saloon.

Trout Creek was even smaller than Thompson Falls, and the people of the community did not welcome the saloon people. They were not happy with this kind of business opening in their town, and the woman were especially cold and unfriendly to Myrtle. But Obe had many of his old customers from Thompson Falls travel over the county line to visit his place, so he tried to ignore the folks who didn't want him in town.

Obe's personality had started to change since he returned from Missoula. Myrtle could see his change in attitude toward a lot of things. He was nervous about where to go if Montana became a dry state. There was a real possibility it could happen, but he wouldn't even talk about changing professions. He was much more impatient and irritable with the girls. He became annoyed if they cried or otherwise made too much noise, which they often did.

Obe was happiest when he and Myrtle had time alone together. Those times with her seemed to be the glue that held the rest of his rickety life together. He was still able to smile and joke with his beautiful young wife. That helped his otherwise-grumpy personality from taking over completely.

In the late fall of 1908, Myrtle's brother John Junior came to live with them in Trout Creek. It was about the same time Myrtle realized she was going to have another child. She and Obe were getting along pretty well, but she knew the news of another baby would not make him happy. She prayed long and hard this one would be a boy. Perhaps a son would change Obe's attitude toward children. Myrtle wondered if he cared about his girls; she knew there was something about a man having a son that made him feel more virile and manly, she thought. She wasn't sure a boy would change anything, but she hoped it might.

It was November before she broke the news of the pregnancy to anyone. She wanted to hold off as long as possible. When Obe noticed the difference in her figure, Myrtle made light of the subject. She joked about how long it took for him to observe the difference. She pretended it was her plan to wait until someone paid enough attention to see the changes. Myrtle teased Obe that he only noticed her if dinner was late or the laundry wasn't done. By making light of the subject she hoped Obe would start out happy. She was surprised he stayed fairly civil in front of John Junior and the little girls.

When they were alone that night, Obe expressed his concerns about the expense and burden of another child. Myrtle tried to rationalize with her husband that everything would be fine. She was strong and could handle the extra work. But she knew that with the pressure of the politicians pushing for statewide prohibition, this added responsibility was not what Obe wanted right now.

Early in March of 1909, when Myrtle was in her eighth month of pregnancy, was when the letter came. She had a hard time holding it due to some swelling in her hands and fingers, but the envelope was so intriguing she couldn't stop examining it. She tried to get some clue of its contents. It was addressed to Obe, but the handwriting was beautiful and the sweet smell of a woman's perfume scented the envelope.

Myrtle put the letter in her dress pocket, taking it out four times before her curiosity got the best of her. She carefully held the letter near the steaming teakettle. Being ever so meticulous, she slowly worked the glue from the envelope loose to reveal the mystery.

In her mind, Myrtle was sure the letter was from a woman in Obe's past and was determined to read it now, before he found out it had arrived.

She slipped the paper out of the envelope and examined its shape and flowery decorations before gleaning the message. The handwriting was surely that of a females. It had curly letters and circles above the 'I's. The words, however, were those of a man, as Myrtle read them to herself.

Obe,

I hear Montana will soon be a dry state. You should leave there before that happens. I'm looking at a place in Sandpoint, Idaho, not too far north of you. We talked about being partners some day. Well, I'm looking for a partner now, are you interested?

Your friend,
Nat Broughton

The letter was short and to the point, but Myrtle was not sure how she felt about the proposition. She hated the thought of moving again so soon. However, she had no ties to the people of this unfriendly town. The house they were living in would definitely be too small when the new baby arrived, so a move would be good in that regard.

Myrtle was so caught up in her own feelings, she almost forgot about the sin she had just committed. She carefully put the letter back inside its envelope and reglued the flap. Obe would never know she had been snooping into his private mail, she rationalized.

When he came home for supper, Myrtle gave Obe the letter. He examined it carefully and then asked, "Well, who's it from, and what do they want?"

Myrtle was startled by her husband's question. He seemed to know she had read his letter, and she almost forgot to lie. "How should I know? It's addressed to you," she replied.

"A man doesn't get a letter that looks and smells like this one without having his wife read it first. Does he, Myrtle?" Obe asked with a grin and a twinkle in his eye.

He looked so impish, the guilty lady began to giggle. "Obe Tooley, you know me too well. How am I supposed to maintain any dignity if you always catch me behaving badly?" she stated. "The letter is from Nat Broughton, but you'll have to read it yourself."

He took his time opening the letter. He was trying to make his wife impatient so she would reveal the contents without his having to read them himself. But Myrtle held firm to her word, and his trick didn't work.

Obe sat quietly and studied the letter for a long while, meditating on the prospects of this new offer. He went to the small desk in the hallway and took out a pen and paper. Before writing anything, he explained to Myrtle that after this new baby arrived he would go up to Sandpoint and look into the situation.

Their third baby came April 2, 1909. This time it was a precious little boy. Obe had finally got his wish but barely had time to give his son the name of Roy Freeman Tooley before setting off for Sandpoint, Idaho.

Obe was anxious to meet with Nat about a partnership deal. Business was not too good in Trout Creek. The prospects of moving on again were all right with him.

Sandpoint was a much bigger place than the one-street town of Trout Creek. Obe had reservations about living in an area with so many people. There was one long main street in town with businesses on both sides and several side streets that supported smaller shops and houses. There was a large grassy park near a marina where folk could keep their boats for fishing and sailing on Lake Pendorilla.

It wasn't until he met with his old friend and heard the sales pitch that Obe even considered living in a place this large. Broughton painted a beautiful picture as only he could. If he could paint on canvas the way he did with his words, Nat would be a rich artist. He took Obe to a boarded-up building with old wood and fixtures and began to paint out in words and descriptions the potential and ideas he had for this place. The structure had previously been a dry goods store, the first one of its kind in town. The owner had built a more modern one at the other end of Main Street, leaving this one vacant. There was a new hotel being constructed across the road, and Nat figured this would be the perfect site for hotel patrons to enjoy some drinking and dancing recreation.

Nat had done all the legwork and found the craftsmen and materials needed to put this old building into shape. All he needed was the capital to pay for the finishing touches and the labor force.

He was a great salesman. By the time Nat had verbally and physically walked his friend through the "mural," Obe was sitting on a throne with his loving wife and children at his feet. The images were too good to be real, but Obe was convinced he wanted to be a part of this picture.

With $200 from Obe, and a handshake, the partnership was sealed. It would cost much more before all was said and done, but the money was enough to let the artist get started.

Obe returned home full of hope and enthusiasm. A FOR SALE sign went up on the saloon and house that very day. He spoke with his brother-in-law John Junior and explained a business proposition to him.

"John, if you would go on ahead to Sandpoint and work with Nat on the renovation, he would pay you a fair wage," Obe proposed. He then added another assignment for the lad. "You could also scout out the town for a house we could all live in. If you did find a good place, you could put down a deposit, move in, and get it ready for the rest of us. I'll give you the money up front to do all of this, if you're willing.''

John was so excited he could hardly keep a straight face when he answered Obe's request. ''Well, sir, if you need help, you can always count on me.''

''Then it's settled. You can leave for Idaho as soon as you can get your things together,'' Obe remarked.

''I can be ready first thing tomorrow,'' the young adult stated as he turned to go pack his gear.

John couldn't remember when he had ever been so full of enthusiasm. He had only dreamed of an experience like this one. The canvas of his thoughts looked bright and secure. He could picture himself as a man with responsibility and income. He could be on his own for a short time, with the security of a ready-made job. He would have a place to stay and money in his possession to make deals with. The young man's excitement was so high he couldn't sleep. He kept repainting the wonderful picture over and over in his mind.

When the sun burst through the small slit of the curtains announcing the arrival of morning, the reality of the adventure was set into motion. With the final instructions from Obe, $100 to save for a house, $20 advance salary, a big breakfast, and hugs and kisses from Myrtle and the little girls, John was out the door and off to become a man.

CANDLELIGHT AND DREAMS

It took Obe about two months to close out his affairs in Trout Creek and get his family and belongings moved to Sandpoint. Everyone was full of hope for this new chapter in their lives. The journey seemed long with three small children. Traveling by team and wagon was never very comfortable, but the little family was content and happy.

The house John Junior had found was more grand and spacious than Myrtle had ever dreamed possible. It was constructed of brick that had been painted white. There was ornate wood fasciae along the rooflines and around all the windows. It was set up off the ground, so a person using the front-door entrance had ten stairs to climb in order to enter. There was a roadway up the hill leading around to the back and another entrance near the kitchen area.

The banker John had dealt with explained that a gentleman from Wales had had the house built for his young bride. After she took sick and died on the passage across the sea, the gentleman only stayed in Sandpoint a year before returning to his native country. After that, another family mortgaged the house through the Sandpoint Bank. They lived in it for five years before moving out, leaving the bank no choice but to foreclose.

The banker was very motivated to sell the house. Obe's money needed to go into the business first, and he didn't have enough to buy the place. With the help of Nat's "silver tongue," they were able to talk the banker into renting Obe the house. The arrangement worked out between the parties provided that part of the rent money would go toward a down payment. This allowed the Tooleys to move into a nice house and a new lifestyle.

The two little girls, Pearl now four and Helen two, were a bit overwhelmed by the size of their new home. They stood at the foot of the long staircase that led to their bedroom and nervously looked up. They both wondered what might be at the top. Two strong arms reached down and scooped the small bodies up. Their kind Uncle John had come to the rescue.

"Come with me, fair maidens; we'll make sure the room meets with your approval before you move in," the young hero stated.

With one girl on each arm, the gallant knight carried the two little princesses up the stairway. They looked for any possible places where dragons might be hiding. They searched every room, inside closets and under beds, to make sure the castle was monster-free. When the girls felt safe and secure, John deposited them in their bedroom to get ready for the night.

Pearl and Helen were still very young, but their personalities and temperaments were quite noticeable.

Pearl was a mild-mannered person with a desire to please her parents. She was very helpful to her mother and willing and able to fetch and carry items for the house and other children. Her outward appearance was like her father's family with straight medium brown hair and a broad smile, when she chose to share it, but she had her mother's mild temperament and patient disposition.

Helen was different from her sister, looking more like her mother's family. The girl had the Knowles's wavy red hair, freckled skin, and hazel eyes. Her temperament was more like her father's, happy one minute and angry the next. She was more outgoing than Pearl and let everyone around her know if she was unhappy. It didn't take much of *not* getting her way to make her angry. As long as everything was just how she wanted it to be, she was fine.

The girls had opposite personalities, but they were the best of friends and got along great together.

The first few weeks the Tooleys were in Sandpoint were exciting ones for Myrtle. There were so many wonderful things to explore. The shopping places were of special interest to this young wife and mother. The extra effort it took to get her three little ones dressed nicely and ready to venture out was all part of the fun.

There were two mercantile stores in town. Myrtle was careful to study every shelf and case to find the treasures offered for sale. The bakery on the corner of Main and Birch Streets emitted heavenly aromas. Anyone who got near it seemed to be lured through the doors. Once they were inside, the sight of the freshly baked breads, cakes, and other treats was enough to make large and small mouths water.

As Myrtle strolled the streets with her three youngsters the smell of fresh-baked cookies caused the girls to tug on her skirt, wanting to go inside. The two little girls pressed their small noses and fingers against the glass cases that protected the goods as their mother made her purchases.

Outside the bakery, Myrtle sat the girls down on a small bench to enjoy the sweet taste of a sugar cookie. They then continued to explore other things of interest.

Down Birch Street next to the bakery was a furniture shop, where the craftsman built beautiful pieces out of wood. Many were ready and waiting for someone to buy. Myrtle examined every piece, making a mental note of the items he had for sale. She had decided to take an inventory of what she thought was necessary to purchase. The next step would be to convince Obe to let her obtain the furniture.

Sandpoint bothered the northwest corner of Lake Pendorilla, where several people made a living in some way dealing with the lake. There were bait shops, a fresh fish store, a boat-building shop, and a boat-rental store. Rich people would rent little cabins lining a grassy area above the sandy shorelines for summer vacations. A lovely grass-and-tree park separated the main part of town from the cabins. Everyone, rich or poor, was free to play ball or picnic in the recreation area.

By the time the little explorers had reached the park, the girls were ready to run and play. Baby Roy was making little fussing noises, telling Mom he was ready for lunch. Myrtle sat on a bench and nursed him while Helen and Pearl climbed a nearby grassy knoll. They practiced their rolling skills on the way down before climbing the little hill again. When lunch and playtime were over, Myrtle put Helen in the buggy with the baby. The two little ones took a nap while Pearl walked at her mother's side.

At the far side of the park was the south end of town. A view of the back corner of the new hotel caught Myrtle's eye. She could see the flags waving above a GRAND OPENING banner, so she knew they were near the new business site. She was anxious to see how much progress had been made on the back hall of Obe's new nightclub.

She crossed the street and poked her head through the swinging doors of the poorly lit saloon. George, the day barkeeper, recognized her and pointed to the side street where the sounds of a hammer striking nails were coming from. As they rounded the corner, Pearl immediately spotted her Uncle John high on a ladder. He was nailing on a sign that read: CANDLE LIGHT ROOM.

"Hey, little girl, what are you doing here?" John called down to Pearl. "Can't you read the sign? It says no one under the age of five is allowed out of their houses."

"No, it doesn't," the clever four-year-old responded. "It says big men should not climb ladders 'cause they could get hurt." She couldn't read, of course, but she liked to tease back at her favorite uncle.

"OK then, I'll just have to come down this ladder and give you a big hug for saving my life," John stated as he descended the ladder, keeping eye contact with the smiling girl as he did. He quickly grabbed her and danced around, acting silly as they laughed and twirled together.

Myrtle walked inside the Candle Light Room for the first time since the new paint and fixtures had been installed. It took a minute for her eyes to get accustomed to the dim light in the room. When she was able to focus, what she saw amazed her. She was sure anyone who saw this beautiful room would like it as much as she did.

The room was large, with three thin but tall windows on one side. They were covered with sheer curtains, providing the sunlight that was softly filtered as it came inside. There were long dark blue velvet draperies that swagged across the top and flowed down to the floor. They could be tied back for daytime light and untied for nighttime privacy.

The wall opposite the windows was covered with a large mirror, giving the illusion of a much bigger room. The remaining walls were painted an ice blue color, with decorative molding around everything. The ceiling was painted a midnight blue, with specks of silver to give a twinkling-star effect.

There was a giant chandelier hanging from the ceiling in the center of the room. It supported crystals, shaped like teardrops in different sizes, dangling all over. The fixture had three hanging circles of graduating sizes, the largest circle being nearest the ceiling. On the bottom circle, which was about five feet in diameter, were kerosene lamps. The lamps were shaped like candles and could be lit to provide the room with a soft glow. The chandelier had a silver chain that held it in place. This was also used to lower and raise the fixture for lighting.

Near the wall with the mirror was a wide but open staircase. It made a half-circle as it ascended to the second floor. At the top of the stairs was a beautiful balcony. Across the railing of the balcony and continuing down the outside edge of the banister were hand-carved cherubs. Each figure had a heart covering its naked private parts. Each little angel had a different expression on its face, which added interest and variety as a person viewed them. The entire staircase and balcony were painted white, thus giving the feel of a cloud rising up from the floor and hovering in the dark blue ceiling.

The floors were lined with marble sheets that had been vanished with a clear coat, making them sparkle.

At the far right of the room was a three-tiered stage with a beautiful white piano. There was a man at the keyboard playing a slow melodic tune. The woman who was next to the piano player was practicing a song. She was quite short but very full-figured. She had mounds of blond curls on her head, with a row of red flowers. She wore a tight-fitting low-cut red dress and shoes, adding to her flamboyant appearance.

Myrtle had the feeling she had stepped into the future somehow, as she tried to absorb all the beauty and grandeur of the room. She had never imagined it was going to be so elegant. This place was going to make them rich, she thought.

A man who had been standing behind the bar watching her finally spoke out. "Well, well, what beautiful sweet thing have we here?" the man commented. "Can I help you?" He opened a latch, lifted a small piece of the bar top, and walked through the opening.

Myrtle studied the gentleman as he walked toward her. He looked to be about the same age as her husband, with reddish blond hair and a small mustache. He was about five-ten and looked to weigh about 190 pounds. His frame seemed solid, and his broad shoulders gave the appearance of a sturdy, strong fellow. He was dressed in a dark green suit with a cream-colored shirt with ruffles down the front. It gave him the look of a man of wealth.

As he continued toward her, Myrtle was transfixed by the way he studied her. It was as if she were a piece of art being examined for purchase.

It was only the sound of Obe's voice coming from the balcony that broke the spell she seemed to be caught in. Her eyes quickly left the stranger and searched for the location of the familiar tones of her husband's voice.

"Myrtle, what are you doing here?" he questioned. "Where are the children?"

Myrtle didn't even have time to answer her husband's questions before the man in the green suit interrupted, still eyeing her intensely.

"This goddess is your Myrtle? Why, Obe, you old devil. You never told me you were married to such a beautiful woman."

The woman by the piano stopped her humming and descended the stage. She strolled her way toward Myrtle, keeping her eyes fixed on the man in the green suit. Obe watched the examination from the balcony, then began the introductions from a distance. He pointed at the women first.

"Myrtle, meet Stella Duncan, and my partner, Nat Broughton."

Nat quickly took Myrtle's hand and kissed it as he bowed slightly before her. "Your husband must have a hard time leaving home in the mornings with an angelic creature like you still there." The words seemed to roll off Nat's tongue in soft, flowing tones.

Stella watched and listened intently as Nat made overtures to this new woman, as he had done to her when they first met. She was hearing the same lines he had used on her, trying hard to lure her under his spell. The words seemed to pour from his lips so easily. Stella now questioned in her mind how many other girls had been thrown the same bait.

Myrtle could only blush and didn't know how to respond to such praise, especially with her husband looking on. She was glad when Stella broke into the uncomfortable situation.

"Nice to meet you, Myrtle. Obe speaks proudly of you and your three little ones. Are they around somewhere?" she asked about the children.

"Nice to meet both of you, too," Myrtle responded before answering Stella's question about the children. "The children are just outside the door with John. We had been walking in the park, and being we were so close, we came to see the progress on the hall." Then Myrtle asked, "Who designed this gorgeous room?"

"I worked in a club for a few years back in New York that was similar to this one," Stella replied. "When we found this place, the idea just seemed to come alive."

Nat was still mesmerized by Myrtle. He called up to Obe, who was now coming down the staircase. "Obe, she would be perfect!" were his words.

"Perfect for what?" Obe questioned.

"As our hostess for the opening of the club," Nat responded. "Picture her in a slim-cut satin gown with long white gloves and her hair curled up with flowers and pearls—"

"OK, OK," interrupted Stella. "We get the picture. Obe, he's right, you know. She would be perfect. Just the type of elegant beauty this place needs."

Myrtle chuckled in embarrassment, trying to pass off what she thought was only a joke to make her feel good.

"Sweetie," Stella remarked as she looked closely at Myrtle, "having a classy lady like you to greet the customers would be like the icing on the cake. We could really use that to sell the townspeople on a place like this. Tell you what; let's you and me go shopping tomorrow and buy everything you'll need to make you a glamorous hostess. We can get you all rehearsed and ready to go by Friday night's opening."

Obe and Myrtle were both speechless as Nat and Stella seemed to suck Myrtle up into their whirlwind of enthusiasm. Obe felt he was being left out of any decision making concerning his wife's involvement. He did agree, however, that the idea of a beautiful hostess, was a good one.

Myrtle looked at Obe with questioning eyes. "Obe?" she started to ask, but Stella interrupted. She took her by the arm, leading her to the door.

"Obe thinks it's a great idea, honey. Now let Stella get a good look at those babies he's always braggin' about."

MAGIC IN MOTION

The few days following Myrtle's meeting of Nat and Stella were full of excitement and new experiences. Stella took charge of the makeover and training of this "stay-at-home mom," trying to mold her into a glamorous and knowledgeable hostess. Besides trying on gowns, painting her face, and experimenting with a variety of hairstyles, Myrtle had to master the techniques of the job. She had to learn all the table arrangements, how many each would seat, and how to balance out the room for waiter convenience. She had always been a quick study when it came to numbers and memorization, so the configuration of tables was much easier for her than trying to be dazzling when she already felt inadequate and unqualified.

John volunteered to stay with the children on Friday evening. Myrtle needed to go early to Stella's dressing room at the club and get ready for the opening. Myrtle was excited about having a female friend and talking about girl things, more so than she was about getting all dressed up. Since her sister, Mabel, had left home so many years ago, Myrtle had been lonesome for the special bond girlfriends can have with each other.

Stella had liked Myrtle right away. She took her under her "more knowledgeable of the world" wings, making sure she would feel good about herself. Stella was a master at doing makeup and hair. She could make it look classy and glamorous, not brash or hard.

Myrtle's hair was pulled up on her head with soft folds held in place by several combs and hairpins. A row of soft pink flowers was placed at the left side near the neck, where three ringlets hung down to her shoulders.

Her gown was a soft pink with dark rose satin trim. The white lace across the bodice gave an illusion of a low cut, but her cleavage and shoulders were covered. The bodice and waist were fitted and dropped in a princess V, with a soft gathered skirt that flowed to the floor. When Myrtle put on the white gloves that extended from fingertip to elbow she truly looked and felt elegant.

"OK, sugar, let's go dazzle them," Stella commanded in an attempt to voice her approval.

The world seemed to stand motionless as Myrtle entered the hall through the dressing room door.

"OK, men. Get your eyes full now so you can get back to work before the doors open!" Stella called out, drawing the attention of everyone in the club.

64

All eyes focused on the beautiful woman who stood before them as she made an effort at modeling her revamped image.

Obe was in awe of how radiant she looked. He realized they had been married for five years and he had never taken her anyplace where she could dress up like this. He had never fully realized how beautiful his wife really was.

"You look real nice," was all Obe could think of saying. He never had been able to enchant women.

Myrtle felt her husband was sincere in his praise and almost blushed. "Well, thank you," she replied. "Your approval is real important to me." She gave him a small kiss on the cheek, then turned to listen to Nat, who was spilling out his endorsements.

"Oh me, oh my. What a stunning creature you are tonight," was the compliment coming from the man of flowery descriptions. "You look absolutely beautiful. You'll turn all the heads in the place tonight."

Stella came to the rescue of the pink-faced lady, taking Nat by the arm and leading him over to the stage, to get a last-minute opinion on one of her songs.

Sensing the tension in her husband's demeanor, Myrtle took Obe by the arm to reassure him.

"Nat was just trying to make me feel more confident about my new experience as a hostess," she explained. "Nothing more."

All of the preparation and advertising that took place prior to opening night paid off. The hall soon filled up with the enchanted patrons. Everyone was drinking, dancing, and enjoying the splendor of the Candle Light Room.

The celebration went on well past midnight. Myrtle had more fun than she had ever thought possible. She danced with everyone who needed a partner and indulged in far too much champagne. By the time the last guest went home, Myrtle was feeling so dizzy her words seemed to all run together as she tried to talk.

Obe had to lift her up on the carriage to leave the club. By the time they reached home, Myrtle had passed out in a stupor. Getting her in the house and to bed was no easy task. She had definitely been an asset in promoting the business venture. She had sold customers on booking the hall for birthdays, weddings, and business parties. On her own, she had twenty-two different reservations lined up for the next six months. Myrtle was great with people, but Obe was still not sure having her part of this nightclub scene was in his best interest.

Waking up, sitting up, and getting up were painful procedures as the sun crested the mountaintops and worked its bright beams into Myrtle's room. Her head felt about three times its normal size and weighed heavy on her neck and shoulders. The excited laughter of her children sounding like shrill screaming, adding to the trauma of her pounding eyes and head. She wanted to stay in bed, buried under the covers. However, the reality of who she was rang loud and clear in the form of a baby crying, wanting to be nursed.

What was usually an easy task of nursing a baby became impossible as the infant tried in vain to suckle the milk from his mother's bosom. Because of her aching head and the added irritation of any noise, the milk to feed the baby would not flow from Myrtle's body. Leaving the child screaming on the bed, she frantically tried to find a remedy for the pain. With an ice bag on her brow, she tried a glass of fresh apple juice, then milk but her head still throbbed violently. In desperation, she climbed on a chair and reached to the back of her top cupboard shelf. She knew a bottle of rye whiskey had been put there by her husband. Myrtle took a big drink and nearly choked as it burned its way down her throat. She steadied herself, then went back to her hungry infant. By the time she had him at her breast again the sharp pain in her head had dulled. She was able to provide the meal her baby needed.

Her body was almost back to normal by midafternoon when the knock sounded on her front door. Nat Broughton was standing there with a bouquet in his hand and a lusty look in his eyes.

"Hello, Mr. Broughton," Myrtle formally greeted the visitor. "If you're looking for Obe, he's at the club."

"Now, now, sweet lady, do you think I would be bringing flowers if I thought your husband was home?" the cunning fellow asked. "Are you going to ask me inside, or do I have to stand on this porch all day?"

Not wanting to seem inhospitable, Myrtle stepped aside and invited Nat to come into the living room.

Once inside, Nat started in on his verbiage of exaggerated compliments. "Please, beautiful goddess, take these flowers as a small token of appreciation for gracing everyone who looked upon your loveliness last night and was privileged to be in the presence of your company. Not just my eyes were fixed upon your every move, but every man there was mesmerized by your charisma. It was like seeing 'magic in motion' as you danced around the floor sweeping each partner up in a wonderful spell of charm."

Myrtle was not wholly taken in by all this praise and was well aware of the underlying intentions of this "wolf in sheep's clothing." She didn't want to be rude but knew Obe's partner needed to realize she was not interested in anyone except her husband.

"OK, Nat. Enough of the flattery," Myrtle stated. "I'm not some brainless bar girl taken in by this kind of talk. What's your real purpose for coming to see me today?"

"My, my, Obe has a tough woman on his hands, I see. Are you sure you really want me to tell you what I want?" Nat retorted as he raised his eyebrows and twisted his mustache like Simon Legree.

"No, perhaps some things are better not said," Myrtle replied and then continued in a pleading tone, "Please, Nat, let's try to be just friends. I don't want any tension in this partnership. All of us have too much invested to throw it away on foolishness. If you have any real feelings toward me, I can't help that. However, you must not let Obe even suspect anything, or he will take his frustration out on me and the children. I know how he can get sometimes. Right now we need peace in our home." As she finished her admonitions she walked to the front door and motioned for the Romeo to leave.

"All right, Mrs. Tooley, have it your way. You don't know what you're missing," Nat stated, winking at Myrtle. "I guess I'll just have to settle with seeing you from a distance at the club tonight."

"Tonight?" she responded. "I wasn't planning on being there tonight."

Nat stopped in his tracks. "Oh, you have to be there tonight. We need you!" The man looked at her with desperate eyes. "We really do need you. Stella is expecting you there at 6:00 P.M. to get dressed and ready. Didn't your husband tell you this morning?" Nat questioned.

"No, we didn't talk this morning. Does Obe know and want me to come again tonight?" she asked.

"We talked about this earlier, and he knows we need you," Nat responded.

"OK. Send John home by 5:00 P.M. so he can stay with the children again," Myrtle requested. "I'll have to hurry if I want to finish my household chores in time."

Obe didn't look pleased when Myrtle showed up to get ready for another night at the club. He knew they needed her talent and personality as a hostess, but he also didn't want his wife at the club every night. But until another solution was found, he would have to just keep quiet about the subject. He didn't like being in this position.

Myrtle had tried hard to be moderate in her champagne consumption that night, but when she awoke on Sunday morning she again had a hangover. This time, however, she bypassed all previous remedies and headed straight for the whiskey bottle. It was like adding "fuel to the fire" but that was the only thing that seemed to work to dull the headache.

Before Obe left the house the next morning, Myrtle had already decided she could not keep up the pace of clubbing every night, not if she still wanted to keep up with her other chores as a nursing mother and a homemaker. Contributing to her decision was the fact that Obe had noticed the flowers on the table and questioned her about the giver. She had tried to explain the innocence of the gift but suspected her husband did not trust his partner's intentions.

"Obe. Could we have a little talk before you leave this morning?" Myrtle inquired. "Would you be angry at me if I didn't come to the club during the weekdays? It will be too hard on our family if I'm away from home so much."

Obe had to force himself not to smile as his wife continued.

"I could make arrangements to be there on Friday and Saturday nights when it is real busy. Stella will just have to cover the rest of the nights." Myrtle knew these words were like music to her husband's ears. She pretended, though, that she thought he would be unhappy.

Obe cleared his throat so he wouldn't choke on the lie he was about to tell. "Well, I guess if you've made up your mind, I can't do much about it. You know what's best. I won't try to persuade you otherwise. I'll tell Nat and Stella we'll just have to get along on the weeknights without you."

Myrtle knew her husband well enough to sense this compromise would work out better as far as their marriage was concerned. The children also would not have to be neglected as much either.

As the week progressed, Nat and Stella both came individually, trying to change Myrtle's decision. She was able to stand firm and only worked Friday and Saturday nights.

HOLIDAY SPLENDOR

Myrtle and the children were very happy with their lives in Sandpoint. The people of the town seemed friendly and accepting toward them. Myrtle became well-known among the socialite women and was invited to join their clubs and organizations. At first she felt flattered, thinking it was her charm and personality they wanted. It didn't take long to realize the underlying motive for their friendship was access to her time and money.

Myrtle joined the Women's Club and the City Beautification League. She spent some of her time participating in different projects around the community. Obe was also invited to join some of the men's organizations. He picked the Odd Fellows only because he liked the men who were members.

Things were going well by Christmastime. Everyone seemed happy and content. The business was holding its own, and the bills were being paid on time. Myrtle was able to hire a woman to come in a few days a week to help with the housework and the children while she fulfilled her civic responsibilities.

Myrtle enjoyed this grand lifestyle and tried to live it to the "hilt." She had many opportunities to promote her husband's business, and a "toast" to more happy days always made her feel good. She never stopped to think how many drinks she was having or just how often she imbided. She didn't feel the drinking was becoming a problem. It was very subtle at first. It took almost a year before she realized she was needing alcohol for more than just social occasions. Myrtle still felt in control, however, and rationalized, *A little drink now and again never hurt anyone.*

By Chrismastime 1909, Myrtle had all sorts of wonderful ideas and plans for decorating the house and the club. She had seen a catalog back in October for some lovely glass ornaments, and the partners agreed to pay for them. When they arrived the first day of December, Myrtle was in the mood to decorate.

The little girls were dressed in their new winter coats and boots. Obe put them up on the wagon between himself and their Uncle John for the ride to the country. Pearl and Helen were so excited about helping select the Christmas trees for the house and club. Myrtle had instructed the tree cutters to get a nice tall one for the Candle Light Room and a smaller one for the living room.

Preparing for Christmas was wonderful for the Tooley children. They helped with making decorations for the tree and baking the wonderful treats to eat. They strung popped corn and cut out snowflakes from white paper. They helped cut out gingerbread men and frosted them after they had been baked. Myrtle knew the children were eating almost as many as they put on the tree. She taught them carols to sing with her and took them shopping for a present. The whole holiday season was filled with joy and pleasant experiences.

When Myrtle's brother Albert showed up on Christmas Eve with presents for everyone, Myrtle felt she was experiencing a touch of "heaven on earth."

Albert had matured into a very handsome young man, with his dark hair and blue eyes. He had grown a few more inches in the last two years since Myrtle had seen him and now stood five-ten in height. He was so glad to see his brother and sister and proud of his nieces and nephew.

After all the gifts were placed under the tree and the children were put to bed, the adults gathered in the living room around the Christmas tree. They listened to Albert tell of his experiences over the last two years. He had been working with a silver-mining company in Montana. He had also become quite proficient in testing the content of silver in the diggings at the mines. The company had expanded their operations to Nevada, and Albert was being sent there to work.

He had been anxious to see everyone in the family before going so far away, not knowing how long he might be gone. He began to relate what had transpired when he went back to Thompson Falls to see his father. John Junior and Myrtle had so many questions about their father and his new wife that Albert had to tell them to stop asking questions and listen as he continued his report.

"When I went to their old canyon home and knocked on the door, a strange woman answered. She told me her husband had bought the place six months prior. The Knowleses now lived in a new place up the road. When I arrived at the new house, Father was very happy to see me, but his new wife, Rosie, was as cold as an Arctic fish."

Myrtle and John both laughed at Albert's description of their new stepmother and encouraged him to continue his story.

Next he described the spoiled boy named Clarence his father and stepmother had adopted.

"This boy is now twelve years old and gets anything he wants from Rosie. Dad didn't say much about the boy. Whenever he did try to correct

70

any bad behavior, Rosie would immediately go to the imp's rescue. This boy is definitely not getting the same kind of discipline we received growing up.''

Albert went on to tell his siblings of the financial situation he found his father in. Not only had Rosie spent every penny their father had got for the old house, but she now had him in debt. He could not possibly live long enough to pay back all his creditors.

Albert felt so uncomfortable with his father's new situation he only stayed for two days. He knew he would feel more comfortable with his sister and her family. It was for this reason he had come before Christmas, instead of after, as he had planned.

"Well, the house is different," commented Albert. "But I feel at home, now I am here with all of you—"

"Albert," Myrtle broke into her brother's remarks, "now we won't take *no* for an answer; you must stay here and celebrate New Year's Eve with us. We're holding the biggest party this town has ever had, at the club, and we really want you to be there."

"Yes, Albert. You have to stay," coaxed John. "I've turned twenty-one now, and this will be my first real New Year's celebration."

"Great. You two have twisted my arm," joked Albert. "If you're going to force me to go to a party and have fun, then I'll try hard to make the sacrifice, for your sakes."

Rolls of streamers and a large box of balloons had been ordered to decorate the club. It took every adult member of the family, plus the workers, to set the ornaments in place. When everything was finished, the club looked very festive.

Welcoming in the year of 1910 was done with class and enthusiasm in the Candle Light Room. New Year's Eve was truly a night to remember. Everyone was dressed in their best party attire, ready to have a swell time. More important, the patrons were willing to spend their money on the beverages for the occasion. The champagne flowed and the money rolled in, making Obe more jovial than usual.

John and Albert looked so dashing all dressed up. The single ladies flirted and teased them both all evening long.

Myrtle was dancing with someone different every dance, making sure everyone had a good time. Albert was surprised at this different side of his sister he had never seen before this night. He wasn't aware she could dance so well or be so outgoing with men. He was even more astonished at the amount of liquor she was consuming. When he mentioned it to John, he replied, "She's going to hate herself tomorrow, but it won't be the first time."

As the countdown for the new year started, everyone tried to position themselves close to the person they wanted to kiss on the stroke of midnight. Myrtle was looking for Obe, but the crowd was so thick, making movement almost impossible. When the count was down to three-two-one, a big hand turned her around. A passionate kiss was then planted on her lips. The body that held her close was warm and inviting. The fervent moment sent her already-swirling head into a captive trance. It was only the sound of Obe's voice behind her and the quick movement of the man embracing her that brought Myrtle back to reality. She realized it was not her husband who had kissed her. Instead, Nat Broughton had stolen the midnight passion.

"Excuse me!" Obe indignantly snapped at Nat. "I think Stella is looking for you."

Nat in his most innocent manner played off the incident as if it were only a joke. "Easy, partner, I was only trying to help you out here. I knew you wouldn't want your wife to go without a New Year's kiss," he replied with a little chuckle.

"I don't need this kind of help from you or anyone else with my wife," Obe retorted. "I'll take care of all the kissing she needs. You find someone else to lay your affections on."

As Nat strolled away, Obe gave Myrtle a hard, stern glare. He then began to quietly scold her in firm, mean tones. "What kind of a tramp are you becoming? What's going on behind my back between you and Nat?"

Myrtle was stunned by everything that was occurring. First the surprise kiss and now the confrontation, with accusations being thrown at her. If the effects of the alcohol hadn't been clouding her thinking powers, she could have replied with firmness about her innocence. But with the drunkenness dulling her senses, all she could say was, "What do you mean? Did I do something wrong?"

Albert, who witnessed the whole scene, came to his sister's rescue. He tried to explain to the jealous husband what had happened. "Obe, it wasn't her fault. The guy took advantage of her. I saw the whole thing."

It took Obe a minute to cool down enough to release the grip he had on Myrtle's arm. He instructed Albert to take her home, as she was too drunk to help clean up.

Myrtle woke up with her usual hangover. She now had the whiskey bottle close at hand, hidden in the pocket of her old gray sweater. If she stalled long enough getting bathed and dressed on these hangover mornings she was able to fool everyone, including herself, into believing that she wasn't drinking too much.

Albert recognized right off the difference in his sister's demeanor but kept his concerns to himself. He would try to help her later to understand the danger she was getting into by drinking. He first wanted to carefully bring up the political topic of prohibition looming heavy over the country. His goal was to do it carefully and not make anyone at the breakfast table angry at him. He figured it would be a sore subject in this home, so he proceeded with tact and caution.

"Has there been anything exciting going on here in Sandpoint that would be of interest to a bachelor like myself?" Albert first inquired.

"No!" John quickly responded. "The best time to be here is in the summer. The rich girls come with their families and stay at the lake cabins."

Albert paused a moment, shaking his head in approval of his brother's answer, then asked his next question. "What's your opinion of the great state of Idaho? How would you rate this state's government?" He was hoping this inquiry would invoke the response he wanted.

"Politicians, hm-m. All a pack of wolves," Obe replied.

"What makes you say that?" Albert asked.

"All they want to do is nose into everyone's business and cause people grief and hardship," the barkeeper answered. "Take this prohibition thing as an example. No one is this town except a few so-called religious do-gooders wants to give up the freedom to buy liquor. But for some no-good reason, those politician guys at the capital can't find anything better to do than to make folks miserable."

Obe had taken the bait, and now Albert could voice his opinion if he did it carefully. "I sure do agree with your thoughts about some politicians—they think they need to change everything once they get elected. But I have met a lot of good people, some very religious and some not, who feel liquor is a bad vice. The religious folks tell me the Bible says alcoholic drinks are against God's teachings and he doesn't approve of their use. But I wouldn't know for sure, because I haven't read the Good Book clear through. I've only read a few passages here and there." He paused for a moment, hoping for a response from Obe. When he got nothing, he continued. "You know, America was founded

73

on the rights of people to make their own lots in life. We also have the freedom to choose if we want to do something or not, as long as we are not hurting anyone. Government shouldn't interfere in this matter.''

Obe thought about what Albert was saying but was more willing to listen than respond.

"What will you do if the whole United States adopts prohibition?'' the young man asked. "You know it's definitely a possibility.''

Obe didn't want to even think about this idea but had a readied answer. "Move to Canada, I guess.''

With the quick response, Obe got up from the table, put on his coat and hat, and went out the front door.

Myrtle had been silent, pretending not to listen to the conversation. When everyone else was gone from the kitchen, leaving her and Albert alone, he again posed questions for his sister to answer.

"You have become quite a socialite, haven't you, Sis?'' he commented.

Myrtle knew her brother well enough to realize she was in for a lecture. She responded with a question back. "Just what are you getting at, *little brother?*'' She emphasized the "little brother'' part with a firm tone in her voice.

"How many glasses of champagne did you end up drinking last night?'' Albert asked. "I counted five myself. You were putting them down like water.''

Alberts' third-degree inquiries made Myrtle defensive. "What did you do all night? Follow me around counting?'' she retorted.

"Myrtle. Stop and listen to yourself. Don't snap at me. I'm your brother and I love and care about you. You took the place of our mother when she died, and I respect you more than any other living woman I know. If I can't speak the truth to you, then who can? I'm only concerned about your well-being and happiness. Your sweet children need you to be healthy and to be assured they will have a mother to raise them. And I need a sister to tell all my troubles and experiences to.''

Myrtle lightened up with the loving words from her concerned brother. "I know, Albert. Just believe me—I have everything under control.''

"I have been reading about studies some scientists are doing on the effects drinking too much alcohol can have on your body,'' Albert reported. "Did you know alcohol can cause the liver to harden, resulting in death?''

74

"Really!" replied Myrtle. "Please don't tell Obe; he would probably call you a liar."

"They also think women who drink have more miscarriages and smaller, less healthy babies. I guess those are some of the reasons certain people are pushing for liquor to be outlawed," Albert stated. He paused to let his sister digest the information before continuing his lecture. "Myrtle, you and Obe are going to have to face the fact that prohibition is going to happen. I've seen a lot of influential people who are in favor of it. These folks are pressing the president and Congress to make it a law. Your family needs to make some serious decisions and preparations. You'll want to be ready when they close down your business. You should encourage your husband to sell out while he can make a big profit. He could start early and go into some other type of work," the wise young man advised.

Myrtle silently contemplated the possibilities. She knew in her soul Obe was not a man to be pushed into something he *did not* want or go quietly when pushed out of something he *did* want. He had become much more stubborn the last few years, and she knew it wouldn't get better as he got older.

Everyone hated to see Albert go when he left for his new assignment in Nevada on the fourth of January 1910.

The Tooleys spent the next few months doing things at home until the winter weather was over.

Little Roy was growing so fast and started to walk by March. He was all boy and, unlike the girls, wanted to be rowdy and play rough. Obe never had time for such foolishness, so when he was gone John spent time with Roy. John played ball and gave all the kids "horsey" rides on his back. The children really loved having their Uncle John around.

When summer arrived John got a job working for one of the boat-rental places down by the lake. Because he was good at working with wood, it was his job to make sure the boats were in good repair and ready for the customers. In the month of August he met a man named Peter Irvin, who owned a boat construction factory in Vancouver, Canada. Mr. Irvin was always looking for talented craftsmen and offered John a good position. The salary would be more than enough to provide for the needs of a bachelor. The only drawback was that he would have to move to Canada. The fact that the man also had two nice-looking daughters, however, played a big part in John's decision to accept the offer.

Myrtle and the children were going to miss him terribly, even though she realized a young man of twenty-one needed to make a life of his own.

DRIVING THE WEDGE

John Junior had only been gone for a few weeks when Myrtle realized she was pregnant again. She was hoping this time it was a mistake. A pregnancy now would just complicate her life. She would have to stop being a hostess at the club on Friday and Saturdays. This would cause everyone there to be unhappy with her. She knew Obe didn't want more children right now, and she wasn't ready to cope with his opposition.

Myrtle kept the information to herself for a long time. She wore loose-fitting gowns and flowing blouses and jackets. By doing this she was able to keep the pregnancy a secret until just before Christmas.

Nat had been keeping a sharp eye on Myrtle, much closer than her own husband, and could tell something was different about her. Besides the loose-fitting clothes, he observed the way she interacted with men, and that while doing her hostess responsibilities she was not her usual self. He noticed she was careful not to dance close. She also tried to keep her drinking down to one glass of champagne each night.

Just before closing one Saturday night the week prior to Christmas, Nat asked Myrtle to dance. He purposely pulled her very close to him, against her will. He could then feel the changes in her body shape. "So, little mother, what does Obe think about you having baby number four?" Nat asked with a chuckle.

"What are you talking about, Mr. Broughton?" Myrtle retorted, hoping he might drop his inquiry.

"Come on now, Mommy," the nosey man continued. "If I can tell, surely your own husband knows by now." Nat pulled her even closer as he continued. "If you were my wife, Myrtle, you wouldn't have to try and hide the news. I'd be the happiest man alive and shout it from the rooftops."

Myrtle reached up quickly and put her fingers across Nat's mouth. "Sh-h-h! I know I'll have to tell Obe very soon, but don't you say anything before I have a chance to tell him myself," she insisted.

After all the customers were gone that night and everyone was preparing to leave, Nat did a terrible thing. The Tooleys were in their carriage ready to depart when Nat yelled at them from the doorway of the club. What he said was meant as a joke, but he was the only one who thought it was funny.

"Myrtle, have you told Obe our little secret about the baby yet?"

Myrtle was speechless. She felt the blood rush to her face in anger. She was trapped in a position she had never wanted to be in. Yes, she was five months pregnant. Her body was showing the bulges of the infant growing inside. She couldn't tell a lie at this point even though she wanted to. But it was a rotten thing for Nat to imply she had willingly told him about the baby before her own husband.

Myrtle tried to explain the whole situation to Obe in a calm, matter-of-fact way. She knew he was angry, however, when he ordered her to shut up until they got home.

The ride home was terrible, as she anticipated her husband's anger. Would he be angrier at the fact that she was pregnant again or that Nat knew before he did? Whatever the reason, Myrtle suspected her home life would be a living hell for a while.

It wasn't until the babysitter had left their house and the couple was alone that Obe began his ranting tirade. His questions to Myrtle started off with shaky calmness but soon escalated to a fit of anger.

"Why were you trying to hide this pregnancy, woman? Don't you think your husband has the right to know about it before the rest of the world? What kind of dignity can a man maintain if another man is the one to break the news?" Obe continued his questions but didn't give Myrtle a chance to respond before starting in again. "Maybe the *real father* was the first to know. Are the two of you trying to cover up your little love affair?"

She could handle all the questions, but not this accusation. Myrtle quickly interrupted the angry man before this train of thought went any further. "Now you listen here, Obe Tooley. I may have been wrong to keep this pregnancy a secret for so long. But if you would have paid any attention to me the last month you would have seen my figure was changing. I can't help it if Nat noticed before you did. He thought he was being *cute* by saying what he did. But I want you to know so you don't have any doubts or say unrespectful words to me again. You are the only man I have ever been with. And the only one who could possibly be the father of this unborn infant. Don't you ever think I am the kind of woman who would be unfaithful to you as long as I am your wife." Myrtle finished her oration with tears streaming down her face. She then went into the bedroom and closed the door.

The couple never spoke of the incident again. But Nat had succeeded in driving a wedge between them that hadn't been there before.

AND BABY MAKES SIX

The Tooleys' fourth child, another boy, was born April 10, 1911. They named him Earl Eugene. With the added work and time it took for this new infant, Myrtle had to rely on the two girls to help with some of the chores.

Four-year-old Helen's job was to keep two-year-old Roy busy and out of trouble while her mother was nursing the baby. It seemed Roy wanted to get into mischief when Myrtle was paying attention to his new brother. Helen would play games with Roy to keep him occupied. His favorites were Ring around the Rosie, Run and Chase, and Roll the Ball.

Pearl was now six years old and was learning to sweep and mop floors. She was also good at dusting carefully and folding some of the laundry. Both she and Helen would straighten their beds each day and clean up the bathroom. Myrtle tried to teach them work could be fun if shared with someone you loved.

Sometimes after all the work was done Myrtle would let the children help her make a cake. They especially liked the activity on stormy days when they couldn't go outside to play. Myrtle also used this procedure as therapy for troubled hearts. Mixing the ingredients, smelling the wonderful aroma, and spreading the sweet frosting was the best medicine ever for chasing away the blues. By the time they got around to eating the scrumptious morsels, the clouds were gone and a bright new day was ahead.

The club and saloon businesses were doing fine. They were bringing in enough revenue to pay their own way and make a fair amount of profit for the partners to share.

Myrtle went back to hostessing on Saturday nights only. She felt she needed some social fun in her life.

Myrtle tried hard to stay away from Nat as much as possible. She knew he still had romantic feelings for her. It was hard to hold a normal conversation with him without his thinking or hoping she was flirting. Stella could see Nat's reaction toward Myrtle and began to resent her being at the club.

Myrtle could only spend a little time with her women organizations, now that she had four little ones at home. But the arrangement was all right with her. Because of all the political turmoil about prohibition and the controversy looming over the country, Myrtle was always uncomfortable when the topic of conversation turned in that direction. The women were especially verbal in a negative sense. They wanted to keep their husbands out of saloons and other drunkards off the streets. Myrtle could agree with many of their points of view, but she would not even mention them to Obe, or he would fly into a fit of rage. Any control whatsoever on the use of alcohol was not a topic open for discussion in the Tooley household. Myrtle just kept quiet about her own opinions.

Obe enjoyed his men's club and got involved in every project the Odd Fellows sponsored. In March of 1912, the club hired a photographer to come and take pictures of its members. As part of the deal, individuals could get family group shots at a reduced price. With Obe on the committee, he insisted Myrtle get the children dressed in their best apparel and meet him at the studio for pictures.

It didn't take any coaxing. Myrtle was excited about getting pictures of her beautiful children. Obe dressed in his club uniform and Myrtle in her best outfit. She wore a soft blue suit with a wide lapel on the coat and large pockets on the skirt. Her hat was encircled with a lot of light blue and white flowers, with a matching bow on the left side. The girls had on pretty white dresses with rows of matching lace down the bodice and around the skirt. Their hair was fixed in long ringlets, with a large blue bow pinned in the back. Roy was dressed in blue-and-white striped knickers with a matching sailor-collared top. He wore stockings that were medium blue and covered is entire leg. His light blond hair was parted on the left side and combed neatly.

Baby Earl, who was almost a year old, was in his nicest white dress with a light blue bonnet.

The family gave the appearance of a happy group, and the pictures became Myrtle's most treasured possessions.

Obe had made a lot of friends living in Sandpoint, one of whom was Wayne Parker, a deputy sheriff. Wayne liked the products Obe sold, and several favors had been performed for under-the-table payments. One of the services was handling the influential or wealthy patrons in a discreet manner. If anyone at the club became drunk and disorderly, instead of an arrest, he received a sheriff escort home. This special service saved him from embarrassment and kept Obe's club in good graces. It was part of the "scratch my back, and I'll scratch yours" theory going on among the locals.

The Tooley Family Sandpoint, Idaho 1912

Helen, Roy, and Pearl

Obe, Baby Earl, and Myrtle

The saloon seemed to be a big source of controversy in town by 1912. The churchwomen were always trying to find ways to get Obe and Nat in trouble. Mr. Parker had to step in several times to keep the peace, but it didn't come for free. The saloon keepers provided many free drinks in order to keep things relatively calm.

Nat and Obe had taken precautions with the construction of the saloon and club to prevent another tragedy like the one in Missoula. They didn't want the churchwomen to take the same kind of action as the women of the Anti-Saloon League.

The windows all had outside shutters, and heavy wooden doors were installed on each entrance. The building could be locked to prevent mob destruction of the inside fixtures. The partners had experienced firsthand the lengths the prohibitionists would go to in order to put their point across. They hoped the same thing wouldn't happen to them again. The only way the business building could be destroyed this time would be by natural disaster or fire, and they had insurance against the latter.

Deputy Parker had been successful in warning the saloon keepers on two different occasions when the churchwomen had organized and marched the streets in protest against their business. It took only a few minutes to seal the building and prevent damage. The few rocks and sticks thrown had bounced right off the wooden protectors. Parker was able to calm down the troublemakers and send them home. He definitely didn't want anything to happen to his source of good liquor.

It was September 1912 when Myrtle received a letter from Mr. James Cox, an attorney hired by her stepmother, Rosie. The letter brought sad news.

To the children of John Knowles: Myrtle, Albert and John Jr.:

Your father John Knowles passed away on August 15, 1912, and was buried in the Riverwood Cemetery.

All of his worldly possessions were left to his wife Rosie and their son Clarence.

If you wish any additional information or have any questions about this matter, you may write to me at 352 North Spring St., Thompson Falls, Montana.

> Yours respectfully,
> James B. Cox
> Attorney

Myrtle was devastated by the news of her father's death. The way the message had been sent was shocking, cold, and cruel. She would miss her father so much and wished she could have been with him at the end.

Rosie's lawyer had made it perfectly clear there would be no inheritance for Myrtle or her brothers. But that really didn't matter to Myrtle. It really bothered her, however, that it took five weeks for her to receive this notice. Why had they waited so long?

This was just the start of many questions that began to surface. What had been the cause of John's death? Had he been sick for a long time or was his death sudden? Or was it an accident? What, Where? How? When? All the unknown questions would haunt her if she didn't get answers.

Myrtle wanted to pack her bags and go to Thompson Falls that very day to get the answers. For once, Obe showed compassion and stopped her. He brought her back to the reality of the situation. He helped her see there was nothing she could do to bring back her father. He explained that John had been a good man and was now in his proper resting place. It would be better for Myrtle to be at home grieving among folks who cared about her than with her stepmother, who obviously didn't want her around. Obe encouraged her to write to the lawyer first to get the details she wanted. If his answers didn't clear up the matter, then she could contact John's doctor or the sheriff.

For the first time in almost a year, Myrtle and Obe actually embraced with tenderness. The hardness wedging their once-loving relationship seemed to soften for a few short minutes as Obe held his sobbing wife.

Obe, too, would miss John's friendship. The two of them had experienced some good times and some rough times together. They had supported each other in the face of danger and had backed each other when necessary. All in all, Obe could say he had liked his father-in-law very much and was saddened now by his passing.

THE OYSTER SHELL BEGINS TO OPEN

Pearl had never seen her parents so sad before, especially her mother, and she wanted to do something to make them happy again. The child's solution was a simple one. Everyone should go into the kitchen and help make a cake; then everything would be better. But when she suggested it to her mother, Myrtle went into the bedroom and started crying again.

When morning came and Pearl had to leave for school, she gave the younger children orders to be good and not bother their mother too much. She promised to tell them stories about what she had learned if they would stay out of trouble until she got home. Even though Pearl was only seven, she was a big help in keeping her younger siblings in line. She knew she could bribe Helen and Roy, but she worried about baby Earl. He was mastering walking and wanted to get into everything. Pearl made five-year-old Helen promise to keep a special eye on Earl so he wouldn't get hurt. Pearl tried to think of everything she had in her little seven-year-old bag of tricks to make sure everyone was OK before she left the house.

She had a hard time keeping her mind on school. When the last bell of the day rang, to let her go home, Pearl was happy. She just wanted to do everything she knew to help her mother get better soon. The quality of taking care of others seemed to be one she had been born with. Even at this young age she was practicing to improve the gift.

When Pearl arrived home from school, Helen and Roy were in the front yard. Mother was staring out the window with little Earl crying in her arms. Her mother's eyes were red and puffy, and Pearl, afraid to see the sadness still in her mother's face, took her schoolbooks and papers inside and gave her mother a hug around her waist.

"I can take the baby for a ride in the buggy. He will probably stop crying when he goes outside," Pearl suggested.

Myrtle handed the youngster to her oldest daughter. "Don't go too far, and be back in an hour. I'm going to my room to rest. I didn't get much sleep last night."

Pearl gathered her sister and brothers and made a game up as they took their walk. "Find a bug," she instructed.

Roy was always the first one to do it. He loved looking for and finding bugs.

"Find a yellow flower," was her next request. The game went on and on, with just enough variety to keep the little group together.

By the time they reached home, the afternoon sun was bright and hot as it made its trek toward the western horizon. Earl had fallen asleep in the buggy, so Pearl put him in a cool, shady spot. She made up stories for Helen and Roy as she had promised. After several tales, Roy began to complain -about being hungry. The little band of siblings picked up their things to go inside. The baby was awake now and held Pearl tightly around the neck as they climbed the front stairs and went inside the house.

Everything was so quiet inside. Only the ticking of the clock in the hallways made any noise. There was no sound of dishes or pots clanking together. No sizzling noises were coming from the stove. There was only eerie silence to little ears.

"Mommy!" Helen called out, but no answer was returned.

"I'm hungry, Momma, and want to eat," was the call from the three-year-old, but the silence continued.

"Go in the kitchen and get the bread and butter," Pearl advised. "Momma must still be resting."

Pearl knocked softly on the bedroom door, and it cracked open at her touch. She cautiously peeked in, with hopes of seeing her mother up and ready to fix dinner. But she was not up. She was on the bed, still sound asleep. She only moved slightly and moaned when Pearl shook her and pleaded for her to wake up. There was a funny smell in the room. But Pearl didn't understand the meaning of the empty whiskey bottle on the night stand, next to her mother's bed.

When she couldn't wake her mother up, Pearl got frightened. She ran to Mrs. Thomas, the lady down the street. She was always nice to the neighbor children, and Pearl hoped she might know what to do. Mrs. Thomas immediately stopped everything and went with the girl to see about Mrs. Tooley. When the neighbor could not wake Myrtle either, she muttered a few words about that *demon alcohol*. She then sent her husband to fetch Mr. Tooley.

"Someone needs to look after you children until your mother sobers up," was Mrs. Thomas's rude comment.

Pearl didn't know what *sober up* meant, but she did feel more secure when her dad came home.

Dinner was simple that night. Obe really didn't want to answer with the truth when Pearl inquired what *sober* meant. He did, however, try to tell the children in a simple way that their mother did not feel good. She was very sad over the death of their grandfather. The children had no concept of death, and Obe could not explain it in simple-enough terms for them.

Pearl finally figured out death was the way a person got to heaven, where God was, and the person was happy when he got there, but the people who loved him were sad. The reason the people on earth were sad was because they had been left behind. The idea was still rather confusing to the younger siblings. However, it made more sense than the way their father had explained.

It took almost three months and several letters to convince Myrtle that her father had died of natural causes. There had been no foul play involved. It was not until her mind was put at ease that she was able to recover from the shock and despair of the incident.

By December, Myrtle was back to her normal self and ready to make Christmas a happy time for the family. Everyone got involved with the tree selection and the decorations. Happiness had returned to Myrtle's countenance, and even Obe displayed a few little signs of a pleasant father. Shopping for surprises was a delightful adventure, and the girls tried their hands at wrapping some of the presents. The house smelled with the delicious aromas of sugar and spice as Myrtle baked her special holiday treats.

Obe spent more time at home than he had for a long time. He even allowed the children to sit on his lap and play tickle games. Most of the time he was aloof from such foolishness, but for now he demonstrated some small traits of a father.

AND THE DREAM CAME TUMBLING DOWN

The peace and contentment in the Tooleys' home seemed to vanish soon after the holidays were over. The year 1913 loomed heavy with bad luck, starting as early as February. Ministers had joined together and vowed to push hard for prohibition to be adopted statewide. The politicians were being pressed to make it happen in Idaho.

Nat and Obe knew it was only a matter of time before some big decisions would have to be made. If they could sell the building and get out from under their obligations concerning it, they could decide what to do next.

Stella had met a rich man from Seattle, and they were married on Valentine's Day. She left that very day with her new husband to start a new life for herself. She had been smart enough to see the "handwriting on the wall" and get out before it was too late.

The Webb-Kenyon Act passed in Washington, D.C., in March, even over the veto of President Taft. With this act, the partners knew operating a saloon was soon going to be illegal.

Myrtle read aloud to Obe from the newspaper the definition of this act: "This law forbids the transportation of intoxicating liquors into a state by any person interested therein to be received, possessed, sold or in any manner used either in the original package or otherwise." She paused to think about what she had read and then asked, "If Idaho adopts this act, we will be out of business. Where do we go from here?"

"Nat and I are putting the building up for sale," Obe answered. "We were told it would make a fine restaurant, but we're not interested in selling food. We've decided to stick with what we know."

"Why don't you try something else, Obe?" the concerned wife carefully suggested. "We could buy some kind of business down by the marina, perhaps a ferryboat—"

Obe cut her words off sharply and began to yell at her. "Don't try to make me into someone else, woman! I don't know anything about boats, and I don't plan on learning a new trade," he snapped. "Don't you worry; I'm working on a way to keep food in all the hungry mouths around here." He stomped out the front door and slammed it, as he usually did when angry.

Communication was becoming almost impossible these days, and Myrtle could tell trouble was brewing. She wondered how long it would be before the family would be on the move again.

The Fourth of July started off with a loud *Boom* from the cannon in the park. Pearl could hardly wait to get ready for the parade that would take place down Main Street. She opened the curtains and looked out her bedroom window, just in time to see Mr. Cohen across the street putting an American flag along the side of his house. Other folks also had flags waving in the yards. The sight prompted the eight-year-old girl to take a deep breath and suck in the grandeur of the scene.

After breakfast, Myrtle got dressed in a new red dress she had purchased especially for the celebration. Pearl and Helen had matching white dresses with a red sash and bow for Pearl and bright blue trim for Helen. The two boys both had short blue pants with blue-and-white matching shirts. Everyone was the picture of American patriotism. All except Obe, however, who couldn't find a good reason to pay tribute to a country that might force a man out of making an honest living. He was dressed in his gray suit and refused to even wear the red-and-white striped tie Myrtle had bought for him.

All the streets were lined with Old Glory for the occasion. There was a parade, with a marching band and clowns. But the best part of the parade for Pearl was the Model T motorcars that carried the mayor and state senator. She could hardly believe such a wonderful machine had been invented and two of them were right here in Sandpoint. A fantastic new era was beginning. The age of motorcars was starting, and she was witnessing it right now.

The parade was a sight to behold for the young girl, and Pearl's senses had marvels to behold all day long. Bright colors, marching bands, the smell of roasting chicken for picnic lunches, and the sweet taste of cotton candy. Pearl wished this day could last forever.

When the man in the park started talking about something called "temperance," Pearl's father insisted the family take a walk to the saloon. He wanted to make sure everything was locked up. After all the doors and windows were latched tight, the family strolled to the marina. Mr. Parker was there laughing and joking with a small group of people.

A ferryboat pulled into the dock, and the children watched all the people. Everyone was dressed in their holiday attire. When the folks got off the boat, they scattered in different directions, looking for ways to celebrate.

Mr. Parker insisted on taking the whole family over to Lakeview, a little tourist town on the other side of Lake Pendorilla. The children were so excited about the boat ride. Pearl pretended she was a beautiful princess, who had been captured by pirates.

After docking at Lakeview, the little band of mariners explored the shoreline and threw small stones into the lake. The children had a great time pretending and playing games as they toured the little shops along the way.

The grown-ups talked the whole time, but Pearl noticed the somber look on her mother's face. Whatever they were talking about, Pearl thought, did not make her mother smile even once. The observant girl could tell by the way her father and mother looked at each other that they didn't agree on the topic.

By the time they arrived back in Sandpoint in the evening, it was time for dinner and fireworks. Pearl thought this was probably the most wonderful day of her life, and she vowed to herself to remember it forever.

Problems began to arise quickly. Critical decisions that should have been analyzed long and hard were made in haste. A meeting between Nat, Wayne Parker, and Obe ended in a disagreement. Everyone was sure Idaho would adopt a statewide prohibition in wake of the Webb-Kenyon Act, but what to do next was the basis for the contention.

Wayne Parker proposed that even though the saloons would be shut down, there could be a lot of money made selling alcohol on the sly. He told them of a house his sister had for rent in Lakeview. It would be the perfect location to set up the operation. He had already talked to his uncle, Sam Parker, the sheriff over there. Sam had agreed to "look the other way," so to speak, if the transactions were done discreetly. With a small cut of the profits to the lawman, a person could make good money. All they would need was a large supply to sell.

Nat didn't like the idea and planned to go up north into Canada. He would look for a business location up around Calgary. He encouraged his partner to come with him, but Obe was more in favor of Parker's scheme.

When Myrtle was presented with the Lakeview idea, she also disagreed. She tried to talk her husband into a different way of making a living. Her arguments fell on deaf ears, because Obe had already ordered the big supply of liquor. He told his wife she had no say in the matter and to prepare to move to Lakeview. The move was to be kept a secret, however, and she wasn't even to tell the children.

Myrtle was miserable and depressed about this decision. The last four years in Sandpoint had been happy and prosperous ones. She hated the thought of giving up the life they had here.

On Tuesday morning, Myrtle picked up the newspaper and read the headline: "IDAHO ASSEMBLY VOTES IN FAVOR OF PROHIBITION, BILL NOW GOES TO THE SENATE." Her heart sank to the pit of her stomach as she anticipated the impact this action would have on her life.

She instructed Pearl to take the children to the park for a picnic and she had to take the paper to Obe and give him the bad news. She fought back the tears that were trying desperately to surface as she got ready to go outside. She didn't want anyone to see her crying as she went to the saloon.

Myrtle arrived at the club just as the two partners were shaking hands with three other men. She didn't want to intrude, but Nat spotted her. He invited her in, to meet the new owners of the Candle Light Club. Mr. Jones, the banker, was also there. He told the partners he would have the money transferred and ready for them within two days. The new owners would be taking over August 1, 1913.

The tears that had been suppressed on the way over to the club were beginning to surface again. Myrtle excused herself and went into the back room. Her whole world was crashing down, and she had no power to stop it.

Obe went to the front door to usher out the new owners.

Nat slipped into the back room where Myrtle was crying. He would only have a few minutes to be alone with her, so he spoke boldly and right to the point. "Myrtle. Don't go to Lakeview with Obe. There's going to be trouble with this deal; I can sense these things. Come to Canada with me," he pleaded with passion in his eyes and voice. "I've loved you since the first time I laid eyes on you. I know I could make you happy."

Nat made an attempt to hold her close in his arms, but she politely pulled away. Myrtle was astonished at the sincerity and tenderness of his words. The way she felt brought the temptation to say yes close to her lips. Yet she was an honorable women, and honor forced her to refuse Nat's proposal. The crying woman wiped the tears away. She tried to be as compassionate as possible toward this man, who had so kindly expressed his feelings for her.

"Nat, you have been such a good friend to all of us and especially to Obe," Myrtle started. "But I made some strong vows the day I got married. I promised to stick with Obe for 'richer or poorer.' I guess we've had a short time of richer, and now the poorer will come for a while. I can't break my vows at the first sign of hardship. What would that say to everyone about my character? I would lose respect for myself; then even a nice guy like you wouldn't want me." She paused as she looked at the man who was ready to rescue her. "You don't know how much your care and concern for me means, Nat. Especially now as my dreams seem to be tumbling down around me."

Nat wanted to hold this frightened lady but was interrupted by Obe coming into the room.

"What's going on here?" the stern husband demanded.

Myrtle was startled by Obe's sudden entrance, but Nat spoke up to answer his question before she even had time to think.

"Well, Obe, I've been trying to convince this pretty lady to leave her bum of a husband and go to Canada with me. But she says she would rather stick it out with her 'old man.' " Nat made the statement in a joking manner. Even though it was the truth, Obe didn't really know it was.

"Nat is such a liar," Myrtle retorted. "Here, Obe, I brought today's paper." She handed the paper to her husband in hopes of changing the subjects. "I thought both of you would be interested in the headlines."

"It sounds like we don't have much time," Nat stated as he read the bold letters. "We had better make Saturday night a real 'whing-dinger' of a party. The people around here won't be able to buy champagne legally for a long time."

NIGHTMARES

The next few days were like a nightmare for Myrtle, with problems and heartache at every turn. It started with a quarrel between the Jacobson children and her own. Mrs. Jacobson had called the Tooleys "white trash." "The Tooley children will not be able to play with respectable families' children," were the final words of Mrs. Jacobson.

Myrtle just shrugged off the incident as a mother standing up for her children. When she went to the general store the following day and was snubbed purposely by the president of the women's club, she knew something was definitely wrong. She had been a good member for four years and didn't deserve the rude treatment.

Mr. Walkins, the owner of the store, also snapped at her, saying she needed to settle up the bill. Myrtle wanted to die of embarrassment. He told her he could no longer extend the Tooleys credit, only cash sales from now on. She wanted to run home in tears but swallowed her pride, maintaining her dignity. Holding her head high and looking the man straight in the eye, she replied, "Certainly, Mr. Walkins, and I sincerely wish to thank you for the kindness and generosity you have extended these past few years. I was about to ask if it would be convenient for you to total my bill. I was planning to settle with you tomorrow. You would prefer cash, wouldn't you?" she asked in her sweetest, most syrupy voice. "If not, I could write you a bank draft right now." Myrtle was bluffing of course, but her intention was to take the "wind out of his sails" and try to humble him a bit.

The storekeeper was taken back by the confident and sweet tones of Myrtle's voice. His harshness seemed to soften as he replied. "No, no. I'll take cash tomorrow," he mellowly answered. "Let me see; your bill is nineteen dollars and thirty-five cents."

Myrtle smiled sweetly and walked out the door in her normal noble manner. She was noticing the whole time how people were intentionally avoiding her. With a lump in her throat and her heart breaking, she maintained her composure until she was alone in the privacy of her own home. She then broke down and cried.

On Thursday Obe went to the bank with Nat and they finalized the deal for selling the club. With cash in hand, Obe promptly walked to Mr. Walkins's store to pay the family debt. Obe would be glad to have a fresh start in a new town. But he knew this time, it was going to be risky. The thought of making a lot of money on the liquor clouded out the danger and consequences he might be facing. Dollar signs were the only thing he could see in his mind.

Obe posted the signs around town for the final party at the club on Saturday night. He luckily arrived back at the saloon just in time to meet the man delivering the wagonload of liquor. This supply would be taken across the lake. Obe was fortunate no one was around to see the shipment. He covered the boxes with a canvas tarp to hide the writing on the sides. He then paid the driver a nice tip to take the cargo to his house and wait for him.

Obe had spent most of his share of the money he got for the club to buy this precious liquor. He was convinced he would make at least five times what he had spent when he sold it. With liquor being hard to get after a few weeks of prohibition, the demand for it would be high. Obe planned to charge a big price for each bottle. Wayne Parker had swayed him into believing that for every dollar he spent on the merchandise he could get at least five back. Surely by the time this supply had all been sold the politicians would come to their senses and repeal the stupid law. He then wouldn't have to "bootleg" anymore.

Pearl had been sleeping soundly when she was suddenly awakened by noises coming from the backyard. She got out of bed and quietly went into the boys' room to see if she could see anything. The full moon was the only source of light for the men moving around in the yard below her. She immediately recognized her father's voice, even though he was talking very softly to the other two men with him. All three men were loading boxes from one wagon onto another one. She couldn't tell in the darkness what was in the boxes, but she sensed it was something valuable. She spotted her mother standing at the corner of the house as if watching for someone. She was making, "Shhhh," sounds when any noise was made. Pearl didn't know exactly what they were doing, but she could tell they didn't want anyone to see or hear them.

When they were finished transferring all of the boxes, one of the strangers and her father guided the horse and loaded wagon slowly and quietly around to the front. The full wagon headed in the direction of the marina. The other man waited for a short time, then slowly led the empty wagon and horse off in the other direction.

The eight-year-old girl was curious. She sat at the bottom of the stairs until her mother came inside the house and locked the back door behind her.

"Momma," Pearl whispered from the darkness. "The sounds in the backyard woke me up. What was Daddy doing outside in the dark?"

The sound of Pearl's voice in the dark room startled Myrtle. She had to clasp her own hand over her mouth to keep from responding with a little scream.

"Oh, Pearl! You made Mommy jump. Don't you know you should be in bed? Girls need their beauty sleep, you know," Myrtle tried to make light of the tense situation.

Pearl wasn't going to give up on her questions until she got a good answer. "Where did Daddy go with the wagon in the nighttime?" the girl questioned.

Myrtle knew her daughter well enough to realize she had better give a logical answer or the same questions would be asked again and again later.

"Pearl, can you keep a big secret?" Myrtle asked the girl.

"I'll try," responded the child.

"No, Pearl. You can't just try. This is a secret you can't tell anyone. Not even your sister or brothers. OK? No one can know that your daddy is taking things from the house at night. You can't tell anyone or it will spoil the secret. We wouldn't want to do that now, would we?" Myrtle shook her head from side to side, and the girl repeated the motion with her. "Now run along back to bed. It will be morning before you know it." She gave the girl a little kiss and watched her climb the stairs to return to her room.

Myrtle had a hard time falling asleep. She really wanted a glass of whiskey to drown out her troubles, but she needed her mind clear, so she could think straight.

When she finely dozed off, she began to hear the sounds of her children. They seemed to be calling from far off in the distance.

"Momma! Momma!" the little voices were calling over and over.

She found herself walking in a thick mist of darkness, trying to find where her children were calling from. When the mist began to clear she recognized she was in the park. She was going toward the old cannon that was mounted there. It wasn't the same cannon she had seen before, but a much larger one. This huge cannon had scaffolding and a platform next to its large mouth opening.

As she got closer, she could see a big man dressed in a long black coat standing on the platform. When the man opened his coat, Myrtle could see her children were under it. They were balancing precariously on the platform with him. The children were frightened and were calling for her to help them. As she started to run towards them, the ground beneath her feet turned to mud. The more she struggled to get to the children, the heavier the mud became, pulling her down into its grasp.

The big man in black begin to push each child into the cannon's opening, as they screamed and scratched to free themselves. But the man was too strong and Myrtle was powerless in the mud. She could only watch in horror as he successfully poked each one inside.

Myrtle looked toward the lake and saw Obe in the distance. He had his back turned away from the children and his fingers in his ears. He looked as if he was trying to escape the sounds of the children crying for help. Myrtle tried calling to him, but he wouldn't remove his fingers.

Then, with one big leap, the man in black flew off the platform. He magically produced a fiery torch to light the oversize fuse of the cannon. With a loud *bang,* the cannon fired. The children went shooting out in different directions up to the clouds and disappeared out of sight. Myrtle tried to scream, but no one could hear her.

She tried desperately one last time, and the effort woke her up. She sat up in her bed and wondered if she had actually screamed out loud. The dream had frightened her so much. She got up to make sure her children were safe.

Obe didn't return until just before dawn the next morning. And it was after lunch before he got up from bed. He instructed Myrtle to start packing the things she couldn't live without; they would be shipping a load over to Lakeview soon.

Myrtle spent most of the day packing things. She kept the children inside and away from the neighbors. She was afraid someone would say cruel things to them. She also didn't want Pearl to leak information about what had she seen the night before. Anyway, the nightmare was still haunting her and she was happy with her children close and protected.

Obe and Nat spent the remainder of Friday doing inventory and preparing for one last bash the following night. They wanted to make sure everyone who came had a good time. It was hoped by the partners that folk would fight to remove any ban placed on liquor before it lasted too long. They were both convinced if prohibition was adopted, it wouldn't last more than six months at the most.

ESCAPE TO ADVENTURE ISLAND

Saturday morning, Obe woke up to the sounds of the church bells ringing wildly and people yelling and hollering in the direction of the church. He jumped out of bed realizing he must have overslept. He quickly got dressed and went to the kitchen to find out why Myrtle had let him sleep so long. He found her sitting at the table reading the newspaper. The worried expression on her face and her head shaking from side to side in a negative motion gave Obe the impression that the news she was reading was not good.

"It's happened, Obe!" she blurted out. "Idaho and several other states have adopted "prohibition," starting right now, today. Why did it have to be today?" she sobbed. But her husband didn't stick around to even talk about the issue. He rushed out the door and headed for the saloon. He intended to hide the remainder of the liquor that was there before the lawmen came to confiscate it.

The front page of the newspaper was plastered all over the building. The flyers he had put up earlier around town were ripped up and scattered on the ground. It was apparent that someone was more pleased about prohibition than he was. There was a crudely drafted sign hanging across the front door reading, OUT OF BUSINESS, OUT OF IDAHO. By all the broken liquor bottles on the ground in front of the door it was obvious that the saloon and club had been broken into.

Obe found the back door had been pried open. He prepared himself for the vandalism he might find inside. When his eyes adjusted to the dim light in the club, Obe was surprised. The intruders had not damaged any of the inside furnishings. They must have at least had respect for the new owners by not destroying what they had purchased. When Obe got closer to the bar, he saw all the champagne bottles were lined up carefully in rows on the top. Each bottle had been opened and emptied. Not a drop of alcohol could be salvaged. In the saloon it was the same way, with all the liquor destroyed.

Obe just stared motionless at the evidence of waste on the bar. He knew he couldn't do anything about it. He had counted on making a good profit on the party tonight and using the money for his new start in Lakeview. It was really going to be a struggle now with so little cash left.

When he went to check the cash register for any hidden stash, he saw the note leaning on the keys. He opened it and read to himself:

Obe,

I arrived this morning just in time to see the last of the "Christian Soldiers" slaying the "alcohol dragon." I ran them off before they could do any damage to the inside of the building. I'm leaving town before a *lynch mob* forms, and I advise you to do the same. Get your family and leave as quickly and quietly as you can.

Give the family my love, until we meet again.
Nat

Obe looked for any cash but found none. He then folded the note and sadly tipped his hat to the empty Candle Light Room. He was leaving another chapter of his life behind.

When Obe got home, he drew most of the curtains closed. He then got everyone busy with the task of packing. They knew they wouldn't be able to take everything, but Myrtle made sure her heirlooms would not be left behind. She removed her precious pictures of the family from their frames. She studied each member's face and reflected on how much the children had grown in a year's time. She tucked the photographs back in the cardboard frames they had originally been in. She wanted to make sure they wouldn't get damaged by the move. She put them in her big purse to carry them personally.

After it was dark outside, the wagon was loaded and taken to the marina. Wayne Parker was waiting to help load the contents on the ferryboat. Obe then made the trip back to the house for the last load. As soon as everything they could take was on the wagon, Myrtle went in to wake up the children, one at a time. Pearl was first, so she could help with the others. Each was dressed in dark, warm clothing, and their bedding was folded. When everything was bundled, it was put on the wagon.

"What are we doing, Momma?" was four-year-old Roy's question, over and over.

Myrtle figured a game of pretend might work to satisfy his question. He needed to be quiet while they were making their undercover escape.

"We are going to Adventure Island. You won't get to go if you don't stop talking. You have to be very quiet or the bad pirates will know we are coming. They might take us as their prisoners." This answer was just the trick to keep all the children very quiet as they prepared to leave the house.

It was important to leave without the main stream of folks knowing where they were relocating if Obe wanted to sell his stock without trouble. Wayne Parker was the only one who knew of the plans to bootleg

97

the liquor. And he was going to be paid part of the profits to keep people from nosin' around. For those reasons, Obe felt they needed to keep their whereabouts a secret.

The ride to the ferry was *eerie* as the family made their way in the darkness. They had to go very slow and be so quiet, the children were uneasy about this journey. When the moon shared its light with them it wasn't too bad. They were able to make out familiar landmarks and knew where they were. But when a cloud or the trees hid the light, it seemed like the darkness was closing in around them.

The ferry ride was not any better. All they could hear was the sound of water slapping against the sides of the boat. The children huddled against the safety of their mother's body. Each one held onto a piece of her skirt.

By the time they reached Lakeview, the faint glow of morning was in the eastern sky. Pearl remembered this place from the July Fourth trip just a few weeks before. She was happy when her mother announced to the children that they were going to live here now. The news was fine with her; she liked it here and was eager to live on Adventure Island.

Lakeview was a pretty little town. It was mostly used as a resort. Down the hill from the Tooleys' new home was a store and confectionary shop. People who were boating on Lake Pendorilla would stop there. There was an old logging road to Lakeview, but not many people used it. The main transportation to and from the town was by boat.

The house they lived in was much smaller than the one in Sandpoint. It had two bedrooms downstairs and a loft up over the living area. The girls used the loft for their room. There was a big room with a fireplace where the family did all their living and a good-sized kitchen with a table and chairs for the meals.

There were several trees in the yard area outside. One big oak had a long swing the previous occupants had constructed and left behind. Most of the yard time centered around the swing, as each child coveted the others' turns to be in it.

Pearl, being the biggest, could make the swing get high. She could see the edge of the lake on the forward climb of the swing. As she swung backwards she could see the bell in the steeple of the little church through the nearby trees. It was a grand experience, being so high in the sky, Pearl thought. She felt it was as close to being a bird as a human could be.

There was a little one-room schoolhouse where Pearl and Helen went to school in September. Only fourteen children attended, their ages ranging from six to fifteen years old. The two girls loved to learn together. They were not allowed to sit by each other, because Helen would just copy from Pearl when they were together. But when they were apart, Helen would do her own thinking and work.

Obe got a job working at logging to provide for his family. He wasn't used to the backbreaking work required and suffered with sore muscles most of the time.

He became a regular miser. He started hoarding every penny he could. He claimed he was going to take the family to Canada after he sold all the liquor he had stored. However, his love for the money itself began to be a problem for the family. Even though Myrtle knew her husband had money, she had to struggle to keep food on the table with the little he allowed her to spend.

The children were never aware of the risks their parents were taking by having the liquor. They weren't concerned or thinking anything could be amiss in this pleasant little town they now called home.

There was a root cellar at the back of the house. The large door covering it was far too heavy for the children to lift. None of them wanted to go in there anyway. It was damp and dark and smelled funny down there. When their father told them never to go in there, it was fine with them.

For the first two months the Tooleys were in Lakeview, Obe was very sneaky about any sales he made. Myrtle didn't even know he had sold about 25 percent of his stock. She also didn't know he had almost two–hundred dollars hidden away where only he could find it. When winter set in early that year and the snow began to fall, the sales slowed down to only a few bottles a week.

Obe found it necessary to work inside the lumber mill for those months. He would sometimes be gone three or four days in a row if the old logging road had too much snow. He bought a lock for one of the small kitchen cabinets and put a few bottles of the now-illegal substance there. Myrtle could get to them if someone came to buy while he was away. At first she was hostile to the whole idea. But after a few weeks and easy sales she was able to make the transactions without being scared to death. She was always very cautious, however, and would only sell to someone if she felt it was safe.

Myrtle became a very good liar and a master of deceit in a short period of time. She did not want her children to know their parents were breaking the law. They could get in a lot of trouble by just having liquor in their possession, let alone selling it. It was now a crime that might bring a stiff fine if they were caught by lawmen who weren't in on the operation. She was very careful to whom and when she sold the few bottles Obe allotted in her cupboard.

Myrtle had a few regular customers who would come around on a regular scheduled visit. There were a couple of older gentlemen and a French woman who cooked at the café the tourists frequented. The cook was famous for her unusual desserts. Myrtle was sure the "unusual" part was being purchased at her house.

She was always delighted when Harry Taggert came calling. He was a man in his late sixties who suffered from rheumatism. Before prohibition, his doctor had prescribed a shot of whiskey as a pain reliever. Harry referred to Myrtle as his favorite pharmacist. He always knew the latest gossip about everyone and enjoyed sharing it with her. Mr. Taggert knew Mrs. Tooley was very uneasy about this sneaky business. He assured her he knew almost everything about everybody in town and that no one suspected her of anything except being a good little mother.

THE PRICE OF GREED

In late November something out of the ordinary happened with the weather in the northwestern part of the country. A warm spell hit and by mid-December the lake was being traveled as if it were spring. Obe stopped working for the logging company and made himself available for any sales that would come from across the water.

Myrtle tried to make Christmas special for the children, but with Obe being so stingy with the money, it was tough. She wasn't able to even bake some of her children's favorite treats, let alone get many gifts. The children didn't seem to mind as much as Myrtle. They were just happy to make snowflakes and sing carols.

By the time the holidays were over, Obe had sold more than half of his liquor supply. He had over $450 in his private stash and was planning to buy more stock when the current stock was gone. He knew he had promised his wife he would take her to Canada when all the liquor was sold, yet how could he leave such a lucrative area when sales were going so well?

Obe was developing a love for money he had never had before. Maybe it was the risk involved or the fact that he was making such a large profit on each bottle now, but the need to acquire those precious dollars was clouding out the really important things in his life. He was now very selfish and greedy with his family. He constantly complained about how much was being spent on food and clothing. Money became the topic of every argument or rude comment he managed to start each day with. He growled at the children at mealtime if they didn't eat every bite on their plates. Yet he complained if he thought they were eating too much. There was no pleasing him. The children tried to just stay away from their father so he wouldn't be mean to them.

One morning in February when Mr. Taggert came to "refill" his prescription, the gossip he had to share sent a cold chill up Myrtle's spine.

"Did you hear that Sheriff Parker had a real bad heart spell the other day? I hear he is going to be laid up for quite some time," the man reported. "I remember when Sarah Taylor had her heart spell, she never did recover. When the second attack hit, she was a goner." Harry loved to tell stories, and Myrtle couldn't get a word in edgewise. "I hear Sam's brother-in-law is bringing his family up from Lewiston to help out while the sheriff is trying to get better. You know, with Mrs. Parker being all crippled up, having her sister come to help out seemed like their only option," Harry stated.

"Yes," Myrtle replied when she was finally able to respond to her talkative friend. "It is nice to have family around in times of trouble."

"Do you have family around here?" Harry inquired.

"No," was all the answer she could get out before the sweet old man asked her another question.

"Where are your kin?" Harry stopped this time to hear her answer.

Myrtle told him about her father's death and where her two brothers were living. But she only remarked in passing about her mother dying before she left Wisconsin.

After Mr. Taggert left, Myrtle reflected for a few short minutes about her days as a young girl in Wisconsin and why her family had left ten years ago. It seemed like a long lifetime of experiences in those ten years with Obe. Most of the first years were happy and secure ones. The last few were different, though, with all the tension between the two of them. It had made her life hard and unhappy. She wanted to believe life somewhere else, without the need for secrets and hiding, would solve the constant bickering between them. However, she knew down deep.she was only trying to fool herself. She wondered if she and Obe would ever again experience the joys they had together those first few years.

Myrtle came out of her daydream when she looked at the clock she had set near the stove. With the hands pointing to eleven and the aroma filling the house, she knew she had better get her bread out of the oven before it burned.

She left the bread to cool while she washed the soiled hands and faces of her active boys and got them ready to take a walk. Myrtle carefully lined a basket with clean towels from her clothesline and put one of the freshly baked loaves inside. After making sure every door and window was locked up tight, the threesome headed for the Parker home. She wanted to give some goodwill and make inquiries.

Emma Parker was cold and spoke harshly when she opened the door and saw there were children at her home. The thought of rowdy little boys bumping against her crippled body and possibly knocking her off balance made her nervous and uneasy about inviting them inside.

Myrtle, sensing the tension, asked if it would be all right for the boys to play outside while she visited with the sheriff. Emma responded positively to the suggestion. After a few instructions to the boys from

Myrtle, Emma welcomed her inside. She then pointed in the direction where her husband was recuperating.

Sam Parker was happy to have a visitor, especially one who brought such a delicious gift.

After giving her sympathies for his illness and other small talk that went along with it, Myrtle got right to the main point for her visit. "How is this illness going to affect our 'arrangement'?" she inquired.

Sam was blunt and honest, and Myrtle was grateful for the truth. "I can't promise you protection anymore, Mrs. Tooley. If I don't get better soon, I will probably turn the job of sheriff over to my brother-in-law. I know for sure he will do no favors when it comes to liquor. He comes from a family of hard-core temperance folks and pushed for prohibition in the state. It is my advice to you and your husband to stop your operation here. You should move on to a place where you can sell legally. One more thing, my nephew Wayne is no longer a deputy in Sandpoint. It was suggested by the new sheriff over there he should leave town or . . ." His voice was getting weak, so Myrtle thanked him for the advice and said her good-byes.

"Be careful, little lady," was Sheriff Parker's warning as she exited the room.

When Obe returned home in the afternoon, Myrtle tried to reason with him about the warnings the sheriff had given her. Obe was as stubborn as usual and wouldn't agree with her about anything. He didn't think this new turn of events would hamper his ability to keep the operation a secret. Anyway, he would no longer have to be paying off the law for knowing about his operation. He could keep *all* the profits for himself.

It wasn't until Sam Parker had the second heart attack, which took his life, that Obe even took better precautions in screening customers.

Myrtle stopped selling to everyone except Harry Taggert. She only kept him because she felt sorry for his suffering.

Homer Remer became the acting sheriff of Lakeview until elections in November. The man was just as Sam Parker had warned Myrtle about before he passed away. By mid-March, everyone knew who was *now* running the town.

Remer was a man in his early fifties and had wanted this kind of power all his life. He was only about five-seven inches tall and didn't weigh more than 140 pounds, but he strutted around the town like a peacock. When he entered a store or café, everyone needed to acknowledge his presence or he would confront them with accusations of wrongdoings. It was easier for people to play along than be harassed by the cocky little man. He stuck his nose into everybody's business, looking for ways to lord his authority over them. He was a *bully* to anyone who was smaller or weaker. He made it a point to hang around the schoolhouse at dismissal time to boss around the children on their way home. He especially liked to make comments to Helen about her red hair and freckles. Helen would always get angry and kick dirt in his direction or tell him to be quiet. Pearl didn't like him at all and would try to hurry Helen away before she did anything disrespectful.

Homer and his wife, Clara, moved into the house Sam and Emma had been living in. The town council provided the house for the sheriff's family because it was right next to the office and jail where he worked. Emma Parker soon had to be moved to Sandpoint to a rest home, because her health had gone from bad to worse with the shock of her husband's death.

The whole peace and serenity of the town had been invaded when the badge was transferred from Sam Parker to Homer Remer. Lakeview was nearly crime-free, so Homer had to find things to do. He had chosen as his Deputy Fred Carson, a big six-foot man who weighed about 250 pounds. Fred had been in a lumbering accident that put him in a coma for three weeks a few years earlier. When he finally woke up, the doctors discovered he was slightly mentally unstable.

The two men would go out on "detecting hunts," looking for undiscovered crimes. They had come across a couple of empty liquor bottles near the lake and determined someone had forbidden liquid in their town. On one of their searches they had spotted a fisherman taking a big drink from a similar-type bottle, but the man was able to get away before they could arrest him.

One Saturday night when the weather had warmed up, Bill Baptist and Carl Evans had been fishing on the shore of the lake. They had caught their limits and decided to build a fire and cook supper right there. In Bill's tackle box was the bottle of whiskey he had purchased the night before from the man people referred to as Boot-Leggier or B.L. for short, as a code name.

Since the new sheriff had taken over, the only way to buy a bottle of booze was to go to a secluded place north of the lake, taking along a lantern. If a person lit the lantern between 11:00 P.M. and midnight and waved it back and forth, a man dressed in dark clothing, with his face covered, would come out from a wooded area. If the first person had the money, the man would produce a bottle of whiskey he had hidden in his boot.

Carl and Bill had been practicing this same fishing ritual twice a year for the past fifteen years. They would go fishing, get drunk, and weave on home about two or three in the morning. Just because liquor was harder to get now didn't stop these two from participating in a calendared event. Both of them were sure it would be sacrileges or something much worse if they let a little thing like prohibition stand in the way of tradition. Sam Parker had agreed with them last summer. They had no idea the new sheriff would be any different.

The two fishermen reminisced, told tall tales, and shared swigs of whiskey in between. It was about 2:00 A.M. when the fire burned out and the liquor was gone. The drunken men began to make their way into town as they staggered home.

As they held each other up, Bill decided it was much too quiet out in the dark night. He felt singing would solve the problem.

"On top of old Smokey all covered with . . ." were the words the drunk man blared out in the off-key tones. The pair agreed that *snow* was the next word but began changing it to silly expressions, laughing, and then singing it again.

By the time they reached the center of town, the drunken pair were having too much fun for this late hour. Sheriff Remer was awakened, grabbed his robe and slippers, and went to wake up his deputy. Before the two crooners knew what was happening, they had been arrested and hauled off to the jail. They were charged with "drunk and disorderly conduct." But the main interrogation was centered on the source of the liquor that had caused the action.

Carl and Bill were held overnight to sober up. After recovering from their hangovers the following day, each was questioned ruthlessly about where they had obtained the bottle. When both explanations matched about the time, place, and signal, Homer fined them ten dollars each and let them go home.

"We have a bootleggin' operation going on here, Fred. I'm going to put a stop to it," Homer stated to his deputy. "It's our job to protect the good people of this town from becoming criminals due to some lawless scoundrel. Whoever is selling this 'devil's brew' needs to be caught and made an example of. Folks need to know there will be no conducting of evil business in my jurisdiction."

Harry Taggert made his usual monthly stop at the Tooley place to get a refill of medication from his favorite friend. The few days of rain in the area had made his rheumatism flare up. The old man's joints were more stiff and sore than they had been for a long time. Myrtle suggested hot water packs and horse liniment to increase mobility, but of course he had tried all the home remedies, with little success.

Myrtle had real compassion for this nice man who always had a cheerful countenance. He tried to be happy even though he suffered with pain most of the time. She even hated to charge him for the liquor he slyly came for. If she wasn't struggling to make ends meet, with her husband becoming more and more stingy, she would have given the healing liquid to him for free.

Myrtle was allowed to use money from her sales for groceries and material. This allowance never seemed to be enough, though, as the patches on the children's clothing were becoming an embarrassment. She would just have to insist that Obe give her enough for new clothes for the children soon.

This new lust for money was like an addiction taking over Obe's soul. Myrtle knew he had once been a good and caring person, but he was different now. Obe was also becoming paranoid, thinking people were out to take away everything he had. He thought by hiding his money in a secret place he would be guaranteed security. Greed was encompassing his whole being. The sickness was affecting the ones he should be caring about by denying them enough allowance for their basic needs. He rationalized his action by reassuring Myrtle that he was saving for the future. He began to think she was like everyone else and resented her constant nagging to have more of his precious stash for household use.

Obe's sin of greed was taking its toll on the family. Myrtle and the children were the ones paying the highest price for his new love.

UNCOVERED SECRETS

The late hours Obe spent by the lake waiting for customers were starting to have an effect on him physically. He was becoming more and more proficient at taking short naps whenever and wherever he found a comfortable place. The big wooden chair on the front porch of the house had become a favorite napping place. The warm sun helped him fall asleep with ease.

Obe had only been asleep for a few minutes in the afternoon when the sound of a child playing skip rope at the corner of the porch interrupted his slumber.

"Yellow, yellow, who's my fellow? Rich man, poor man, beggar man, thief, doctor, lawyer, merchant, chief. . ." The chanting went on and on as Pearl jumped in the rhyme.

Obe listened for a few repetitions before telling Pearl to stop the blasted noise and go elsewhere to play. It was just another way of being grumpy with his family, a trait he had mastered and used much too often these days.

The young girl quickly obeyed, moving to the backyard and away from her irritable father.

Mr. Taggert had stopped in a secluded spot on his way home from the Tooleys. He was very careful not to be seen taking a dose of painkiller he had just purchased from Mrs. Tooley. He made sure the cork was in tight and the bottle tucked safely in the upper inside pocket of his jacket before proceeding on his way. He wanted to make sure no one could tell he was carrying the precious medication.

The old gentleman waited patiently for the team and wagon to go by before venturing to cross the rain-soaked road. Mr. Taggert had started to go across when he caught sight of Homer Remer coming out of the general store. The new sheriff was coming right in the direction Harry was headed. Harry didn't like Remer at all. Homer was always trying to start trouble by taking the old man's cane or pretending to trip in front of him. It was Remer's sick way of bullying the weak or crippled. He enjoyed taunting them and getting them to react. He could then possibly provoke a reason for arrest.

As Taggert tried to stop his forward progression to avoid the sheriff, the traction beneath his feet gave way. He slipped down to the muddy street on his sore hands and knees. This was not a position he wanted to be in with Remer nearby.

A woman close by had seen Harry go down. She yelled to the man behind Harry to help him. Everyone in close range stopped to look as Deputy Carson reached down and lifted the old man out of the mud.

Sheriff Remer was observing the scene from the other side of the street. Not only he but everyone around saw the bottle as it became dislodged from Harry's coat pocket. All eyes were fixed as it broke in a hundred pieces, splashing its illegal substance on everything nearby.

Harry could only glare in horror as he watched the coveted liquid disappear into the ground. Worse, however, was the anticipation of the punishment he knew was coming from the sheriff and his deputy.

"Well . . . well . . . !" were the long-drawn-out words of the sheriff as he strolled to the scene. Like an actor on a stage trying to get noticed by his audience, Remer squatted down by the broken glass. He touched his finger to a drop of liquid on a piece of the broken bottle and tasted it. With a grotesque expression on his face Remer looked at his audience. "Hm-mm! I don't think this is hair tonic. Now pray tell, old man, what is this stuff?" He was hoping his onlookers would support his gestures with laughter, but everyone remained quiet.

With the negative reviews, the lawman rose to his feet and announced in authoritative tones, "You're under arrest for possession of liquor, Taggert, and you're going to jail right now." Homer pushed at the crippled man's sore body in an effort to make him move faster. Poor Harry could hardly walk now, due to the new pains from the fall.

"Mr. Remer, give the man a break. He only uses the stuff for his rheumatism!" a lady called out in Mr. Taggert's defense.

Remer looked around to see who was talking. But everyone was quiet, protecting the source of the protest. "All of you people know having liquor is against the law. No one is going to break the law here and get away with it!" the sheriff yelled so everyone could hear. He gave Mr. Taggert another push and herded the aching man off to jail.

Now Harry was old but definitely set in his ways. He had a stubborn streak that was normally hidden deep in his personality. As Homer began to question Harry about where he had purchased the liquor, the stubbornness was jolted and started to surface.

The arrogant sheriff spoke softly at first. He leaned in close to the man across the table. "OK Taggert, let's make this real simple. You tell me where you got the bottle and I'll only fine you five dollars."

The silence in the room was not the sound the lawman wanted to hear or expected. He had figured the old man would "spill his guts" right away and be done with the matter. The sheriff hadn't counted on the strong will of this crippled-up guy.

"Now don't play games with me, you old goat," the interrogator ordered. Remer stood up and paced slowly across the room. "You tell me right now where you got that liquor," the lawman demanded again.

Harry began to tell lies in order to mask the real truth from Homer. Harry liked Mrs. Tooley and didn't want her to get in trouble. He needed to protect the product she could supply, to relieve him from an otherwise-painful existence. He would say or do anything to protect his friend.

As the investigation continued, the tone of Remer's voice became louder and harsher. When the answers were not the ones he wanted to hear, Homer would slap the old man or punch him. The harsh punishment was too much for the stubborn prisoner. Harry finally collapsed with pain and fright. The two men locked him in the jail cell.

"You'll tell me what I want to know soon enough!" the bully yelled at the silent man. "But right now, I have bigger fish to fry." Remer got his rifle down from the rack and stomped out of the office. Carson was left on his own to guard the prisoner.

It was cold and wet as Bryce Chappins sat at the edge of the wooded area trying desperately to light his lantern. His hands shook, not from the cold, but from the d.t.'s his body was experiencing. He seriously needed a drink. He had only been able to raise the needed money for the high-priced brew an hour ago. He had been trying for at least fifteen minutes to produce the needed flame. He couldn't seem to get his matches to light. Getting his lantern lit in time was the only way to put an end to the grief he was undergoing. When he was down to his last match, a feeling of panic started to take over his mind. He rubbed his hands together and took a deep breath in preparation for one final try. At last, the flame flared bright and the fuel began to burn. Chappins had successfully got the lantern to exhibit light.

He checked his pocket watch; 11:57 it showed. Both hands were nearly on the twelve. He swung the lantern two, three, four times, in hopes the salesman was still out there somewhere. Chappins didn't know how he would make it another day if he didn't get the liquor he needed tonight. He waved the lantern again, just in case it hadn't been seen the first time. He then waited, trying without success to see any movement in the darkness.

The next five minutes seemed like an hour. It took that long before a man dressed in black appeared out of the thick underbrush. He was wearing a long coat, dark hat, and black neckerchief over his nose and mouth, obviously trying to keep his identity a secret.

"It will be four dollars tonight," the man in black announced as he reached for the bottle hidden in his boot.

"Four dollars? But I only have three-fifty. Last time, it was three-fifty," the shaking man stated. "Please! Please! I'll bring the extra fifty cents next time. I'm a man of my word," Chappins pleaded.

There was a pause of silence before the salesman replied, "All right. But remember, next time it's four dollars plus the extra fifty cents you'll owe me."

Mr. Chappins shook his head in acknowledgment of the deal as the two men made their exchange.

It was the sound of a shell being loaded into the chamber of a Winchester that broke the silence. The shocking tone put fear in the hearts of the two men making their deal. Their eyes turned to a group of trees about fifty feet up the hill. Although it was dark, they could plainly see the barrel of a rifle pointing in their direction. The man in disguise started to reach for the gun he had concealed in a shoulder holster but knew the effort was too late.

"There won't be a next time, Mr. Bootlegger, whoever you are," Sheriff Remer announced as he descended the hill behind the aimed gun. "Now, both of you, put your hands in the air or be shot right here and now."

The two men were both stunned and frightened with a loaded gun pointing right at them, especially with Remer holding it. Both perpetrators knew Homer was just crazy enough to really shoot, if he even thought of making a run for it. Consequently, both men surrendered peacefully. The two were cuffed, the liquor and money collected as evidence, and they were led off to jail.

When the three men arrived at the jailhouse, the sheriff had no trouble finding out the identity of his two new prisoners. Harry Taggert knew Bryce Chappins, and Deputy Carter recognized Obe Tooley from the lumber mill.

"Obe Tooley, huh. So, you're the infamous salesman who's been causing all the crime in this town," Remer stated as he strolled around the room like a proud rooster.

"I guess you have the upper hand here, Mr. Remer," Obe responded. "I suppose you can call me, and accuse me, of anything you want."

"Tooley? Tooley?" Homer said, trying to thinking of where he had heard the name before. "Don't you have a funny freckled-faced little girl with carrottop hair?" He laughed, making jest of the child and her father, in order to get a rise out of his latest prey.

Mistakenly Mr. Taggert went to the defense of the young girl. "Stop making fun of an innocent little girl; she is a beautiful child just like her mother. You have no right—"

His words were interrupted by the sheriff, who had picked up on a clue from the old man's comments.

Obe held his breath. He hoped Remer had not realized the significance of Mr. Taggert's response about Myrtle's beauty. Obe really didn't want his wife to be arrested, too; he might be required to give up some of his precious loot for her. However, Obe's worse fears were to be experienced, as Homer began to question the old gentlemen again.

"Mrs. Tooley? So, you know Mrs. Tooley. She's the one you've been getting your booze from, isn't she?" Remer demanded Harry Taggert admit.

"No, no. I got my bottle from Mr. Tooley, just like everybody else," Taggert lied, trying to convince the sheriff it was Obe and not his wife.

Remer turned to the crippled man and in a manner only a sadist would use, grabbed Harry's hand and began to squeeze it tight and rough. "Now don't you try to lie to me, you old geezer. Mrs. Tooley sells this stuff, too, doesn't she?"

"No! No! Please stop!" the old gentleman yelled in fear and pain.

"You're lying, aren't you? Tell me the truth, you old fool. Mrs. Tooley sold you the bottle, didn't she?" Homer yelled. He squeezed the man's hand harder and harder.

The eerie sound of bones breaking brought Obe to his feet. But the deputy quickly hit him with the butt end of the rifle, sending him to the floor.

Poor Mr. Taggert could endure the pain no longer. He couldn't stop himself from screaming out, "Yes! Yes! She's the one." He wanted to die as soon as the words escaped his lips. He hated himself and wished he hadn't uttered them. Like feathers in the wind, however, they were out and could not be retrieved.

THE PRICE OF STUBBORNNESS

Pearl awoke to the sounds of a child crying. It was still dark in the room, and it took a little time for her eyes to adjust enough to see. She looked at the little clock on the dresser. When she could finally make out the time, she saw it was only four o'clock. The family usually didn't get up until six. *Why is little Earl crying?* she wondered. With her natural caretaker's instincts, she climbed out of bed. She put on her hand-knit slippers and sweater and started down the stairs to help the three-year-old.

Her mother was already up. She was pacing back and forth in the living room holding the screaming child. She was going from window to window looking through the narrow cracks in the otherwise-drawn curtains. She looked as if she was trying to see something. She was nervous and obviously startled when Pearl asked from the doorway, "Mother, what's the matter with Earl?"

"He's sick with fever, and won't stop crying," was the mother's uneasy response while still looking out the window.

The sick toddler reached for his oldest sister. He was looking for another source of relief or comfort. He hadn't found any in his mother's arms.

"He needs to have some cold wet towels rubbed on his head and body to help bring down the fever," Myrtle hurriedly explained. "Pearl, could you help me do that?" she questioned her daughter with pleading eyes.

Myrtle went to her room and returned a few minutes later, fully dressed. She felt the cheeks of her sick child's face, then reached for her heavy sweater. The strange actions of her mother had frightened Pearl.

"Mother. What's the matter? Where are you going?" the girl questioned with a trembling voice.

"I have to go out for a little while, sweetie" the woman responded, not wanting to say more than necessary.

But Pearl could tell something was very wrong and didn't want her mother to leave. "Where's Daddy?" were the intuitive girl's words. "You stay here and make Daddy go out in the dark," she urged.

"Daddy didn't come home tonight," Myrtle answered with quivering lips. "I think I need to go and look for him."

Myrtle put on her sweater and started toward the back door. She stopped, however, when the sounds of loud voices and pounding at the front door made her motionless.

112

"Wake up in there and open the door!" was the command echoing throughout the house.

Myrtle froze in her tracks, unable to move. The only thing she could think was that something terrible had happened to Obe. She tried to prepare herself for the worst.

The command was repeated again, this time with more force of pounding on the wooden door.

"Open this door or we'll break it down!" a man shouted.

"Momma!" Pearl desperately cried. "Should I open the door?"

The woman came to her senses and hurried to open the door.

The two lawmen pushed their way through the unlocked doorway and grabbed hold of Myrtle.

"Are you Mrs. Tooley?" Homer asked as he glared at the woman.

"Yes," the startled woman answered. "Is something wrong with my husband?" The words blurted from her mouth.

"Yeah. There's something wrong with your husband," Homer gloated. "He's been arrested for bootleggin'! And we're here to arrest you, too," he replied, making gestures to intimidate the already-frightened woman. "Mrs. Tooley. You are under arrest for selling an illegal substance in the state of Idaho. We're here to take you to jail." He spoke the formal words and motioned his deputy to handcuff the now-sobbing lady.

"Please, sir. Please don't do this," Myrtle begged. "I have a sick child. Can't you see? I couldn't leave my sick baby."

"Shut up, woman!" the sheriff demanded as he pushed her down into a kitchen chair and slapped her sharply across the face.

The noise had woke Helen and Roy. They arrived at the kitchen just in time to see and hear the slap.

Pearl saw them running toward the lawmen with their little fists doubled up and reached out and caught Helen by the arm, but five-year-old Roy got by her. He started to strike at any male body part he could reach.

Homer grabbed the boy and threw him back toward the other children. Pearl was able to hold onto his nightshirt and tried to calm him down.

"Well, now isn't this just the picture of a trashy American family" were Remer's intentionally cutting words. He bent down and, with his eyes staring straight into the female prisoner's eyes, stated, "I'm only going to ask this question one time, lady. You better give me the right answer or you'll be real sorry. Tell me where you folks hide the liquor.''

Myrtle was so frightened and tearful the lump in her throat prevented the words from coming out soon enough to satisfy the sheriff. Remer opened the cupboards and began throwing the precious glassware, causing it to shatter on the floor below.

"Stop! Stop!" Myrtle choked out. "Please, please stop."

Remer turned around to strike her again, but the children were already at their mother's rescue.

Like wild animals they attacked the oncoming blow with a vengeance. The feisty red headed girl grabbed the backswinging hand and sank her teeth into it. Like a lion, she bit down hard in hopes of stopping any forward movement. Roy lunged forward like a ram and butted his head into the sheriff's midsection. The hit caused the little man to fold in the middle as he screamed from the bite on his hand. Pearl had stepped in front of the victim and, like a faithful dog, was preparing to receive the blow in place of her mother.

The children screamed out like frightened innocent lambs when attacked by hungry wolves. "Leave our mother alone! Go away and don't hurt her!" One after another they yelled their demands at the cruel man.

The whole episode was like a terrible nightmare that wouldn't go away. Myrtle's only thought was to say what she had to in order to protect her little ones.

"Children. Stop! Stop!" she commanded in tones they had learned to respect. "Come over here right now and stop hurting Mr. Remer."

The children huddled around their handcuffed mother, trying to protect her the only way they knew.

Looking toward the hook on the wall holding her apron, Myrtle spoke to the Sheriff. "There is a small key in the top pocket of my apron. It opens a locked cabinet in the pantry. You'll find what you're looking for in there."

"What is he looking for, Mother?" Pearl questioned.

"Sh-h-h. Just keep still and cooperate. Maybe if the men find what they want, they won't be so mean to us," the tearful mother responded.

Homer emerged from the pantry with two bottles of the outlawed potion. He was not at all satisfied with such a small find. He glared at the huddled group and yelled, "There's got to be more than two bottles around here! I'm going to keep looking if it takes all night." He stomped around like a madman. "Fred, take the baby. Let's see if she'll talk when she hears him sing."

The deputy obeyed his leader and took the small child from the arms of his sister.

Myrtle yelled out in horror. "Don't hurt the boy! He's sick! Please don't! He's sick!" The sobbing women cried.

"Oh, dear God. Please don't let them hurt the baby," Myrtle prayerfully pleaded.

"Hey, Boss. This baby is real hot. I think he really is sick," Carter responded with the only compassionate words that had been uttered by either man.

"I don't care," the crazed man replied. "I'm going to find that liquor."

In a steadfast tone demanding respect and consideration from a man of his size, Fred spoke. "You can stay and search if you want. I'm going to take this kid to a doctor. He's really hot, Homer."

Remer was shocked by the firmness of his deputy and for a moment was speechless.

"Let me go with him," pleaded the mother. "He'll be too frightened if I'm not with him."

The sheriff paused for a minute to think. He could tell Fred was going to leave with the child, no matter what he said. He didn't want to show this woman he didn't have complete control of everything, so he conceded to the deputy's decision. "Fine. We'll go to my house. The doctor can come there, where my wife can keep an eye on the prisoner. But, mark my words. I'll find the rest of that liquor if I have to tear this house apart board by board," the determined man stated while ushering the little band out into the cold air.

The first glow of morning was beginning to hide the few stars that had broken through the otherwise-cloudy sky as the children marched dutifully out to the paddy wagon. They were off to jail, by their mother's side. They did not know why all this was happening or what bad thing she may have done, yet they were willing to go to the depths of *hell*, if necessary, to be with her.

Myrtle and the children were taken to Sheriff Remer's home, next door to the jail. They were housed in the basement room. The room was sometimes used as an extension to the small two-cell jailhouse when the occasion arose. The windows were high and had bars on them. The only way in or out was by the stairs. There was a heavy metal door at the top

115

that could be locked from the outside. In the room were six cots with mattresses and blankets. There was also a small table with four chairs in one corner.

Mrs. Remer's personality was nothing like her husbands', and she seemed, to Myrtle, to be a fine Christian woman. She immediately sent for the town doctor when she learned of the sick boy. She showed compassion for the other children by bringing some hot cereal and milk for their breakfast.

After his own breakfast, Homer went back out to the Tooleys' house. He again started looking for the place where the rest of the liquor was hidden. He rummaged through every room in the house before going out to the backyard. When he discovered the root cellar, he was sure he had found the site. After lifting the door, he went down inside the black hole. There was just enough light from the opened doorway to see the boxes. He gazed inside each carton that held a supply of alcohol. He loaded the full boxes in his wagon to take back to the jail with him. He counted all the empty cases and tried to figure out just how much money Obe had made selling the stuff here in this town.

"Somewhere around here, Mr. Tooley has a lot of money," he said out loud.

The more he thought about the money, the more Homer wanted it for himself. As he drove his team and wagon to his house, he formed a scheme to get it from his prisoner.

"OK, now, Obe Tooley," the arrogant sheriff addressed the man behind the bars. "I have your little Missus and those bratty kids of yours next door. They're all locked up tight at my house."

Obe tried to restrain his feelings outwardly, but inside he was very angry.

"Look out that window. See what I found in your root cellar." Remer laughed as he taunted the man.

"Fred. Go outside and count the bottles I just brought in," Homer instructed his deputy, in order to be alone with Obe.

After the deputy went out, Homer moved close to the jail cell. He wanted to speak quietly to the prisoner.

"Look, Tooley. I'll make you a deal. You pay me five hundred dollars and I won't take you to Sandpoint for trial," the crooked sheriff ordered. "I know you have the money. I counted all the empty cases in your cellar, and I figure you have plenty." Remer paused for a minute to give the man a little time to think before continuing. "You give me the money and I'll let you and your family move out of this town. You'll all be free of this messy situation.''

A normal, reasoning person would have thought this deal over long and hard. But Obe was not that kind of person any longer. His love for his money seemed to shadow any logical thinking. It didn't matter how much suffering the decision might bring.

Obe immediately answered firmly, "*No!* Mr. Remer, you're just a criminal yourself. No better than I am.'' Obe spouted back at the sheriff, ''Not you or anyone else is going to extort my money away from me. I earned it myself and I'm going to keep it.''

"Why, you stubborn fool,'' the angry sheriff retorted. ''Don't you know you and your wife will go to jail if you don't give me the money?''

''I don't care. Maybe we will go to jail. But I'm not giving a crook like you a dime!'' Obe yelled back.

The hotheaded man with the badge stormed out of the office and walked to the wagon where Fred was counting bottles. Homer said something to his Deputy, then both men started unloading the wagon. They took the confiscated liquor and began placing the bottles on the fence posts behind the jail. When all the posts were topped with the illegal juice, they began shooting their pistols in that direction, aiming at the brew. Each time they were lucky enough to hit one, they hooted and hollered like little boys. They laughed and jeered as the liquid and glass splashed and shattered to the ground.

The sounds of gunshots made Myrtle jump to her feet and run to the window. She instructed Helen to bring her a chair so she could see outside. She wanted to view what she feared was happening. As she watched the lawmen shoot the bottles one by one, she cringed at the effect this might have on her husband's ability to think clearly in this tense ordeal.

Obe sat silently on his cot as the men outside continued to break his precious supply of potential profits. Each time the gun fired, he hit his own leg with his clenched fist. He rigidly resolved that he would not give up his money, no matter what price he had to pay for that decision.

After what seemed an eternity of gunshots piercing the air. Remer strutted back into the office. He would give Obe one more chance to reconsider his offer.

"Are you still sure you want me to take you and the wife to Sandpoint?'' Homer asked.

"I'm not giving you my money, and that's final," Obe replied with hate and anger in his voice. "Just get on to doin' whatever you have to, and don't ask me the question again."

Homer went down to the lake and took the ferry across to Sandpoint. He wanted to brag to the authorities there about his great arrests. He needed some other lawman's advice on what to do about the woman and children.

After determining what should be done, the sheriff of Sandpoint told Remer he would be sending two of his deputies over in the morning to help him bring over the prisoners.

The morning broke in Lakeview on that April day with the promise of a beautiful new spring. It was a promise of wonderful beginning for almost every creature. But for the Tooley family it heralded in a different kind of beginning, one of sorrow and hardships.

The deputies from Sandpoint arrived and helped Sheriff Remer take Obe, Myrtle, and their four children across the lake. The two adults needed to go to court and appear before a judge.

When they saw each other for the first time since the arrest. Obe could see Myrtle had been through some trauma by the cut on her swollen lip. Her eyes were red and puffy, a trait he knew showed when she cried a lot.

"Are you all right?" Obe asked his wife.

"Look at me, Obe Tooley. Do I look like I'm all right?" Myrtle responded in tones that meant no.

The two of them were silent the rest of the way to Sandpoint.

The children sensed the tension of the situation and sat quietly next to their mother. The baby was still sick, but with the medicine the doctor had given him he slept until they arrived at the Sandpoint jailhouse.

Obe was placed in a cell at the sheriff's office. Myrtle and the children were taken to the sheriff's home next door and placed upstairs in a bedroom.

It was such a humiliating experience for Myrtle to be under arrest and brought to the town where she had been one of the leading citizens just the year before. Myrtle was glad to be in the sheriff's home and out of sight. At least she was away from the view of any old friends who might stop by the office next door. She wasn't concerned too much about Obe's feelings. After all, if it hadn't been for his big scheme to get rich illegally they could be in Canada, not in this terrible predicament he had got them into.

118

It was the middle of the afternoon that day when the deputy and the sheriff's wife, Mrs. Jensen came up to the room Myrtle and the children were in. Mrs. Jensen would be sitting with the little ones while their mother went with the officer to go before the judge.

Obe was already in the courtroom when Myrtle arrived. She looked at him with questioning eyes not knowing what to do or say. But Obe just hung his head as they waited for the judge to come in.

"All rise," the bailiff announced as Judge Raymond Woods entered the courtroom.

Myrtle trembled as she forced her weak body to stand. She hadn't slept for almost two nights, with the traumatic arrest and the sick baby. Her soul seemed drained of its will to keep going.

"Mr. and Mrs. O. A. Tooley. You have been charged with a misdemeanor and accused of the possession and selling of alcoholic beverages. Do either of you have anything to say before we proceed with this trial?" the judge asked.

"Your Honor." Myrtle spoke up immediately. "I have a very sick child and I need to be with him right now."

"Yes, Your Honor. We ask the court for some time before trial to prepare our case," Obe added as an excuse to stall.

"So granted," the judge proclaimed. "You have ten days, until April 17, 1914, at ten in the morning, to declare your plea and be ready for trial. Mrs. Tooley." The judge looked at the frightened woman straight in the eye. "You are remitted to bail in the sum of one hundred dollars and are awarded to the care of the sheriff until such bail is given."

Myrtle gave a slight gasp at the high amount of the bail. She knew Obe would probably not pay it.

"Mr. Tooley," the judge went on, looking this time at Obe, "you are admitted to bail in the sum of two hundred dollars for your appearance and are to remain in the custody of the sheriff until such bail is given."

Obe never expected bail would be so much. He wasn't going to give the crooked lawmakers that much of his money. He decided he and Myrtle would stay in jail at those prices. He choked on the words but managed to get them out somehow: "Thank you, Your Honor." At this point he didn't want to make a scene and have contempt charges added. He could just as well vent his frustrations later.

"Court dismissed," was the judge's statement as he pounded his gavel on the desk.

119

"Please, Your Honor." Myrtle spoke up in a pleading tone before the judge left the room. "I need to speak with my husband in private for a few minutes."

"OK, Mr. Jensen, they can have five minutes," the man ordered.

The two weary people waited until the sheriff was across the room before Myrtle began pleading with Obe.

"Please pay the bail money, Obe, at least mine. I know it's a lot, but the children and I are cooped up in a bedroom at the sheriff's house. The kids need to be home in their own beds. Earl is sick, and the doctor is pretty sure he is coming down with the measles. He said all the children will probably get them within the next month. I need to be home, where they can be cared for properly." Myrtle could tell her reasoning was falling on deaf ears. Her husband already had his stubborn mind made up, and no amount of talking was going to change it.

Obe tried to convince her it would be better for everyone if they all stayed in Sandpoint. He reasoned the doctor here was more experienced and could give the children better care than the one in Lakeview.

Myrtle could see right through his phony excuse. "Obe Tooley. You stingy old goat. It's not the children you're concerned about. It's that wretched money you have stashed away somewhere. I can't believe you have turned into such—"

Myrtle hadn't finished her chastisement before the Sheriff broke into her sentence. "Time's up," he stated. "If you're going to pay the bail money do it now, or you're both going back to jail." His words were sharp and to the point.

"Take us back to jail," were Obe's only words. He stood up and walked toward the lawman, leaving his tearful wife to trail behind him.

There was one more day of fever before the red rash started to appear on Earl's body. The little guy cried a lot during his waking hours. Myrtle tried to keep him quiet, knowing the noise was probably annoying Mrs. Jensen. But the strange living quarters along with the itchy spots made the boy miserable.

One night when all the children were asleep except Pearl, Myrtle tried to explain to her questioning daughter why her parents had been arrested. Pearl listened carefully to her mother's explanation. It was hard for the girl to understand. Her daddy had been selling liquor ever since she could remember, even to the lawmen. They had never got mad at him before. Why was it OK to sell drinks before but not OK now? The logic of the matter didn't make sense, but the reality of the consequences was something even a young, maturing mind could grasp.

All that was important to Pearl was that she was a part of a family, and she loved them all. She even loved her now-grumpy father, who no longer allowed any of the children to show their feelings for him.

Pearl crawled up on her mother's bed and cuddled up close. She put her arms around her mom's neck and whispered, "I love you," words that were not always expressed openly but were always in her soul. She held tight for a long time before falling asleep snuggled up next to her momma.

Sheriff Remer had gone back to the Tooley house in Lakeview to see if he could find where Obe had his money hidden. While the sheriff was searching, he found two more cases of whiskey in an old shed by the outhouse. He was angry about not finding the money, so he took the two cases of alcohol over to Sandpoint to taunt Obe another time.

The sounds of gunfire, glass breaking, and loud laughter awakened the Tooleys on the morning of April 16 before the trial.

Obe stood on his cot to see what the men outside his window were shooting at this time. The rising sun made the objects lined up along the wooden fence sparkle like large pieces of amber jewels.

Homer Remer and two of the Sandpoint deputies were taking turns shooting in the direction of the sparkling objects with their revolvers. They laughed loudly when they hit one of the bottles, to allow everyone nearby to marvel at their accuracy.

Remer had been watching to see when Obe would appear at the window so he could get in one more episode of irritation before the trial.

"Good morning, Mr. Tooley. Looky what I found in the shed by the outhouse. You wouldn't happen to know how they got there, would you?" the sassy man asked, but he didn't wait for an answer before turning and firing five bullets in the direction of the full bottles. Three containers immediately exploded, sending liquid and glass particles in all directions.

"Oh no! Not again," Myrtle uttered as she looked out the bedroom window. "Please make the terrible man stop tormenting Obe. Especially right now, with only one day left before the trial." She knew the destruction of more of her husband's investment would make an already-obsessed man go crazy. She was afraid of what he might do or say in such a state of mind.

He sat back down on his bed. His jaw began to tighten, and his hand formed into a fist. *"Damn him! Damn him! Damn them all!"* Obe cursed. "All they want is my property and my money. It all boils down to that. Everyone wants my money. Well, they're not going to get it. I'll rot in hell before I give one penny to any of them."

The greed and lust for money had become like a growing cancer to Obe's soul. Acquiring the "filthy lucre" was like an addiction, and the desire engulfed his being. All truth or reason was blocked out if it contradicted this one desire. He had become estranged from his wife and children and had no desire to make friends with anyone. He was always suspicious of people's motives for wanting to be sociable. His mind also rationalized that everyone who offered him friendship was in some way trying to get something from him. He resolved he wasn't going to fall into that trap again. It seemed to this disturbed mortal everyone was out to take advantage of him. The frustration of trying to build businesses only to be forced to leave and move on had taken its toll on this haunted man. Providing homes for his ungrateful wife and kids, and being expected to give more and more, was like a painful sore. All of these new frustrations had come to a festering head at this time, this place, this moment of life. With this stubborn mind-set, bad actions or decisions could destroy and shatter lives. But this doomed man could not see beyond right now. Everything that had happened up to this point was now condensed in his own selfish, stubborn soul. Obe was determined to keep his precious money, and nothing or no one was going to get it from him.

The afternoon of April 16, Pearl came down with a fever similar to the one her little brother had experienced. The doctor was again called up to the room in the sheriff's home, and the diagnosis of pending measles was announced.

A high fever can play delusional tricks, especially on a child's mind. The onset of the illness that encompassed her body sent nine-year-old Pearl in and out of sleep for the first twenty-four hours. It was difficult to distinguish between dreams and reality in this strange bedroom enclosure. Pearl's thoughts took her from dark places to light places, back and forth, back and forth. She was in a beautiful field of flowers. The air around her was sparkling with drops of mist, but they didn't seem to get her wet. She was wearing a soft white dress and silver slippers. She had the ability to run through the flowers and stay suspended in the air for long periods, longer than she could with normal gravity. Gravity did not seem to have the same pull on her as usual. The more she leaped, the longer she could stay suspended in the air. It was a wonderful feeling, and she desired to go higher and higher. She yearned to sail away and see what was above the soft, billowy clouds floating gracefully in the sparkling air.

She touched the earth for a final leap that would take her up to the clouds. But the toil-worn hand of a woman reached up through the flowers and caught hold of Pearl's white dress. The hand held tight, preventing her from going up higher. She tried to leap again, but the woman called out to her, "Pearl! Pearl! Come back, sweetheart. I need you to stay here. Your sister and brothers need you to take care of them. They will get lost if you aren't here to keep them together." The sound of her pleading voice made the light disappear, and Pearl was in the darkness again.

All she could see was the silhouette of her mother sitting by her side. She was dipping a rag in cool water and rubbing it on Pearl's feverish forehead. Mother was trying to keep the fever from destroying Pearl's body. She could feel her mother's love radiate around her and struggled to keep her burning eyes open. She desperately wanted to obey the caring woman's commands as she fought to make her child well again.

DECISIONS AND DECISIONS

When the morning of the seventeenth finally arrived, Myrtle was exhausted. She had been up all hours of the day and night tending to the sick children. She had only been able to keep going because she knew this situation was temporary. She figured the judge would not be easy on Obe, but surely he would show mercy to a mother with four young children. Even if the fine was high, Obe had at least six hundred dollars hidden away somewhere. And after all, they were only charged with a misdemeanor. No one had been injured or killed from buying the liquor. They would simply pay the fine and move on to another state or to Canada and start again. To Myrtle the solution to this problem was easy and logical. She and Obe were not strangers to moving. They had pretty well mastered the technique after doing it three times in the past ten years.

Myrtle was not at all happy about this situation she was in but was glad the day of trial had finally arrived. They could soon put an end to this tense part of their lives. She had made a solemn vow to herself she would never be a part of selling liquor again, as long as it was illegal. She would just have to convince Obe and help him find another way to make a living.

She was filled with new hope and resolve until she was escorted into the courtroom just before 10:00 A.M. and looked at her husband. At that point her stomach began to churn. She had seen the same bizarre look on Obe's face and countenance before, and it always meant trouble. Myrtle's heart began to pound, and her throat felt like it was being strangled with fear.

Their eyes met for one short blink, but Obe lowered his head and would not look at her. Myrtle tried to silently get his attention, but he still would not look her way. She became desperate. *If he would only look at me,* she thought, *perhaps some of the hardness he surrounded himself with would soften.* She needed her husband to be soft and compassionate today.

"Obe," she finally said out loud.

He raised his head, but the look he gave was neither soft nor compassionate; it was mean and cross. The devil himself could not have given Myrtle a more dreadful glare. Obe lowered his head again and only looked at the handcuffs around his wrists.

Myrtle didn't try again to talk to him. Her heart was aching and she felt so abandoned and alone. The hopes she had brought into the courtroom had been dashed by the hate radiating from her husband's eyes.

124

"All rise," the bailiff announced. "The Honorable Judge Raymond Woods presiding."

Everyone obediently stood up.

"Be seated," the judge commanded. "Bailiff, are the defendants both present?"

"They are, your Honor," the bailiff responded.

"Present the first case," the judge instructed.

"Case Number Four Ninety-six, the *state of Idaho versus O. A. Tooley*" the bailiff announced, handing the judge a document.

The judge paused to read the papers of the case. He then looked at Obe, who was now standing.

"Mr. Tooley. You are charged with a misdemeanor, for the possession and selling of liquor. How do you plea?"

There was a deafening silence in the courtroom as Obe faced the man wearing the black robe. With no visible expression on the defendants' face and a demeanor as cold as ice, he looked at the judge and answered, "Guilty!"

"Do you wish to say anything in your behalf before I pronounce sentence?" the judge questioned while looking back at Obe with a stone-cold glare.

"No. It wouldn't make any difference, would it?" the guilty man responded.

The two men's coldness toward each other sent a chill through Myrtle's weakened body.

"Just get on with it," Obe demanded.

The judge looked carefully at his paper and made some calculations with his pen. He then announced his decision.

"The court fines you two hundred dollars plus court costs and taxes, in the amount of sixty-six dollars and forty cents making the total two hundred, sixty-six dollars and forty cents."

A gasp escaped from Myrtle's lips. She had not expected the fine to be so much.

"If you cannot pay the fine, you can spend one day in jail for each two dollars of your fine, up to one hundred and thirty-three days." The judge paused to see if the man in front of him would humble himself but never expected the reaction that followed. The judge had been told by a good source that this man had been selling the liquor at inflated prices. The person had reported that Mr. Tooley had the money hidden someplace. As he had obtained it illegally, Judge Woods felt the state of Idaho, and particularly Bonner County, should share the pot.

125

"It seems to me a pretty high price to pay for a simple misdemeanor, Your Honor," Obe retorted.

"Well, it is not a simple misdemeanor, Mr. Tooley. I don't want alcohol bought or sold in this county. Maybe when people like you know they will face a stiff penalty for bootlegging in the Sandpoint area, they won't be coming here to sell their liquor," Woods spouted back. The veins in his neck were now enlarging and coming to the surface.

"What will it be?" the judge asked while trying to regain his composure. "Pay the fine, or go to jail?"

Obe stood up straight and with a slight grin spoke out. "I'll go to jail!"

The answer took everyone in the courtroom by surprise. It was definitely not the one the judge wanted to hear. He had planned to go easy on Mrs. Tooley. With Obe's attitude and refusal to part with his money, Woods's reaction resounded in anger. "OK, Mr. Tooley, if that's your decision, you may take a seat while your wife comes forward," the judge ordered. "Next case."

"Case Number Four Ninety-seven, *the State of Idaho versus Mrs. O. A. Tooley,*" the bailiff announced.

"Mrs. Tooley, please stand," Judge Woods instructed.

Myrtle was trembling as she tried to rise. The first attempt was futile and she slipped back to her chair. She grabbed the table in front of the seat. By using both arms and legs, she successfully made it to an upright position.

"Mrs. Tooley. You are charged with a misdemeanor for the possession and selling of liquor, which has been outlawed in the state of Idaho. How do you plead?" The Judge recited the charges with even more coldness in his tones than he had with her husband.

"Your Honor," Myrtle tried to explain, "I was only trying to help a couple of old men who needed the liquor for their pains, sir."

"I wasn't asking you *why* you did it, Mrs. Tooley," the judge snapped at the trembling woman. "I was asking *did you do it or not do it?*"

"Yes, I did do it," she replied with her head bowed.

"Then are you pleading guilty?" he questioned.

"I guess I'm guilty," Myrtle answered as the tears began rolling down her flushed cheeks.

With the compassion of a wooden Indian, the judge doled out his sentence to the sobbing defendant. "The court fines you the sum of two hundred dollars. . . ."

"Oh, no!" The words escaped from Myrtle's mouth as she tried to cover her lips. A numbness started to take over her body as she listened to the judge finish.

"Plus court cost and taxes in the amount of twelve dollars and fifteen cents for a total of two hundred, twelve dollars and fifteen cents. Or you may be committed to the country jail of Bonner County Idaho, at the rate of one day for every two dollars of the fine and costs, not exceeding one hundred and six days."

"Oh, Your Honor," the humble woman responded. "I can't go to jail, there is no one to care for my four young children. Mr. Tooley will pay my fine," she stated as she looked at Obe with desperate, pleading eyes.

But Obe only tightened his jaw and proclaimed loud enough to send Myrtle's soul to the depths of hell. "I'm not giving this court *any money!* Not for me and not for you!"

His words cut like a dagger, ripping at Myrtle's already-broken heart. "Obe Tooley. You can't do this to me. I'm your wife and you promised to take care of me. Think of our children. They need at least one of their parents. Even if you hate me for some reason, don't do this to your innocent babies!" Myrtle screamed hysterically at the hateful, stubborn demon who was wearing her once-loving husband's face and clothing.

"Woman! Can't you see it's the government's fault? The politician forced us to be in this mess. They were the ones who made us close down our business in the first place. Now let this *damned government take care of all of us,* for a while," Obe cursed.

Everyone in the courtroom listened in disbelief as the man rejected the pleas of his tearful wife. Even the judge was amazed at Obe's lack of compassion. However, Woods also was a stubborn man beneath those black robes. There would be no changing of his decision, or any leniency in his courtroom today. He was the law enforcer and could not afford to back down on a judgment.

"Order in the court!" Woods demanded as he pounded his gavel sharply on the desk. "Order in the court."

The pounding by the judge brought the reality of her husband's refusal to Myrtles' mind. She dropped to her knees in the center of the room. "Oh, God in heaven, please, please don't let this be happening." She put her face in her hands and wept for the whole universe to see.

"Sheriff. Take Mr. Tooley back to his cell and hold him until we can transfer him to the county jail," the judge instructed. "Bailiff and Mr. Williams. Help Mrs. Tooley to the cot in my outer office. Stay with her so she can rest until I finish with my eleven o'clock appointment. I'll speak with her privately. Court dismissed."

HOOKS AND CROOKS

Myrtle lay on the hard cot and closed her burning, tear-soaked eyes. The darkness was an escape from the harshness of the daylight. She wanted to lift her lids and find the last hour of her life had only been a bad dream. The stiff bed under her frail body reminded her this nightmare was reality. She wanted and needed sleep but forced herself to stay awake and think.

What could she do to soften one of the men who held so much power over her life and freedom? If only Obe would pay her fine or the judge would put her on probation. She could be with the children and find a legal way to support them on her own.

Whom could she turn to? Whom could she borrow the money from to pay the fine? Whom could she get to care for her children while she served the time in jail? Myrtle's mind began to analyze all the possibilities. *Daddy, daddy,* her thoughts called out silently. She had always been able to go to her father for help. If only he hadn't passed away, he would have been here by her side to rescue her. The crack in her heart seemed to widen as she continued in her desperate plight.

John or Albert, if either of her brothers were closer and could have been reached, would be here to help. But John was somewhere in the Yukon. She hadn't heard from him for the last five months. He could be anywhere in the wide expanse of the isolated mountainous region of Canada. If there were any way to reach Albert, he, too, would come to save her. But the chances of locating him in the mining camps of Nevada would be almost impossible. He would never be able to get here in time to do any good.

She kept trying to think of anyone who might help her. But, she really had no one, not even a close friend to turn too. Stella Duncan, now Mrs. Frederick Cooper, had been the only woman Myrtle had ever had as a close friend since moving from Wisconsin. Just where in Washington State Stella was living now Myrtle had no idea.

If she had only been able to foresee this moment a year ago, she would have left Obe and gone to Canada with Nat Broughton. Surely living with him would have been better than the torment she was now facing. If Nat were here, she reasoned, he would be able to talk some sense into her heartless husband. Nat could usually make Obe see things in a clearer light. *Oh, Nat Broughton, where are you?* she again cried out in silence. *I need you now.* She wanted to scream the words loud enough for the ex–business partner to hear, but she knew the effort would be foolish. She just lay on the cot numb and motionless.

"Mrs. Tooley, the judge can see you now," were the words that reincarnated Myrtle's dying soul. The bailiff motioned for Myrtle to get up and enter the opened door to the judge's chambers.

"Well, now, Mrs. Tooley." The judge spoke low and deliberately from behind the large desk where he was sitting. "Events in the court-room didn't go the way they were supposed to today. Did they?" He looked her straight in the eye. At that moment, Myrtle could see in the man's face the same glimmer of greed that had possessed her husband.

"If you would like, madam, I could allow you to try and convince your husband in private. Perhaps a womanly touch could get him to at least pay your fine," Woods suggested. "Sometimes a woman can exert a lot of. . . ." he paused. "Should I say 'sweet persuasion' over a man?"

The more this man of authority spoke, the more Myrtle's skin began to crawl. She could tell by his words and gestures she was being used as a pawn in an elaborate game of extortion, where the ramifications for the losers could be devastating. She tried to maintain an appearance of respect, but down deep she knew the purpose she was being used for and the thoughts made her sick inside.

"I can try to talk to Obe again, Your Honor. But what if he won't pay?" Would you consider probation for me if I promised to work off the fine? I'm a good cook and I could clean the courthouse or your home, or teach school to the children. I have been a teacher, you know." Myrtle kept talking faster and faster, trying to suggest all the possibilities of her skills, in an effort to keep from serving the sentence in jail.

"I don't want your service, woman!" the judge snapped at the pitiful creature. "I want the. . . ." He stopped himself before blurting out the rest of his statement.

Myrtle fully understood now just what the judge was after. He wasn't really interested in true justice. What he wanted Obe had perceived from the beginning. Woods, too, just wanted the money. Her future and the future of her children both revolved around *money.*

"Sir, what about my children?" Myrtle inquired soberly. "What will happen to my children if I have to go away from them, to jail?"

"Yes, there is the matter of the children," the man in black robes responded. "Do you have any relatives or neighbors whom the court could give temporary custody to?"

"No, Your Honor, no one. That is why it's so vital you consider probation," Myrtle responded.

"No close family or friends can be a problem in these cases. If you can't persuade your husband to pay the fines, the children's home in Lewiston will be contacted. Your children will be sent there and put up for adoption. Then respectable, law-abiding people can raise them," he threatened.

His words were sharp and slashed another piercing blow to her heart. She had never in her most terrible thoughts imagined the children would be sent so far away. And to be put up for adoption, that was unthinkable. How could this so-called lawman even suggest such a cruel horrible thing to a mother, for such a minor crime?

A gasp of horror escaped Myrtle's lips. "You wouldn't be. . . . No, you couldn't be that mean and cruel to innocent little children, your Honor. Do you have any idea what that kind of experience would do to the feelings of a child?" Myrtle pleaded.

"I am not hired to consider feelings, madame. My job is to see that justice is carried out. I will do the only humane thing I can do for abandoned children. I will try to find them decent homes to be raised in. If you go to jail, your children will be taken to the state children's home," the judge concluded.

Homer Remer had come over to Sandpoint to testify against the Tooleys if necessary. He was now at Sheriff Jensen's office, where the prisoner was.

Obe was lying on a jail cot staring at the ceiling when Myrtle was brought in to see him. He didn't want to face her; he just wanted to be left alone.

"So the 'little jailbird' has been brought to see the 'big jailbird' " Homer said, laughing at the joke he had made.

"Mr. Remer, the judge said my husband and I could be alone for a short time," Myrtle stated in a firm tone. "Now please, you can lock the door if you think you have to. Mr. Wood said we could be *alone.*"

The nosey man did not approve of these directions. He did leave, reluctantly however, when the bailiff confirmed the judge's orders.

"So what favors did you have to promise to get the judge to let us be alone?" the cynical husband asked.

Myrtle tried to ignore her husband's rude remark. She did not want to get into a fight about some silly suspicion or accusation. She had much more important matters to present to the man. "Obe, we needed to talk privately, and the judge allowed us to do it," she stated. "You need to *listen carefully* to what I have to say. There is too much at stake for you to continue this stubbornness. You need to pay one of our fines," Myrtle stated firmly. "One of us needs to be free to take care of the children."

"Here we go again," Obe complained. "This whole thing is about *my money*, you know. All everyone wants is to get ahold of everything I've worked for all my life. They drive us like some sort of cattle all over the country, trying to keep us from making a living. Now, just when I have a little bit of savings, they want to take it all away. Well, they can arrest Obe Tooley and fine him a big fee, but they will never force him to pay for it. Not with money."

Myrtle listened to her husband and could empathize, in part, with what he was saying. But his views of life were too narrow. How could she remove the blinders he seemed to be wearing? How could she help him see the "bigger picture"? He needed to stop focusing on the money and see the value of his children's happiness.

"I know, Obe. You are right," Myrtle admitted.

Obe was almost startled by his wife's admission of the court's motives. He listened as she continued.

"When I was talking with the judge earlier, I could tell he wanted you to pay the fine. He really does want that money, and it sickens me. It is plain to see you and I are not the only criminals here. If it were just me and you facing these problems I'd be willing to serve the sentence. Especially after what I gleaned from talking with the judge today. I would agree to go to jail and keep the money. But the real problem, Obe, is our children. These men have the power to destroy all our lives. If we don't pay at least one of the fines, that's what they are going to do," Myrtle explained.

"Myrtle! I just don't care what they can do! I am not paying the fines!" the man snapped at her.

Myrtle cleared her throat. She wanted to make sure the father of her children could plainly hear and understand what she was about to say.

"If you refuse to pay at least one of our fines, they will send the children to Lewiston. They will put them in the orphans' home and possibly adopt them out to other families. Obe, if that happens, I will die inside. *Please* don't take my children away from me," she pleaded. "You have the power to stop this from happening. Hate me; beat me; divorce me, whatever you wish. But please, please, don't let them take our children away. Don't punish the innocent little ones and cause them unnecessary grief and suffering. The two hundred twelve dollars and fifteen cents is so insignificant in comparison to what we will be losing. I'll find a way to pay it back to you myself if that's what you want. But for heaven's sake, give the judge the money!"

The pleading had fallen on deaf ears. The man was more stubborn than a mule and would not budge an inch. "Insignificant! You think two hundred and twelve dollars and fifteen cents is insignificant. Well, let me tell you a thing or two, woman. I worked hard for that money. I'm not giving it up and that's final!" Obe shouted as he raised his hand and struck his wife. "Go away and leave me alone!" the cantankerous fool yelled.

The sting on Myrtle's cheek from Obe's hand paled in comparison to the wounds he had made to her heart and soul. With more tears rolling down her already-soaked face, Myrtle articulated one more thing to this man who now seemed like a stranger. "Obediah Tooley! With the witness of all my ancestors in heaven who have passed on before me, if you let them take away our children, and I can't get each one back when this is over, you will never know or see me again!" She then called for the sheriff to take her back to the house where she could be with the children.

ANGELS WITH SPOTS

Myrtle felt like she had aged forty years as her drained spirit and body were herded back to the sheriff's house. The weight of the universe seemed to have been placed on her shoulders. How would she ever convince her sweet angels she had tried to save them in vain. She hated for them to face this hardship. She could tell them the truth and blame their father. But the knowledge of his rejection could cause all sorts of mixed-up emotions in such young minds. She was afraid they might feel guilty. She couldn't have them thinking they had been the reason for the rejection. They were the only ones who were innocent in this whole ordeal.

Roy and Helen were sitting at a table under the big apple tree. The two of them were eating a lunch Mrs. Jensen had prepared. When their mother was brought back to the house, they stopped and ran to meet her.

"Mommy, Mommy, you're back," the five-year-old boy gleefully announced as he grabbed her leg and held tightly.

"Momma, Mrs. Jensen had the doctor come over to be with Pearl. She's real bad sick," reported the concerned girl.

Myrtle bent down and gave each child a soft hug. "Helen, you stay here with Roy. Mrs. Jensen will tell you when it's all right to come upstairs," the worried mother instructed. "I'll go help the doctor with your sister."

When Myrtle went into the room, the doctor was sponging Pearl with cold towels. He was making an effort to bring down the high fever.

"Thank you for coming," Myrtle said to the kind healer. "I didn't want to leave her this morning, but I had no other choice. How is she doing?"

"I think the worst part of the fever is over. But you will need to check her temperature every two hours. If it goes up over a hundred and one degrees, then start the cool bathing again," he instructed. "I advise you to wait until the day after tomorrow before you take her home."

Tears welled up again in Myrtle's eyes. She asked the doctor if she could speak with him privately in the hallway. It took a few minutes of sobbing before she was able to talk to the man. "You see, Doctor, my husband has chosen not to pay our fines the judge ordered, and so. . . ." She broke down in quiet sobbing again before she could say the words. "I am going to jail. The judge is going to have the children taken to the children's home."

The doctor stood close to the woman and offered her a clean handkerchief to dry her eyes. "Well, well," the medical man uttered. "Raymond Woods is up to his old tricks again. I see. Well, I have a few strings of my own to pull here. I suspect before this illness is over your other two little ones will also come down with the measles. I will be informing the judge neither you nor your children are going anywhere until the disease has run its course. When everyone is well and healthy again then I will lift the quarantine. I suspect it will take at least a month or more for that to happen. We'll postpone this action as long as we can," he told the young mother.

"Oh, God bless you," she thanked him as she gave him a hug. "I'll be grateful for any amount of time I can have with my children."

When the fever finally broke completely the following morning, the red itchy spots began to appear. Pearl felt as if her skin were on fire.

The doctor brought over some calamine lotion for Pearl and insisted her fingernails be cut and filed smooth. "And don't scratch whatever you do, young lady," he commanded. "You don't want to end up with scars all over this pretty skin when the bumps go away now, do you?" The doctor was firm but had a happy twinkle in his eyes. He wanted to reassure his patients he was only trying to do what was best for her.

The worst part of the rash lasted for more than a week before it began to cool down and slowly disappear. By this time, Earl had completely recovered. However, Roy was now starting with the fever.

Helen was assigned to help her mother keep an eye on the three-year-old boy. He was regaining his strength and ready to run and play. Mrs. Jensen would keep a lookout on the two children as they played in the backyard. She would give them small tasks to do to keep them busy. Helen would help her fold some of her laundry, and Earl was assigned to gather twigs and sticks for the stove.

Myrtle was not allowed to leave the upstairs part of the house. She was glad when Pearl began to get well and could help out a little. By the time Helen came down with the fever, Pearl was getting her strength back and could help out more and more each day.

Mrs. Jensen would let Pearl come and help deliver meals to the rest of her family. She also helped hang some of the laundry on the low wires, where she could reach.

At her mother's request, Pearl was allowed to run little errands. She was old enough to go to the store by herself. She was a big help with Earl and would make sure he was clean and dressed each day. She could also keep him busy with work and play. This was a big service to her mother, who couldn't even go outdoors.

Dr. Greer had informed Judge Woods of his quarantine of Myrtle and the children. The judge had passed the message on to the children's home in Lewiston. Mr. Chase, the superintendent of the home, had informed the judge he would be in Sandpoint the first week of June. He would bring all the necessary paperwork to pick up the children.

By the last week in May, all of Myrtle's children were over the measles and back to full health. She was happy they weren't sick anymore, but she also knew what this meant.

The day Mr. Chase rode into town, in the black horse-drawn carriage, the sky was dark with the threat of an early summer storm. He asked directions to the sheriff's office and went there to inform the authorities of his arrival.

Mr. Chase was a man in his early sixties, with thinning gray hair and a very slender body. He wore a dark suit of clothing and carried a cane. The cane was not used much for walking but as a discipline tool for unruly youngsters. The sharp turned-down creases in his face gave the impression he was very stern and unhappy.

"I'm here for. . . ." he started, then pulled a document from his pocket and read the name. "The Tooley children. Where are you keeping them?"

"Mr. Chase, I presume? We have been waiting for you. I'm Sheriff Ronald Jensen. My deputy will go and get Mrs. Tooley. We will meet them at Judge Woods' office. Come with me and I'll take you there," the sheriff responded.

Myrtle was shaking all over when she was led into the judge's office. She was now face-to-face with the men who were about to rob her of her offspring. There were no smiles on any faces. Somberly the men prepared the proper papers required by the state of Idaho for their custody.

There was silence in the room as the judge read the documents. He then put his name on the line requiring his signature.

Myrtle in her quivering meek voice pleaded with the judge one last time. "Your Honor. I have served nearly half of my sentence already. Wouldn't you please just put me on probation now, and let the children stay with me?"

136

The judge glared at the woman with no mercy in his eyes. "Mrs. Tooley. You had your opportunity to keep your children, but you failed. It's my duty to see the children are placed in a safe environment. A place where they can go to school and grow up to be good citizens. It's my opinion they can best be served by having Mr. Chase take them to a better place than they're in now," he sharply stated.

"Madame. We have a nice facility in Lewiston," Mr. Chase added. "The children will receive the best of care. The state will also provide food and clothing. I'm sure if you could see our home, you would agree it is a fine place for youngsters to learn and grow. There are good schools nearby, where the children have a variety of subjects to study. Many more than the small one-room schoolhouses the rural areas provide."

"But it's so far from here," Myrtle stated. "I want to get my children back after I have finished serving my sentence. It will be a hardship for me to travel such a long distance."

"Mrs. Tooley. You need to stop thinking so much about yourself and consider the children's needs first. There is no place any closer than Lewiston for these sort of things. You will just have to live with your mistakes and let the children be where they can be cared for," Mr. Chase advised. He then handed her the document to sign.

Myrtle looked the paper over. Her eyes were so teary, the words were blurred in front of her. She tried to read all the small print, knowing loopholes were often added. But between the shaky hands and watery eyes she just gave up and put her signature on the dotted line.

"OK, Mrs. Tooley," Mr. Chase commented after reading her signature. "I will be at the sheriff's home by eight in the morning to pick up the children. The youngsters must have a good breakfast before traveling. They need to be clean and dressed and their belongings packed. Make sure they are ready to go on time. Now good day, Your Honor," he said to the judge. Mr. Chase then exited the room.

Myrtle made no such acknowledgment. She got up from her chair and walked to the door where the deputy was waiting for her.

As she climbed the stairs to the room where her children were waiting for her, Myrtle fought with every ounce of strength left in her aching soul to keep from breaking down in front of the little ones. She needed to be strong so they could be strong. She needed to show her courage so they, too, could be courageous. But first and foremost she needed to make sure each one knew she loved them. They would need a lot of love to be sustained for the next few months.

Just before opening the bedroom door, Myrtle took a deep breath. She needed the strength to began the arduous task awaiting her on the inside.

"Mommy, Mommy," the four little ones seemed to be saying in unison. "We're glad you're back, Mommy. We missed you."

Myrtle smiled in response to their cute, innocent gestures. She then sat on the bed and held out her arms. "OK, I need a big hug from each of you," she requested, then sucked up the sweetness of their hugs and kisses. "Children, I have something I need to tell you," Myrtle softly spoke. "Remember back a few weeks ago when I told you Daddy had to go away for a while? Well, now I have to go away for a little while, too. I'm not going to be allowed to take any of you with me."

"No, Momma! You can't go away without me. I'll sneak and follow you," the precocious five-year-old Roy announced.

"Oh, how I wish it could be possible," the courageous mother continued. "But you won't be able to do it. All of you are going on a long trip."

"Where are we going?" Helen questioned quickly.

"You are all going to a big house in a town called Lewiston. There will be a lot of other children to play with," Myrtle explained.

"I don't want to go to a big house," Helen blurted out. "I'll run away and come and find you."

"No, no, you must not think or try such a thing. You could be in great danger if you tried to run away," the mother warned. "Pearl, I need you to be my helper." She looked at her oldest daughter with firm concern. "Children, Pearl is the oldest. You follow where she goes, and do what she does. Listen to her and mind what she tells you," the mother commanded. "Pearl. I know this is a very big responsibility for such a young girl. But I need you to be strong. You must be real grown-up and help your sister and brothers. They need to do what they are told by the man who will take you to Lewiston. When you get there, you must do what the adults in charge at the big house tell you. Can you do that?" Myrtle asked the nine-year-old.

The girl listened to the commanding tones in her mother's voice and realized what she was being asked to do was very important. She shook her head in a "yes" motion as her mother looked her firmly in the eye, then smiled ever so slightly.

"Let's pretend this is a big new adventure," Myrtle said as she changed the tone of her message to relax the seriousness of separation.

"You can see new places, meet new people, and do a lot of new and exciting things. I bet this trip will be real fun if you make it that way," she explained.

The little ones changed their frowns into smiles with the thoughts expressed by these words of encouragement. But Pearl could sense the anxiety in the countenance of the weary woman who held her tight.

After supper the incarcerated group entertained each other with songs and stories. Myrtle tried to soak up as much of the happiness and joy radiating from her youngsters as possible. She would need every bit of this cheerfulness to sustain her in the empty days that lay ahead. She wanted to leave the children with wonderful memories of her love for them. She desired to leave them with a belief that they would be together again soon. She didn't know what the future would bring for her sweet ones when they were out from under her protecting wings. She could only pray for God and the angels in heaven to watch over them until they were reunited again.

"Mommy. Does Daddy still love us, too?" Roy questioned as the group snuggled up to each other.

The question brought the horrible truth to the tip of Myrtle's tongue. But she held it back to spare the pain it would cause. Instead she answered the boy with a lie. "Of course he loves you. Sometimes Daddy doesn't show his love like Mommy does. Each one of you always remember: you are loved." She sweetly pinched the little guy on the cheek and gave him an extra kiss.

The children fell asleep one by one at the sides and feet of their mother. However, she stayed awake to watch over them one last night.

THE RIFT

The dawn seemed to come earlier than usual the morning of June 4, 1914. Myrtle forced her tired body out of bed, hoping not to disturb her sleeping darlings. They had never looked so beautiful to her as they did that breaking morning. The mother watched her little ones as they lay asleep on the bed. If she only had a photograph to remember them so peaceful and sweet. She tried to convince herself two months would go by quickly. Surely by then things would be better with Obe. Perhaps this time in jail would be good for him. It might make the stubborn man appreciate what he had and was now losing. She somehow had to renew her hope and faith in the future. She was going to need it to endure the rest of her sentence in the Bonner County Jail.

She moved quietly as she gathered the children's clothing and sorted through them. She set aside the clothes best suited for traveling and folded the rest neatly. She then packed them in the box Mrs. Jensen had provided. Myrtle stood back to take a silent inventory. She wanted the people at the children's home to see these children had been properly cared for. They were not just someone's abandoned whiffets. She also wanted the people to realize these children were only to be there on a temporary basis. They would be returning home as soon as their parents could arrange it.

At 7:00 A.M. Mrs. Jensen knocked on the door and brought in a pot of mush for the family's breakfast. "The children need to be fed, washed up, dressed, and ready to leave in one hour," the woman advised. "Mr. Chase will be here with the carriage at that time. Mrs. Tooley, I personally want to say I will miss you and the children. I have grown quite fond of them. If I were younger or my health better, I would keep them for you myself. I'm sorry they will be taken so far away."

"Thank you, Mrs. Jensen. Those words of concern mean a lot to me," Myrtle responded.

The children got out of bed, took turns on the toilet, then washed up for breakfast. After breakfast, the three oldest washed their entire bodies under the careful supervision of a mother's watchful eyes. They were then sent to put on the clothing she had laid out for them. Myrtle carefully bathed the three-year-old and made sure a few tickles were added to make him giggle. She dressed him meticulously, making sure each button was buttoned and each lace was tied. She wanted her children to be properly dressed when they left her presence.

140

Myrtle brushed each daughter's hair, taking care to remove every tangle. She pulled the sides back and put clips in to hold the locks in place. She then added a matching ribbon to each sweet head. She took the time to survey the individual beauty of each girl. Myrtle got the boys and wet down each little head. She combed their hair until it met with her satisfaction. As she was tucking the comb and brush in the box, Mrs. Jensen called up the stairs to inform of Mr. Chase's arrival. The sheriff came up to the room and offered to carry down the children's belongings.

With Earl straddling her right hip, Roy holding her left hand, and the two girls following behind, Myrtle took her most prized possessions out to the man waiting by the carriage.

The grumpy look on Mr. Chase's face scared Earl, and he grabbed his mother around the neck and began to cry. Myrtle tried to soothe the boy, begging him not to cry anymore. But with tears running down her own cheeks she wasn't a very convincing example.

Mr. Chase reached for the boy and pulled hard to take him as he screamed even louder.

"Mommy! Mommy! Mommy! I don't want to go! Don't take me! I want my mommy!" the three-year-old shrieked.

The man ripped the baby from his mother's arms and held him tight. The boy scratched and kicked to free himself.

The sight was so heartbreaking for the mother. Each child was wailing at the separation.

"Don't worry, Momma. I'll take care of all of us!" Pearl called out as the carriage drove away, carrying the precious cargo.

Myrtle watched until they passed far from her sight. She then buried her tear-soaked cheeks in her hands and muttered quietly, "Obe Tooley! Someday you are going to pay. Maybe not in this lifetime, and maybe not with money, but someday, you mean, stubborn, wretched old man, you are going to pay for the crime you have just committed against your children." Myrtle then bowed her head in a quiet prayer. "Please, God, watch over those innocent little souls."

THE JOURNEY OF TEARS

The carriage loaded with the sobbing cargo only went two blocks from the jail yard before it stopped in front of a building. There was a wagon and team in front of it. A man and three middle-aged women were waiting for Mr. Chase to arrive with the children.

Only a few quiet words were spoken before the children were instructed to climb down from the carriage and get into the wagon. As they did what was instructed, a woman took hold of each girl and one of the crying three-year-old. Mr. Chase kept the five-year-old boy with him. The man transferred all the children's possessions from the carriage to the wagon and then climbed up to take over as the driver.

Mr. Chase and the three women each took out a tether from the wagon. They each fastened one end to the ankle of the child they held and the other end to their own wrist. It was a scene too heartbreaking for a caring parent to view. Mr. Chase had not wanted Mrs. Tooley to see how her children were being transported to the home.

The four little children were already so frightened, this last gesture made their fears even worse.

"I don't want this belt around my leg!" Helen demanded as she wrinkled her little face in a pouting manner.

"It doesn't matter what you want, little girl," Mr. Chase stated. "We want *no* foolishness or attempts at running away. This just helps keep little people where they are supposed to be," he retorted.

Earl kicked and screamed the whole time the strap was being secured. The wagon driver had to help the woman hold his little leg still.

"Maybe he'll stop crying if he sits on my lap," the brave nine-year-old girl suggested after listening to her upset brother's violent sobs for several minutes.

The woman who was holding Earl looked at Mr. Chase. When he nodded his approval, she gave the boy to his eldest sister. As soon as the small boy was in his sister's familiar arms, his loud crying mellowed to sobs, and then he was quiet. He laid his little head against his sister's chest and stayed motionless in her arms for the next hour.

It took several hours of slow riding in the wagon before they reached Coeur d'Alene. They could catch a train there that would take them the rest of the way to Lewiston.

Once aboard the train, they traveled the rest of that day and all night before arriving at the Lewiston station on June 7, 1914.

The children's home was in a nice location set at the northern end of the city. It had an extra-large house and a few other buildings on the property. There was one small guest house, a barn, and a good-sized storage building.

The house itself sat about four hundred feet from the main road, with a long driveway leading to the front porch. It was a three-level facility with bedrooms on the upper level, the kitchen, dining, workrooms, parlor, and a large office on the main level. There was also a recreation area and storage room in the basement.

The grassy area in front of the home was bordered with several rows of flowers. There was also a vegetable garden on the southeast side of the property.

As the group rode up the road to the house, Pearl noticed several boys who looked to be of different ages from about ten to fifteen. They were working in the big green yard in front of the house, all pulling weeds from flower beds or hoeing in the garden. The boys stopped working and gazed at the carriage for a few minutes. Each one seemed to be looking for a familiar face. On seeing Mr Chase they went back to the work they had been doing.

A woman in a blue dress was in a swing on the front porch. She rose when she saw the carriage and yelled to someone inside the house, "They're here!"

Two other women wearing dark dresses and large white aprons came from the house to greet the superintendent and his newly acquired cargo. A third woman came a few minutes later, and Mr. Chase greeted her. She seemed to be the one in charge as she spoke to the other women.

"Carol, Laura, take the children in to be bathed," she ordered. "Get their clothing and show them where they will sleep. I will brief them on all the rules after Mr. Chase and I have a chance to get their papers in order," Mrs. Chase concluded.

Mrs. Chase was a tall, thin woman in her late fifties. She helped her husband manage this home for orphaned and abandoned children. Between the two of them they ran a pretty tight and disciplined program, both being very stern when dealing with the youngsters.

The Chases were not exactly the ideal caretakers. They were unscrupulous and used whatever means possible to make their jobs profitable.

Mr. and Mrs. Chase went straight to the office. He then took out the papers he had on this new family of children.

"I don't like this situation much," Mr. Chase commented as he shook his head. "The mother of these four is quite a feisty and educated woman. She will only be in jail for a short time and plans to come and get the children back when she gets out. It looks like we will need to work fast if we're going to take advantage of this situation."

"Do you think she will have the means to hire a lawyer?" Mrs. Chase inquired.

"I don't know. But I've been told her husband has a fortune hid somewhere. That's the reason we were able to get these children. He wouldn't part with any of it, even to keep his own kids. That's why Raymond contacted me. I have my doubts if the father will be a problem. I just don't know about the mother, though; she seemed pretty determined."

"So." Mrs. Chase smiled a little as she continued. "You're saying the father's greed is our gain. It will take a good lawyer to undo these signatures. You're right, however, we will have to get things moving quickly."

"Bring in our folders. We'll see if any of these children will fit with our former applicants' requests," Mr. Chase ordered.

The woman went into a side room to retrieve the information her husband needed.

HOME, DREADFUL HOME

The children followed one of the women in the black dresses with the white aprons while the other one pushed them along from behind. The smallest boy began to cry again, so Pearl picked him up and hugged him tight.

"It's all right, Earl," she told him in comforting tones. "Big Sister will take care of you."

The boy held tight and was OK in his sister's arms. Roy and Helen held hands, and the four frightened children forged ahead.

They were taken through a large room with several sofas, tables, and chairs and a lot of tall shelves filled with books. At the back of the room was a double doorway. When the doors were opened, a short hall with two sets of stairs at each end was revealed. One staircase on each side went upward to the bedrooms, and the other two went down to the basement.

It was at this junction the girls and the boys were to separate, each to go up to their assigned staircase.

"Girls to the left and boys to the right," one of the chaperones announced.

The Tooley children stood still as if waiting for different instructions.

"I said girls to the left and boys to the right. Don't you understand English?" the woman snapped sharply at the children.

"I'm sorry, ma'am" Pearl responded firmly. "There must be a mistake. Our mother told us to stay together and we need to do it."

"Yes, Momma said," Roy chimed in quickly.

"Well, listen to me, and listen closely if you know what's good for you," the woman in front instructed as she glared with frowning eyes and wrinkled forehead. "Your mother isn't here. And you will probably never see her again. I'm giving the orders now."

"Our mother is coming to get us; she said so. When she does, we're going to tell her what you said. She'll be mad at you!" Helen yelled out.

The woman lashed out and struck the little red-haired girl sharply across the cheeks and mouth. The motion was so quick and without warning, Helen was stunned and motionless for a few seconds.

Pearl reached out to her wounded sister. With her free arm she pulled her close. Helen buried her stinging face into her big sister's side and sobbed bitterly.

Roy lunged for the cruel woman but was restrained by the woman in back of him.

"Let me go!" the five-year-old screamed as he struggled to free himself.

"Stop, Roy!" Pearl ordered. "If you don't stop, they'll hit you, too."

"Mark my words," the woman stated as she shook her finger in the children's faces. "There will be no sassy talk here. Do you understand?" She paused and waited for a "yes" nod. "The next time there is any disrespect from any of you, you will get a strap across your bare backside. Have I made myself perfectly clear?"

The woman who was giving the lecture reached out and quickly took Earl from Pearl's arms. She gave him to the woman standing behind the children. "Laura, you take the boys and I'll handle these sassy girls," she instructed.

The woman named Laura grabbed Roy by the arm and whisked him up the stairs on the right. Pearl and Helen could hear Earl's cries when he was out of sight.

"*OK*, you two, March!" the stern woman ordered.

The girls were taken up the left stairs. They then entered a room with latrines in stalls along one wall and a long white basin on the other. Helen and Pearl had never seen such a place and stood in awe at the sight.

At one end of the room were large bathtubs with hot and cold water. The girls were instructed to remove their clothing and scrub from head to toe with soap. The woman watched carefully to make sure every nook and cranny was fully soaped and rinsed. She checked their heads, looking for head bugs. When she didn't find any she let the girls dry off. They were each issued soft white shower robes and pink knit slippers.

"You will bathe every three days," the woman instructed. "Before you come, you will take off your soiled clothing. Put them in your basket under the bed that will be assigned to you. Put on this shower robe and slippers to come to the bathing room. Take your bath and return to your room in your robe. Do you understand?" The woman spoke so harshly and coldly the little girls only dared to agree. Silently they nodded their heads.

The girls were then taken to another room with a lot of cupboards and shelves full of linens and clothing. Each girl was measured, then issued two of everything. Their stack consisted of light gray dresses, white aprons, slips, undershirts, panties, and stockings. They were also given one yellow and one pink pinafore. These both had wide ruffles at the shoulders and bottom. The gray dress was to be worn every day. When one got soiled, the other one was to be worn while the first was laundered, and so on. The white aprons were to cover the dress while working or playing at home. The yellow pinafore was for school or errands in town, and the pink one was for church or parties.

The instructor next took down some white sheets and gray wool blankets. "These are for your beds," she explained. "They will need to be changed and laundered every Saturday morning. OK, now, follow me."

Both girls were so overwhelmed they wanted to cry. But when Pearl saw her sister start to weep, she gave her "don't do it, be brave" look. The two girls marched forward and down a hallway to the big sleeping room.

The bedroom was a long, wide room with single cots. There were also standing wardrobes along both sides. The space was broken up into small sections. Each section had a double standing wardrobe closet, in the center next to the wall, with a single bed on each side. On the other side of the bed away from the closet were a small desk and a chair. Above the desk were three shelves where books and trinkets could be stored. Next to the desk was a standing room divider. It extended about three feet out from the wall toward the center. This allowed for a small amount of privacy on one side.

Helen was assigned a bed at the west side of the room near the back. Pearl's was on the east side near the front.

"You might as well get used to being separated right now. You won't be together for long," the woman stated with an almost evil tone. "Now get dressed. Do it in this order; panties, shirt, slip, dress, white apron, socks, and shoes. Then make your beds. I'll be back in fifteen minutes. Hurry up; don't dillydally around," she commanded as she exited the room.

Pearl looked at the stack of clothing and bedding before her. The overwhelming new tasks, the added burdens, along with her feelings of responsibilities for her siblings, were too much for this nine-year-old. Her bottom lip began to quiver, and for the first time since Mr. Chase had taken her from her mother Pearl could not hold back the river of tears that flowed from her eyes. She turned her face from Helen's view, sat on the edge of the bare mattress, and wept.

147

A small hand touched her shoulder, and Pearl looked up to see her sister standing by her. She, too, had tear-soaked cheeks and eyes.

"Sister, I just want to go home. I hate this place," Helen sobbed.

In a sobbing reply Pearl stated, "I hate this place, too, but I don't think they will let us go home."

The two frightened homesick girls sat on the bed holding hands, both trying to just survive the heartache they were experiencing.

After a few minutes alone, Pearl's and Helen's private crying was interrupted by two girls in their midteens. They came bursting through the door into the large bedroom. They were wearing their yellow pinafores, and each carried a small package. The teens were chattering about some boy they had been talking to. When the older girls eyed the two sobbing sisters huddled together, they paused and looked at each other with sober faces. Together they approached the little girls and with cheerful voices spoke to the crying pair.

"Hello there," the golden-haired girl greeted them.

"Do you need some help?" the brown-eyed girl questioned as she pointed to the stack of clothing and bedding lying on the mattress beside Pearl and Helen.

"We both just hate this place," sobbed Helen. "And we want to go home, but we don't think that mean old lady will let us."

"I know how you feel," the brown-eyed girl replied. "Why don't you tell us your names?"

"I'm Helen, and this is my big sister, Pearl."

"Well, hello, Helen and Pearl. I bet you just arrived here, didn't you?" the golden-haired girl inquired. "My name is Anna and this is Francis," she stated as she pointed to the brown-eyed girl with her. "I think we understand just how you're feeling right now. We would be more than happy to give you a hand."

Anna gave a soft tug on Helen's arm. "Come on, missy. Show me where your new bed is located."

Like angels sent from heaven, the empathetic young ladies guided and befriended the seven- and nine-year-old girls. With the older girls' help the little ones were able to make their beds and get dressed. The older girls had saved them from the cruel words and actions of the caretakers. It was truly a gift of service sent from heaven.

At 5:30 P.M. sharp, the supper bell rang. Anna and Francis took Pearl and Helen by the hand and cheerfully guided them down the stairs and into the dining room, then carefully prompted them on how to line up and act at mealtime. The teens taught them how to protect themselves from getting punished for bad behavior.

The eating tables were divided into three separate areas, one side for the girls, the other side for the boys, and the adults in the middle. Soft conversation while eating was allowed, as long as it did not disturb any of the adults.

The meal was hot and tasted good. But of course the girls decided it was not as good as Momma made.

Pearl sat quietly just trying to learn the dos and don'ts as quickly as possible. She wanted to avoid any confrontation with the caretakers and try to stay as invisible as she could.

When one of the caretakers came to the doorway of the dining hall and called out for, "Pearl Tooley," she almost died of fright. She looked at Francis with terror in her eyes, searching for a clue as to where they were going to take her and why.

Anna and Francis just looked at each other and shrugged their shoulders.

"Pearl Tooley!" the caretaker called out again, but louder this time.

Anna nudged her and whispered, "It will be OK. You haven't done anything wrong. They probably just want to ask you some questions."

The reasoning and encouragement helped Pearl to rise to her feet. "I'm Pearl," she answered softly.

"Come with me; we need you." the caretaker remarked.

As she followed the woman, Pearl could make out the screaming and crying of a child. The cries were almost familiar, but more intense and different somehow from anything she had heard before. As she got closer to the sound, she became frightened. She realized the cries were those of her baby brother.

The woman opened the door of the room the sound was coming from. Pearl was appalled at the sight of her sweet brother naked and screaming. He was throwing his arms in the air and kicking wildly. Pearl had never seen such a tantrum before. She was petrified. *He's acting like he is going to die,* was her thought. When she got closer to the table he was on, Pearl could see his little naked body was covered with long red welts. The nurse standing by the table was trying to apply healing balm to the stripes.

"What have you done to my brother?" Pearl boldly demanded. "Earl, tell me what they did to you."

The naked child stopped the thrashing when he heard his sister's command. He reached to grab ahold of any part of her he could find. Pearl gathered the damaged little body into her arms. She hugged him tight as he whimpered and trembled. His flesh felt like ice. She tried to wrap her apron skirt around him for warmth.

"He's just barely three years old," Pearl informed the nurse. "He doesn't understand everything yet like the older kids do."

"I know," the compassionate woman remarked as she continued to apply the balm. "This kind of treatment should not be allowed to happen. It's only singleminded fools, who haven't got brains enough to think of intelligent solutions, that would treat a three-year-old baby this way."

When enough balm had been applied to douse the flaming sting from the child's welts, Earl rested his little head on Pearl's loving shoulder and closed his swollen red eyes.

Mrs. Chase arrived in the room about five minutes after the boy was warmed and calm.

"I'm going to report this cruel punishment of a baby to the Health Department," the nurse boldly stated. She removed the sheet that was over the unclothed child.

Mrs. Chase gasped as she viewed the red, swollen skin. "Who did this?" she asked of the caretaker who had led her to the room. "Was it Laura again?"

The woman did not want to be a snitch but she knew this kind of treatment was happening all too often with the small boys. "Yes, ma'am. I heard the screaming, but by the time I got to the bathroom, the lad was already beat pretty bad."

"Mrs. Chase," the nurse spoke in an authoritarian manner, "it is also my recommendation that Pearl be allowed to help out when this boy needs correcting. As you can see, her love did much more for his behavior than the strap did."

"Well, perhaps, under the circumstances, it might be better if the boy stays with you tonight, Pearl," Mrs. Chase hesitantly conceded.

"Dr. Morgan will be here tomorrow," the kind nurse added. "I want him to examine the boy again. Pearl, could you come with him? I think your brother will feel better if you are with him, don't you? Mrs. Chase, I also recommend you do something about Miss Laura. If you don't, then I will." The boldness in the nurse's voice made even Mrs.

150

Chase uneasy. She certainly didn't like the prospects of an investigation by outside authorities. So she agreed to the woman's demands.

The trauma of seeing his little brother being struck over and over with a strap had a marked effect on Roy. He had never even dreamed such cruelty could happen. All the baby had done was want his momma. The once-feisty spirit of the five-year-old youngster had been tamed. When he tried to stop the woman from hitting his little brother, he, too, was struck with the belt. He was then dragged off to bed without any supper. Unlike the girls, the little boy had no guiding older fellow to help him.

"Boys are supposed to be brave and take the lashes," an older guy told him. But the little five-year-old didn't understand why he had been forced into such a hostile environment. He had always tried to be a good boy and mind his parents and older sisters. He couldn't understand what he had done that was so bad. Why had his mother and father sent him to a mean place like this?

Roy lay on his newly assigned bed and curled up into a little ball. He tried to remember the words of the songs his mother often sang to the children at bedtime. If he could just sing those songs, maybe he could get back to his mother's waiting arms.

In the morning when the boy was still curled up and refused to respond, Mrs. Chase sent for Pearl instead of ordering the strap, knowing the visiting nurse was serious about reporting the harsh beatings to the authorities and she didn't need people coming to snoop around.

"Pearl Tooley!" the call came again as the girl was eating breakfast.

Little Earl was seated between his two older sisters. Again Pearl was startled by the summons.

This time she was taken to the nearly empty boys' sleeping room. Roy all curled up like a "potato bug" was something she had never seen before. He almost looked like he was preparing for some sort of game. But Pearl knew this was not the time for playing games.

"Roy," Pearl softly spoke as she shook the cocooned boy, "Roy, it's Pearl. I'm here to give you a morning hug."

The sound of her voice and familiar words brought the dying soul back to life. They reached for each other and both clung like vines on a wall.

"I think that mean lady killed our baby!" Roy cried. "She kept hitting him and I couldn't get her to stop."

"It's all right, little brother," she answered while stroking his hair and rubbing his back, the same tender caresses she had seen her mother do when trying to make someone feel better. "Our baby brother will be all right. They didn't kill him," she continued, trying to reassure the traumatized boy.

"They took him away last night. I tried to stop them," the boy repeated.

"I know," Pearl told him. "They took me to the doctor's room where they were trying to put medicine on the blisters. He wouldn't stop crying until I held him. They let Earl sleep with me in my bed last night."

"I wish I could sleep with you, too, Pearl," Roy pleaded as his little eyes filled with tears. "I tried to remember the words to Momma's songs. But all I could think of was, 'Lullaby, lullaby,'" he sobbed.

"Tell you what, Roy. I'll ask if you can sleep with me or Helen tonight. I'll teach you the words to a song, so you won't feel so lonely," Pearl promised. "Now get up and get dressed and let's me and you eat some breakfast."

Pearl's mothering was good medicine for the homesick boy. She helped him get dressed and down to the meal room in time for hot cereal and milk.

Adjusting to this new way of living was as difficult for the Tooley children as it had been for all the other children who had passed through this home. After two weeks of adapting and starting to understand what was expected, the children were beginning to fill some measure of happiness in their existence again. The knowledge their siblings were near was a comfort. Knowing one of them was just down the hall or would be out in the yard at playtime gave each Tooley child the feeling of security.

The food was good and nourishing, and many of the people who worked there were kind, caring adults. Even the work could be made fun with other hands helping to get it accomplished. The chores were rotated. Older children were assigned a younger one to work with. Everything was starting to go OK for the children until one day about three weeks after they had arrived.

GOING, GOING, GONE! SOLD!

The day Mrs. Sleighter came to the children's home looking for a young boy, Mr. Chase knew exactly who would be leaving.

Mrs. Sleighter was a woman in her early thirties and was very heavy with an expected infant of her own. She explained to the superintendent that her baby would be born in a few weeks. She felt her child would be much happier with an older brother to be with.

Before she explained her full story, she opened her purse and took out an envelope. It contained many five- and ten-dollar bills. Mrs. Sleighter placed the money on the desk in full view for Mr. Chase to see as they talked.

"Tell me, madame," Mr. Chase inquired as his eyes perused the money on his desk. "Just how can I be of assistance to you?"

"Well, sir, I don't live in the state of Idaho. I have only been here for a year visiting my cousin in Grangeville. My home is in southern Alberta, Canada, near the small town of Cowley. My family owns a good-sized piece of land there that we farm. I could provide a home for a boy to learn and grow. There is a school only a few miles away with a fine instructor," Mrs. Sleighter reported.

Mr. Chase looked hard at the woman before speaking. "Taking one of our boys out of Idaho and especially out of the United States can prove to be a pretty messy situation, madame. One requiring a lot of extra paperwork and trouble. I just don't know . . ." He paused, rose from his chair, and slowly paced behind his desk.

"How much trouble?" the woman questioned as she spread the bills slowly in a fan shape on the desk.

"Now if you legally adopted the boy before you took him to Canada, the governor's office couldn't say a word," Mr. Chase reported.

"How long would it take to adopt the child?" the woman asked as she started to fidget.

"It takes about a year for everything to be 'set in stone,' you might say," he informed her.

"Oh no, sir. I plan to go into Canada as soon as this baby is born. I can't wait a year." She put her hand on the money and began to reassemble the bills back into a stack.

"Well," Mr. Chase responded as he cleared his throat and watched the woman handle the money, "perhaps some 'special' arrangements could be made in this case. But we would need to keep very quiet about the matter.''

"Keeping quiet about delicate matters is one of my better qualities, sir,'' Mrs. Sleighter said in an almost-whispered tone. "Now just how much will these 'special' arrangements cost?''

The superintendent studied the bills to get a sense of how much was on the desk. He thought for a short moment and then stated a price. "I think perhaps about two hundred and fifty dollars might do it,'' the greedy man answered.

"Well, sir, there is two hundred dollars on your desk. Do you think you might be able to do the extra work for this amount?''

Mr.Chase reached for the money and flipped through the bills slowly before putting them in his pocket. "Yes, I think this will cover it. Now I'll send for the boy.''

The children were in the yard for leisure time when Mrs. Chase came to get Roy. The bluntness of her attitude alerted his siblings that something terrible was about to happen.

"Roy Tooley!'' she called. "Come here right now. I need to get you ready.''

Roy looked at Pearl with questioning eyes. *Why am I going somewhere and not the others?* he thought.

"I don't want to go,'' he answered as he shook his little head in a negative motion.

"Roy! You come right this minute! There is a lady waiting for you,'' Mrs. Chase scolded.

Pearl was on her feet and heading toward the calling woman with questions starting to flood her mind. Three more pairs of legs followed close behind her.

"Where are you taking my brother?'' were the inquiring words of the protector.

"That is none of your business, Miss Tooley,'' the coldhearted woman snapped. "Now get out of the way and give me the boy.''

Roy was clinging to the back of his sister's skirt. "I don't want to go!'' the frightened boy stated as he began to cry.

"It's not your decision to make you little scamp. Now come here before I get the strap. There is a nice lady waiting to take you home with her,'' Mrs. Chase stated as she reached around Pearl for Roy.

154

Pearl moved to keep her brother behind her as the woman grabbed. "My mother gave me instructions to take care of my brothers and sisters until she can come and get us. He doesn't need to go home with anyone," Pearl snapped back.

After missing her grab for Roy, the woman went for Pearl, snatching her with both hands on her upper arms. "Now you listen to me, all four of you. Your mother and father are *bad people.* They are not coming to get you in a few weeks, or months, or ever!" the cruel-mouthed woman growled as she shook the girl. "Your parents' *don't want you* anymore. They are in jail for breaking the law and have signed papers so you can live with other people. It is now our responsibility to find folks who are willing to take disrespectful and undisciplined waifs like you. Maybe honest people can make you into suitable citizens."

The lecture was like ice-cold water splashed in their faces. All four of them were stunned with the realization of their fate.

"Our mother does too care about us!" Helen yelled. "She told us; she promised."

The woman reached out to strike the redheaded girl, but Pearl moved in the path and received the blow instead. By this time two other caretakers had come to help Mrs. Chase. The superintendent's wife glared at Pearl with the look of a demon. *"Don't you ever interfere with my punishments or authority again!* You will sorely regret it if you try, Miss Tooley!" she threatened. "I know how to deal with your kind. Now both of you girls go to your room and stay on your beds for the rest of the day. There will be no reading, no dinner, just *thinking time* for you two."

Roy's own clothing was already laid out when the caretakers were finished cleaning up the sobbing child. These two ladies were kind and gentle and tried to console the unhappy child. They told him the lady he was going with was nice. She would give him a good place to grow up and go to school.

The five-year-old was easy to mold when tenderness was used. The clay of his personality was still pliable. He desired to have the love and care of a tender mother again.

One of the kind caretakers peeked inside the girls' bedroom while the other one stood guard outside. Roy was allowed to go in to see his sisters and get one last hug.

"You be good, Roy," was the advice of the eldest exiled girl. "Just remember, when Mother comes to get us, we'll come and get you. No matter where they take you, we'll find you. I'm going to be real good and follow all the rules here from now on, Roy. Maybe then they will let me send you letters," Pearl confessed. "Promise me when you learn how to read and write you will write back. We can never forget each other. I'm going to make sure of that."

"I promise," the brave little boy said. "I'm going to be real good and follow the rules, too, and learn to write and everything." He hugged both sisters tight and blew kisses to them as he exited the room.

Mrs. Sleighter took hold of the five-year-old boy's hand as she pushed him into her carriage. "Come, little boy," she said harshly. "Now what's your name again?"

"My name is Roy Tooley," the youngster blurted out as his bottom lip quivered.

"Now listen, Roy Tooley; you are under my care now and you had better do everything you are told. We are going on a long train ride and you are not to talk to anyone but me. But only if I ask you a question. Is that clear?" the coldhearted woman instructed.

Roy looked at this woman with a new fear. He had been told by the caretakers this was a nice lady. But they had lied. She was grouchy and mean. He didn't want to go anywhere with this woman. "I want to go back with my sisters," Roy answered as he hung his little head. He tried to hold back the tears forming in his eyes.

"Hey, little mister. I don't want any more of the sniveling. You straighten up and act your age. I don't want anyone to think I've got a five-year-old 'baby' tagging after me," Mrs. Sleighter firmly scolded. "Now if you don't want the back of my hand, you better be quiet and act like a gentleman."

The young boy wiped his eyes and sat up straight. Even though he was young, he was determined to receive as little punishment from this woman as possible. He was so terrified. He really wanted to curl up in a little ball again and just go to sleep. Maybe this bad dream would go away if he could. But that was not possible. Every time he even slumped, the woman next to him would poke his side and tell him to straighten up.

Mrs. Sleighter took Roy by the arm, and they boarded a train at the Lewiston station. The train headed back up north, the direction he had come from only a few weeks before. They were on the train for almost two days before reaching Bonners Ferry, Idaho. It was a small town about twenty miles from the Canadian border. They rented a room near the town doctor's office, so the woman could prepare for her infant to be born. It only took two weeks of waiting there before the woman gave birth to a baby girl.

After the infant girl was a week old, Mrs. Sleighter, the new baby, and Roy traveled across the Canadian border. They continued north, to Cowley, a small town in southern Alberta. She had purchased illegal papers from the children's home showing Roy as being legally adopted. She had to have these documents in order to take Roy across the border.

When they arrived at the farm, Mrs. Sleighter, who had been divorced from her husband for about three years, introduced Roy and the new baby girl as being a brother and sister she had adopted in Idaho. She needed some way to cover up the fact that she had just given birth to an illegitimate baby.

AND THEN THERE WERE TWO

"I just don't know," Mrs. Lewis said as she looked at her husband with a questioning expression. "What do you think?"

"It's up to you, dear," he responded. "You're the one who will be with the child most of the time."

"I'm sorry for being so unsure, Mr. Chase. It's just . . . we were hoping for a tiny baby," Mrs. Lewis added.

"I understand, madame," Mr. Chase acknowledged. "But we have had your application four years now. And, well . . . , we just don't get many infants. This little boy just barely turned three in April and is in perfect health, with no deformities. We may not get another one this good for months, maybe years."

"Why don't you take a look at the youngster?" Mr. Lewis encouraged. "If we don't like what we see, we'll simply wait longer."

Mr. Chase rang the bell on his desk. His wife came scurrying to the sound.

"Where's little Earl Tooley?" he inquired of the woman.

"He's in the nursery room right now, sir."

"Take Mr. and Mrs. Lewis to the nursery, to observe the child," he requested. "I'll join you in a few minutes."

Earl was in the room with Beth Ritter, a six-year-old lame girl, and Garret Sawyer, a five-year-old dark-skinned boy. The three of them were playing with some wooden blocks, making stacks and knocking them down. The fun task was making the three-year-old squeal with joy.

The more Lottie and John Lewis watched this healthy sandy-haired lad, the more their hearts were touched.

"He's a lovely child." Lottie expressed out loud. She looked at her husband with tender mothering eyes. "John," she said as she stared at him.

He knew what that particular look meant. She used it every time she wanted something special. "Are you sure?" he questioned.

"I'm sure," she answered and then turned back to look at the small boy again.

"OK, Mr. Chase. We'll take this boy," John stated. "When can we take him home?"

"We can have him ready to go by the time you get the proper papers filled out. We already knew you're an acceptable couple or we wouldn't have notified you about this child,'' Mr. Chase continued as he walked the couple back to the office.

"Helen! Helen!'' the little lame girl called as she made her way from the house and on to the play yard. "It's your brother,'' she panted from the effort of the quick movement. "They're going to gave him away,'' Beth continued to report. "Pearl isn't here; she went to town on the trip.''

Helen was on her feet, running toward the study where her sister would normally be at this time. But when Beth reported the trip to town, Helen remembered where her older sister was, made a quick turn, and headed straight for the office area. She dodged anyone who came near or reached for her. Helen darted fearlessly down the hallway on her mission to rescue her baby brother.

"You can't have my brother!'' the fiery red-haired girl shouted as she entered the superintendent's office. Mrs. Lewis was now holding Earl on her lap.

"I'm supposed to watch him when Pearl's not here,'' Helen explained as the tears began to surface on her determined face.

Mr. Chase stood up quickly behind his desk, with noticeable anger in his eyes. "Miss Tooley! You are forbidden in this office unless you're summoned here,'' the superintendent sternly stated. "Now go back—''

Mrs. Lewis, holding the now-squirming boy, let him go and stood to look at Helen. "Hello, Miss Tooley,'' Lottie Lewis greeted as she extended her hand to shake the hand of the troubled girl. "My name is Lottie Lewis. Is this your littler brother?'' she inquired in friendly tones.

"Yes,'' Helen answered. "We're only here till our mother comes to get us. So, you see, you can't take him.''

"Is this true?'' Mrs. Lewis inquired of Mr. Chase.

Mr. Chase only shook his head in a negative motion, acting as if he were trying to spare the girl from some horrible truth.

"Do you have a first name, Miss Tooley?'' Lottie asked the seven-year-old girl, trying to change the tender subject.

"My name is Helen,'' she reported in softer tones.

"Well, Helen, I would be honored if you would allow my husband and me to borrow your little brother for a while. But only until your mother comes to get you. We promise to take real good care of him. Maybe you can come and visit sometime, just to make sure he is in good hands. You see, we haven't been able to have any babies of our own. We have so much love just going to waste, we would like to give it to

159

your brother. What do you say?'' she asked with sincere kindness in her countenance.

"Would you really let me come and make sure he's OK?" Helen concernedly asked.

"Yes, we would," Mrs. Lewis confirmed.

"And will you give him back when our mother comes?"

Mrs. Lewis shook her head yes.

With all her demands met, Helen agreed to turn loose of her clinging brother. She would allow Mrs. Lewis to take him.

"Helen, it's been nice to meet you. I'm glad you care so much about your brother. This is a brave thing you did to come in here. Now I'm sure Mr. Chase will view this as an act of love and not scold you for your actions." Mrs. Lewis looked at the superintendent with an almost "don't you dare punish this girl" look. "You be sure and tell me about it if he does, the next time I come," she instructed the girl. "Come on, little man; give your kind sister a kiss good-bye."

Earl didn't cry this time as Helen gave him a hug and kiss. Somehow, he felt safe and warm in Lottie Lewis's arms.

By the time Pearl returned from town and learned the fate of her youngest brother, Helen had already resolved in her mind a plan of action for the future.

"I've made up my mind," Helen stated while standing before her sister with hands at her waist and elbows bent. The determination on her face matched the fire of her hair, and Pearl knew her younger sister meant business. "They might be able to send me away to live with other people. But if the people don't like me they will send me back to this home. Then I can be here when Mother comes."

"Why wouldn't someone like you?" Pearl inquired.

"If you do or say mean things to the people, then they'll just send you back. Beth told me so," Helen boasted.

"Helen. You could get in a lot of trouble by doing *mean* things," Pearl explained.

"Well, Beth said that *I* probably wouldn't get in much trouble. 'Cause people expect red-haired kids to cause more trouble than normal kids. You see, normal kids like you would get in more trouble than me. So that's why you should be nice, Pearl and I will be the mean one," Helen rationalized. "One of us needs to be here to tell Mother where they have sent all of us kids. So we can go home and be together again."

160

Helen's logic and information made sense to nine-year-old Pearl. Anyway, who was she to dispute Beth Ritter? Beth had been here her whole life.

Mr. Chase opened the letter that had been delivered to his desk earlier in the morning.

Mr. Chase, Lewiston, Idaho

July 21, 1914, Sandpoint, Idaho

Dear Sir,

Your kind letter rec'd Sunday. Am so glad the children are well and happy and hope they will continue so.

Am glad they are learning to do things.

Hope you will keep them all for me as am going to do all I can to try and get them back again. Do you think it would make them discontented if they were to write to me? Would like to have them write and write to them but do not wish to do anything to make them unhappy.

Hope to hear from you soon,

Mrs. O. A. Tooley

He put the letter back in its envelope and stored it in the top drawer of his desk. Then he rang the bell on his desk for Mrs. Chase to come to the office.

"Have you had any success in finding placement for the Tooley girls yet?" he questioned.

"No," she admitted. "Almost every request of late has been for boys or older girls who can work. There is only one application for a girl, but we have been reluctant to fill the request."

"Get the application and let me look at it," Mr. Chase ordered.

The woman returned with the information and handed it to her husband.

"Oh yes, I remember this request," he remarked while looking over the pages. "Well, if there's no one else, I guess this will have to do for now. Bertha, get Pearl Tooley ready. We'll leave first thing in the morning. I'll deliver her myself."

The two sisters only had a few minutes together the next morning before parting. But they vowed to write and tell each other everything.

161

BLIND TO LOVE

They arrived in the northern Idaho town of Stites in the late afternoon. Mr. Chase gave Pearl strict instructions of behavior before taking her to the woman's house where she was to stay.

"Now, listen, Miss Tooley. The woman who will be in charge of you is Dr. Jett. She is handicapped with blindness. But I understand she can see more things with her remaining senses that most people see with open eyes. Don't think you can get away with poor manners or disrespectful behavior just because the woman is blind. I expect your actions to be just as good or better than they would be if she could see. I hope I've made myself perfectly clear," the superintendent directed.

"Yes, sir," the frightened nine-year-old girl acknowledged.

Susan Jett was a doctor of osteopathic healing. She lived in a house large enough to rent out some of the rooms to folks traveling through the area. Most of her boarders only stayed one or two days. However, a few stayed as long as one or two weeks.

Pearl was put to work immediately. She was assigned to make beds, scrub floors, and do other various chores Miss Jett found for her to do.

"There will be no time spent on frivolity at this house. Wasting time is the devil's tool," the doctor would say if she caught Pearl resting. "You can rest at bedtime."

It was difficult for Pearl to please this taskmaster. Because Miss Jett couldn't see, Pearl was many times accused of not doing jobs she was instructed to do.

One very hot August day, the young girl was told to scrub the kitchen floor. She was in the process of toiling with the soapy water and scrub brush making sure to do a good job. The air was thick and hot inside where she was kneeling. The young Cinderella opened the outside door to let some cool air inside. Not only did a cool breeze come in, but it brought with it miraculous quick drying powers. Pearl soon realized she had to wash and rinse one spot before moving to another. The breeze was drying the water on the floor too fast. The scrub maiden soon had a routine down. She would scrub a small section, then rinse it with clear water, and the air would quickly dry it for her. By the time she had her buckets empty and put away, the entire floor was clean and dry.

Pearl had just closed the back door when Miss Jett came into the kitchen. She rubbed her cane on the dry floor and immediately began to yell accusations at Pearl. "Pearl! I told you to scrub this floor an hour ago. You haven't even started yet. Now you stop lollygaggin' around and get to work right this minute,'' the blind woman demanded.

With pride and a sense of accomplishment in her voice, Pearl announced, "I have scrubbed it already."

"Don't you dare lie to me, you little rascal!" the woman yelled. "Just get this floor scrubbed right now or I will lock you in your room for a week. Then we'll see if that helps you to tell the truth and do as you're told."

Pearl was crushed. She had been so proud of her method for making the floor so sparkling clean. *If the old woman could only see, she would know I'm not a liar,* she thought to herself. *OK, if she doesn't want a dry floor, then maybe a wet one will make her happy.* She filled the bucket with clear water and took it into the kitchen. She dipped her rinse rag into the water and wrung it out directly onto the clean floor. After repeating the action on several areas of the floor, she spread the puddles around. She then sat and waited for the blind floor inspector to come back for another check.

"That's better," Miss Jett stated as she moved her cane across the slippery water. "Just remember, liars go to hell and burn. Now go and do your other chores, you lazy orphan."

Pearl was starting to grow, and the clothing she had been wearing was now too small and ragged. Just before school started in the fall Miss Jett had three dresses made for Pearl from some material she had stored away. All three were black and very loose-fitting. There was plenty of room for growing in these dresses.

The woman insisted Pearl wear her hair braided and looped around the crown of her head. She told Pearl that proper girls shouldn't wear their hair hanging. Only gypsies and harlots wore it that way.

There were no mirrors in Miss Jett's house. After all, the blind woman had no need for them. Pearl had no idea how pathetic she looked on her first day at school in Stites.

When she was walking home from school, she saw a reflection of herself in a large glass window of a downtown building.

"No wonder the kids at school laughed and whispered behind my back. I look so funny and ugly. Mother would be so mad at Miss Jett if she saw how terrible she has made me look," Pearl said softly to herself as she continued to walk to the house where she was staying. "It will be so wonderful when Mother comes and takes me back home where I belong."

Life in Stites, Idaho, was neither pleasant nor easy for Pearl. But the spirit of tenacity and survival was strong inside her. She continued to forge forward, one day at a time.

The eagerness for the holidays to come way back in May had been dashed early in November when a short carefully printed letter came from her seven-year-old sister.

Dear Pearl

They sent me to some people's house, but I was too mean, so they sent me back. Mommie has not been here and I have been waiting every day. If she comes, I will write again. Anna is helping me write. She says hello.

Love
Helen*

The Christmas season was particularly difficult for a girl who had always loved the holiday. Miss Jett belonged to a Christian religion, but celebrating any holiday was a waste of time for her. It was also sacrilegious, she told the chore girl. As a result, there were no decorations, no wonderful smells of special treats, and no presents for Pearl that December 25, 1914. There was only a morning church service to go to, wearing a black dress.

Pearl knew in her heart that something must be terribly wrong. Her mother should have gone to Lewiston by now to get here. She prayed the things Mrs. Chase had said about her parents not wanting or loving her were not true. Pearl could still remember how she had felt when she was home. There was warmth, caring, and security there, feelings she had not been shown in the last six months. She tried to think of all the reasons or possibilities for her family still not being back together. But some of the thoughts just scared her young mind.

"If I don't hear from my mother by my next birthday, I will ask the pastor at church if I can be baptized," she resolved. "Maybe if I am a baptized Christian and not a 'heathen,' as Miss Jett calls me, then God will listen to my prayers more closely."

---

*Letters in this book from Helen to Pearl are actual letters, published here compliments of the Helen Hoffman estate.

It was June 1915 before the lake water was warm enough for baptizing. Pearl was ready even though the water would be very cold. She wanted to be immersed and become a Christian. Along with two other people who were also going to be baptized and some other members of the congregation, Pearl made her way to the water's edge for the "Praise the Lords" and "Hallelujahs." The prayers were said and Pearl waded out with the pastor far enough so the water was up to her waist. It was cold, and she shivered enough that her teeth made clanking noises in her mouth. She had never learned to swim, so she held onto the man for dear life. He plunged her freezing body all the way underneath the water and brought her up again. Even though she was so cold her lips were blue, Pearl felt a renewed warmth and hope. A hope that had been lost for several months. Now that she was a Christian, she told herself, surely her future would be brighter.

It didn't take long for Pearl to realize her hopes and dreams were just that, hopes and dreams, not reality. Summer ended, school started, and Christmas 1915 rolled right on past. She had only received a few letters from Helen, who by now had also lost hope.

Some of the members of the church where Miss Jett and Pearl attended took a liking to the downtrodden young girl. A very nice young woman by the name of Katherine Wallace got permission from Miss Jett to allow Pearl to go on a Fourth of July picnic. Even though she had protested at first, the blind taskmaster allowed her worker to be gone for a few hours, as long as Miss Wallace promised not to "spoil" the girl.

The parade with all the red, white, and blue flags and banners, the picnic with children running free and playing games, brought back memories of another time in Sandpoint. A time that had been one of the happiest days of Pearl's young life. A life that was now gone. A life she had conceded would probably never return.

When summer was coming to an end and the beginning of school was just around the corner, Katherine Wallace decided to check into the conditions this now-eleven-year-old girl was enduring. Miss Wallace would see Pearl at church and invite her on Sunday walks and ask her subtle questions about her responsibilities and activities. Some folk would call the woman just plain "snoopy" but Miss Wallace was sincerely concerned about Pearl's circumstances.

Katherine was aware Pearl's dresses were now two years old. They had been patched so many times, there were now patches on the patches, a pretty deplorable situation for Miss Jett to let happen, as she was getting money from the state each month to use for the girl's care.

The day before school was to start in the fall of 1916, Miss Wallace went to Miss Jett's house and presented the budding young lady with a beautiful soft lavender dress. The material had a very small purple flowers and green leaves all over it. Miss Wallace also had two purple ribbons she had made to go with the dress for Pearl to wear in her hair.

"It's the most beautiful dress I have ever owned," Pearl told the seamstress. "I will never forget your kindness."

The happiness Pearl felt as she put on her new dress the next morning was almost overwhelming. She wished she could wear her hair brushed out and long but feared the wrath it would bring. The braids on her head even looked more beautiful adorned with the ribbons. Pearl couldn't remember how long it had been since she had been this happy.

The beginning of school was much better that year as Pearl entered her classroom in lavender instead of black.

Christmas 1916 was one of the worst times Pearl had experienced since being in Stites. It started the day before Christmas when Miss Jett could not find a dollar she knew she had put in her purse. After several minutes of hunting, emptying the purse, and hunting some more, the blind woman concluded that Pearl had stolen it, called the girl in, and started questioning her about the missing dollar. Pearl tried to explain that she did not see or take the money. But the interrogation went on and on. Miss Jett accused Pearl of being a thief and a liar and of trying to take advantage of her inability to see. The woman would not believe the girl's continued denials of guilt. The questioning seemed to go on for hours. Pearl finally stopped answering the woman's accusations. She had stated her innocence over and over. She was tired of the futile attempts to convince the woman.

Pearl was told to stay in her room and think about her sins. The fuming woman then left. After about thirty minutes of exile, Miss Jett returned to give the sinner one more chance to confess. When Pearl again denied the alleged crime, the heartless but cunning blind woman reached out with her left hand and grabbed the girl by her hair. With her right hand Miss Jett rubbed a bar of lye soap across the cheeks, lips, and teeth of the screaming victim.

The deed was quick but nasty and painful as the lye burned Pearl's delicate skin. She fought to free herself from the wicked woman's grasp and was finally able to get away to rinse the vile blistering chemical from

166

her face. The acid soap had already done its damage, though. The open sores it left were a raw reminder.

When Pearl didn't show up for church on Christmas morning, Katherine Wallace left early to find out the reason. She only feared the young girl might be ill and needing care and definitely wasn't prepared for the sight she saw when Pearl responded to her constant knocking at the door.

Pearl tried to hide her mouth with her hands, but the battered young maiden couldn't cover all the unsightly marks.

"Oh, my Lord!" Miss Wallace gasped. "What happened to your face?"

Pearl was reluctant to speak. She feared the nice lady whom she liked so much would think the same as Miss Jett about the missing money.

Katherine took Pearl's hand away from her face to view the full extent of the wounds. Both of Pearl's cheeks were swollen and dotted with red sores. Her bottom lip was split and swollen to twice its normal size. Her tongue was also enlarged and spotted with white sores.

"She punished you with lye soap for something, didn't she?" Miss Wallace angrily questioned. "That mean old woman tried to wash your mouth with strong lye soap. I can tell by the sores" the young woman continued, making it unnecessary for Pearl to answer the question. "Only a nonseeing person would miss the mouth by that far and make a mess like this." Katherine paused for a moment to examine the swollen face before asking the reason for such severe action.

"I didn't steal her dollar," Pearl babbled. "She said I did, but I didn't. Please don't think bad of me, Miss Wallace. I would never take anything that wasn't mine. I try to be a good Christian and obey the commandments. Please don't think I did it and get me in more trouble."

"Oh, Pearl. How could any decent person think bad of a good girl like you?" Katherine informed the innocent child. "As for trouble, it won't be you that is going to be in trouble," Miss Wallace stated. She then turned and marched off as if she were going to do battle with the devil.

Pearl's face healed much faster than her broken spirit. However, that, too was on the mend when Miss Wallace came to visit the first week of January. Katherine had brought a present for the wounded young girl. It was all wrapped up so pretty, with fancy paper and ribbon. It was a brand-new Bible with a note in the front: "To Pearl, I hope you will always remember me as your friend, Katherine Wallace."

167

The young girl loved the gift and read it every night before bed. Pearl felt Miss Wallace was not only her friend but also a person to emulate and hoped she could grow up and be just like her.

Katherine was not only a giver of tangible gifts to Pearl. Her real gift came in the form of a letter and a telephone call to the children's home in Lewiston.

Miss Wallace had written a letter and had several people in the community also sign it. The letter stated that Miss Jett's home was not a proper placement for a young girl. It asked the managers of the home to make an investigation and suggested very strongly it should be done soon. When action hadn't been taken by mid-January, a telephone call was made. Miss Wallace wanted to make sure someone would be out to look into the matter before the end of the month.

As a result of Miss Wallace's vigorous pursuit for justice, a caretaker was sent out. After two and a half years in Stites, Pearl was taken back to the home in Lewiston.

A NEW START

Pearl finished the sixth grade in Lewiston while living at the home. The next summer, she was sent to a home in Grangeville. She was able to help a young mother and her eighteen-month-old baby boy. Pearl was having a hard time remembering what her own little brother looked like, so that summer she pretended the boy was her own brother.

In the fall, Pearl went back to the home to start seventh grade in Lewiston. She had accepted the fact that her parents did not want her anymore. What had been said to her when she first arrived at the home she finally acknowledged as the truth. Her family had been separated for three years, and she had decided to make the best of whatever experiences were thrown her way.

Mr. and Mrs. Chase were no longer the managers of the home, having left rather unexpectedly one day. Soon after, the caretakers who had been so cruel also left. Mrs. Williams, a nice woman, assumed the superintendent's responsibilities until a new one could be hired. Mrs. Williams tried to make up to the children for all the hard times they had suffered when the Chases were in charge, planning parties and excursions, things she knew the children would enjoy.

On Halloween 1917, the children at the home were given a party down in the basement. They dunked for apples and played games. They pulled taffy and had cookies and apple juice for treats. Mrs. Williams dressed up as a fortune-teller and told all the children their fortunes.

"Come into my chamber and Madame Zenya will reveal the secrets of your future through my magical powers," the gypsy woman uttered as she pulled back the blanket curtain that separated the chamber from the rest of the basement.

Pearl was excited to play the games. She waited in line while four other children entered the magic den before her. She didn't know why her heart seemed to be pounding; it was only a game, not a real fortune. Perhaps it was the thought of hearing of a wonderful future that caused the fluttering in her young body. Yet for some reason, Pearl was sure this woman would renew her hope concerning the issue that troubled her the most.

Madame Zenya held back the curtain, and Pearl entered the chamber. She sat in a chair on one side of a small table, across from the fortune-teller.

"Let me see your right hand, palm up," the seer instructed. She studied Pearl's hand as if she knew what to look for before telling the future. Using the lines and creases of the girl's palm, the gypsy fabricated the story as Pearl listened intently.

"I see by this line that you will have a long life. This crease shows you will marry a handsome man and have ... hm-m ... let me see ... three children," the woman announced.

Pearl blushed a little at the anticipation of a handsome husband. The teller continued with all the things the young girl wanted to hear about jewels, a mansion, and furs.

"... and you will live happily ever after."

Pearl was all smiles as the woman told of all the marvelous things awaiting her in the future until she stood and graciously invited her to exit through the back curtain. The young girl's whole demeanor changed as she looked at the gypsy with questioning eyes.

"You left out the most important part," Pearl blurted as she held her palm up to the woman. "You know, the part about my mother and my sisters and brothers, when we're all going to be back together again."

Madame Zenya seemed to disappear as the kind Mrs. Williams took ahold of Pearl's upturned hand. "Pearl, not even the great Madame Zenya can tell you the answer to a tough question like that one. However, if you will keep up the desire of a reunion, someday your dream will come true."

It wasn't exactly the answer Pearl was hoping to receive, yet it did restore her faith in the future.

After several bouts with sickness in the fall and early winter, the doctor determined that Pearl's tonsils needed to be removed. Unfortunately, the best time to do it was right before Christmas. Even though she wasn't feeling her best and couldn't participate in the singing, Pearl was just happy to once again celebrate Christmas in the traditional way.

In February 1918, one of the girls at the home came down with scarlet fever. Everyone was put under a quarantine for five weeks. No one could leave the house, and no one could come in. Even the adult staff had to stay. Pearl felt lucky she did not contract the disease. She did her part by helping with the extra chores that couldn't be done by the sick and filling in for those nursing the sick also. After the quarantine was lifted, the job of fumigating was backbreaking work and took several days.

In June 1918, Pearl was sent to Pardee, Idaho, to stay with a young couple named Lou and Carroll Moore. Carroll was the depot agent and postmaster. Lou, his wife, had been a schoolteacher. Lou had her first baby soon after Pearl arrived. She was a little red-haired girl they named Alice Lilly. Pearl thought the baby was the most beautiful infant she had ever seen.

Pearl really like Pardee and the Moores. Helping with the housework and the baby was enjoyable to her. It didn't seem like work at all.

That summer Pearl learned to swim and dive in a small lake near the house. The Moores treated her like she was family, taking her every-where with them. They took her to a friend's home a few miles away for a birthday party they had been invited to. It was a big beautiful mansion, with well-kept lawns and gardens. Inside were lavish furnish-ings and other things Pearl had never seen before, except in magazines. Pearl wondered how a palace like this got way out here in Pardee. The lady who owned the home was named Mrs. Bethmann, and she treated Pearl very graciously.

"Lou! Come in," the woman greeted as she opened the door of the splendid house. "Let me see your precious infant." Mrs. Bethmann reached for the bundle in Lou's arms and removed the white lace bonnet. "Oh!" she squealed with delight. "Look at her red hair. I always dreamed of having a girl with red hair. You are so lucky," the lady con-fessed.

After fussing over the beauties of little Alice Lilly for several mi-nutes, Mrs. Bethmann noticed the shy thirteen-year-old girl standing be-hind Lou Moore. "You must be Pearl," Mrs. Bethmann acknowledged. "Lou has told me what a nice girl you are and how much you have helped her with the baby. I'm glad you were able to come today, so I could meet you."

"Thank you," Pearl responded.

"Ester!" Mrs. Bethmann called for her maid. "Take Pearl out to the porch where the other young people are and introduce her. Make sure she gets a glass of lemonade. Lou and I will be out in a few minutes."

Pearl was treated with grace and respect by this woman and immedi-ately like Mrs. Bethmann.

The young girl was very happy in Pardee and with the Moores and would have loved to stay with this family. Unfortunately for Pearl, there were no schools close by. The nearest one was in Woodland, a place too far when it meant going by horse and buggy. At the end of summer, Pearl was taken to the train station to go back to Lewiston.

"Pearl, I really wish things were different here so you could stay, but. . ." Mrs. Moore's voice choked up as she tried to explain away another disappointing parting in this girl's life.

"It's all right," the brave girl spoke up. "I'm used to moving around. I try not to get attached." Pearl hung her head and brushed imaginary dust from her skirt in order to hide the tears welling in her eyes.

"Yes, I understand," Lou responded. "I know you don't want to feel attached, but would it be all right if we wrote to you once in a while? I could send you some pictures of Alice if it would be OK."

"Oh yes! I would really like that," Pearl replied with a broad smile. "I will miss you and Alice."

Everyone exchanged hugs and handshakes, and Pearl boarded the train back to the home.

On the long ride back, she thought about her own brothers and sister. She had moved around so much the last few years, she had lost contact with them. She wondered where they were and how they were getting along. She prayed silently, in the best Christian form she knew, that God would watch over and protect them. Pearl resolved somehow she would get all of their addresses this year and keep in touch by mail. The vow she made to her mother so long ago was still in her heart. She planned to live up to her promise to keep the children close, even though her mother hadn't kept the promise of coming to get them. Pearl would do her part any way she could.

Roy

Roy had been taken to a small town in southern Alberta, Canada. He was to live on a farm owned by Mrs. Sleighter's relatives. The family farmed about 640 acres, and Roy was expected at a very young age to be part of the workforce.

He began school at age six and walked about one and a quarter miles to school and back each day. The name of the school was the Tennessee School House, and it was located on the southwest corner of the postmaster's land.

The winters in Crowley were extremely cold. For at least two weeks each year, the temperature would drop to forty degrees below zero. Regardless of the weather conditions, Roy consistently attended school. It was very seldom the school was ever closed because of a blizzard.

172

Roy was treated very badly. He felt like he was just another "horse" in the barn. No affection was ever given to him at any point in time. Before leaving for school each morning he had to milk three cows and do numerous other chores. After school, he was required to also do chores. He would bring the cows up from the pasture, milk them, and feed the chickens and the rest of the animals.

Doing the work and going to school were things expected of all boys of the day. It was the noncaring and lack of love shown to Roy that were very hard for the young boy.

Christmastime was especially bleak for Roy. Mrs. Sleighter would inform him he was not "one of the family." He should not expect to receive presents like the other children. Even on the holidays when the other children were given a little extra money to spend, he again was left out. For a boy his age, this treatment was extremely hard to cope with. He felt unwanted, rejected, and abandoned.

Earl

John and Lottie Lewis lived in the town of Orofino, not too far from Lewiston. They had tried for several years to have children, without success. When they took little Earl home with them in July of 1914, their lives were much more happy and fulfilled.

At first they lived in constant fear Earl's parents would come and take him back. So they filled out the legal papers necessary to adopt him. They also changed his name to Robert Earl Lewis to make it harder for his people to find him.

Unlike his older brother, Roy, Robert Earl was loved "too" much. The couple spoiled the youngster and gave him very little discipline. He was allowed to do pretty much what he wanted and thus grew to be an unruly boy.

Helen

After Pearl left the children's home for the first time to live in Stites, Helen kept her word about being a mean little red-haired girl. After three different homes in two years and a backside full of healed belt welts, Helen gave up on her mother and decided to live a more sensible way

173

of life. It just wasn't worth all the spankings if her mother wasn't coming to get her anyway.

Mrs. Lewis had kept her word about letting Helen see her little brother, now named Robert. In 1917, Lottie Lewis got permission from the home to have Helen live with them. At first the arrangement was fine. After a while, however, Helen and Robert had a hard time getting along with each other. Robert was very spoiled and Helen wanted to be his boss and make him behave. Lottie was a very mild-mannered woman and didn't know how to handle both strong-willed siblings. Helen stayed with the Lewises for about two years.

THE DIARY

When the train pulled into the station on Sunday morning, the folks from the home were there to meet Pearl. There was a new superintendent at the Home named Mr. Howland. His wife and sister-in-law, Laura, had brought Pearl's friend Bobbie along with them to greet her.

Mrs. Howland had driven to the train station in a new Ford motorcar. Pearl was thrilled to finally experience riding in an automobile.

The new superintendent's in-laws, Mr. and Mrs. Waters, also now worked at the home. Mrs. Waters was the head cook, and Mr. Waters was a sort of handyman and janitor. They had a daughter named Laura, who was the same age as Pearl. The two girls immediately liked each other and became best friends.

The children's home had some changes in living and sleeping arrangements with the new people in charge. The girls were divided into two groups and slept in separate dormitories. There was now a room for the little girls twelve and younger and a place for the big girls, thirteen and older. The boys were on the other side of the house with the same kind of arrangements.

The dining room had also been changed, and everyone was allowed to eat together. The stern military atmosphere had changed to a less rigid structure. Pearl was glad for the change, and the happier attitude of the people.

Mrs. Howland knocked at the bedroom door before entering the older girl's room.

"Before you turn out the lights, I would like to share something with you that meant a lot to me as a teenage girl," Mrs. Howland stated as she held up the small book she had carried in. "This is my personal diary. I started it when I was fourteen. I would write something in it each day about what I had done, or the people I had interacted with. This little book was my confidant and many times my very best friend. I could tell this book anything and it would never repeat my secrets to anyone. I could trust this book to save important dates and experiences that would otherwise get lost in the back part of my mind. Now that I am older, I can go back and read my history to evaluate the growth or decline of my attitudes and feelings. I am so grateful now for taking that five or ten minutes each day to record my life in this book and the several others I have. If any of you girls want to start a diary, come and see me tomorrow and I will provide you with your very own book. Goodnight, girls,'' the superintendent's wife said before leaving the room.

Pearl contemplated the challenge Mrs. Howland had given her and decided she would start her own diary the very next day. At first, the task was more difficult than Pearl had imagined. It seemed to her just starting with that day would be meaningless in years to come, so she asked Mrs. Howland for advice. She advised Pearl to do a summary of when she first came to the home and where she had been up to then. After the summary, Pearl could start with her daily activities. Pearl sat down and began a work that would become a pleasant habit for many years to come. The now-thirteen-year-old girl took a pen and started to write.

My Diary

Pearl E. Tooley

Will start first with just an introduction of myself. I came to the Children's Home at Lewiston, Idaho, on June 7, 1914, with my two brothers and one sister. Will not go into detail on why I came here for I will always remember that anyway. I was ten years old, my sister seven, my oldest brother five, and my youngest three. Of course we all *"hated"* to leave our mother and father because we had been with them all our lives, my little brother would cry sometimes for them. But now I realize it was better that we did come here.

Pearl paused as she tried to convince herself of the truthfulness of the last sentence before going on.

My oldest brother Roy went away just a little while after we came here and my youngest brother Earl Eugene (the people that took him and adopted him called him Robert Earl Eugene) went away soon afterwards. Then about a month afterwards I went to a home in Stites, Ida. I stayed for two and a half years, then came back here and went to school.

The young author tried to skim over the parts of her history that were painful and stick only with the facts for the summary. After telling about last year's scarlet fever epidemic and her summer in Pardee, Pearl brought the writings up-to-date and started her first daily entry.

Friday, Oct. 4, 1918

I went to school, I got my English all right. In History we had a test, not a final, but just a little test so the teacher could tell about what we were able to do. We had six questions. I got five of my questions alright but the last one was, "Who was James Buchanan?" I didn't know who he was so I guessed at it. But as it happened I told all about Horace Greeley instead.

When we came home we had lunch in the kitchen and Mr. Howland took us down to the train depot where we expected a car of returned soldiers and marines. Nearly all of them had been wounded. One had his eye out, one had to walk with a crutch and another pulled up his sleeve and showed a wound in his arm. There were Canadians, French and I think Italians, and of course lots of Americans too. They spoke to us on the real thing soldiers had to endure "Over There." They said that about this time of year the men in the trenches were in the water up to their waist, most of them having bad colds. When they came out of the trenches their heavy coats and boots and other clothing weighed about one hundred and seventy pounds, and they were expected to go "over the top" with that on.

Sometimes they would be so dead tired they would stick their bayonets up and try to rest their coats on them and if they would take their boots off the rats would just gnaw holes in the soles of their feet. And when the guards were on duty in the fields, sometimes the Germans would flash a light on them in order to see where they were so they could get them. So the guards would "flop," if they didn't the Germans would "flop" them. When they did that, they would probably have their head in between the ribs of some dead comrade who had probably been dead for five days.

They showed some of the big machine guns and shells the Americans had captured from German battlefields.

Goodness but it was certainly crowded, we were jammed in like sardines, everybody trying to crowd to the front.

Monday Oct. 8, 1918

Everything went as usual today, but tonight when we came home we didn't change our dresses as we usually do, we went to helping with supper. We had salad, chicken and a lot of other good things. Mr. and Mrs. Howland, Dr. Flesher and Governor Alexander ate in the office, Laura served their table.

When we got through eating, Governor Alexander shook hands with us girls and asked our ages. We did the dishes, the boys washed and dried, then I set the tables. We girls stayed up until nine o'clock and got our lessons, then went to bed.

The following day the governor spoke at the school. Pearl felt special that she had helped serve him dinner the night before and had shook the hand of such an important man.

On Wednesday a Dr. Bryon King came to the school and started a month's worth of lectures on English poetry and literature. Pearl looked forward each day to listening to him and wrote in her diary about him.

He told us several stories and no matter how sad they were, you could always look for something to laugh at. He told a funny story about a man getting stage struck and Dr. King acted as if he were the man. And if he didn't make the funniest faces and funniest expressions, he kept you laughing every minute.

Oct. 11. 1918

. . . Mr. Simmonds told us today that we couldn't have institute next week. We had been planning to have some "big men and women" from all over the country. But Spanish influenza is all over and there can't be any more public meetings held for quite a while, church, picture shows, or nothing. Some of the towns have closed their schools, but we don't have to yet. . . .

Monday Oct. 14, 1918

Last night when we went to bed it was lightning a little, but about half past ten, Elizabeth came in and got in bed with me and then Mrs. Howland, Mrs. Waters and Miss Quiggley came in the dormitory. It had been thundering and lightning and also pouring down rain. All the beds on the porch were soaking wet. Elizabeth, Florence, and Mrs. Howland began bringing in the beds. It thundered and lightning all night but this morning the sky was quite clear.

Saturday Oct. 19, 1918

We got up this morning, Miss Quiggley is feeling pretty "bum," throat sore, back ache and a bushel of other things the matter with her.

We did our work and other peoples' too. I scrubbed the kitchen and helped with dinner besides doing my other work. Mrs. Waters is feeling bad too but we made her go upstairs, so's Mrs. Howland but she *will stay up*. Miss Quiggley went to bed. We called Dr. White but he is so tired from being in Nezperse chasing "flu" germs so much that he isn't coming up just now, but said, "If anybody gets worse to call." Dr. White came about six o'clock when we were eating supper. He announced that Miss Quiggley, Mrs. Waters and Mrs. Howland have the Spanish flu, so of course next morning, Dr. Bruce came up and tacked a beautiful big red sign with "QUARANTINE" with Scarlet Fever XXXXed out, I guess they were signs left over from last year.

Sunday Oct. 20, 1918

. . . We were doing our work, Mr. Howland scolded us because, I guess, he thought we didn't do enough work. He said on account of "those" being sick we would have to double up on work. It caused me to be rather "peeved" so I hurried just as fast as I could. I went to the kitchen and washed and scoured all the pots and kettles and set the tables in the time I usually set tables. (I guess it does some good to get scoldings sometimes.)

Friday Oct. 25, 1918

I got Miss Quiggley's breakfast for her and made the beds on the porch, cleaned Miss Quiggley's room and fixed her up. Then I came downstairs, sprinkled some cloths and ironed them, did a few other things and ate dinner. I fixed Miss Quiggley's dinner and helped do the dinner work.

Saturday Oct. 26, 1918

I got up this morning feeling pretty good. Got Miss Quiggley's breakfast and gave her a hot water bottle. But the hot water bottle leaked all over the bed, I must not have screwed the cork in quite tight enough. I had to change her bed, mend the clean sheets first, and I brought a flat iron up and ironed the mattress dry. I then cleaned up the room, made the beds on the porch, swept the room upstairs where the little girls sleep, went downstairs and sat down awhile. About that time I was feeling pretty "bum." First I felt awful cold, no matter where I would go it seemed as though I couldn't get warm, but I stayed up and around. I fixed Miss Quiggley's dinner, sprinkled and ironed some napkins for Mrs. Grange. I was sitting in the sewing room and my head ached. Mrs. Howland came in and took my temperature, it was 100.5, so Mrs. Howland said they had a bath ready for me upstairs, so I went and occupied it. After I got undressed, which was a rather hard job for I felt so dizzy. I had broth for dinner and supper. Dr. Todd had sent Miss Savage up for our nurse.

The Spanish flu epidemic hit the children's home quite hard. Many of Pearl's friends and staff came down with it. One day it was Hazel, the next day Laura, then Viola and Elizabeth. Just about the time Pearl thought she was over the flu and would try to get up to do her normal chores, the fever would return and she was back in bed. It was about five days before Pearl felt well enough to write in her diary again.

Thursday Oct. 31, 1918

Today is Halloween and I think most of us feel like ghosts. I did the front room hall and office this morning and brushed the tables off and set them. Then I went in the sewing room and sewed some buttons on Lynda's shoes and mended stockings. Today is donation day, of course people can't bring their donations here and go through the house as they generally do because we are in quarantine, but they are leaving them down at one of the grocery stores and the delivery wagon is bringing them up.

We have had a lot of things come up already, apples, squash, and pumpkins. One wagon came with six boxes of apples in it. We got outing flannel, stockings, all kinds of food, soap, coats, hats, and all kinds of clothing.

I was doing the dishes when Mrs. Savage came in and took my temperature, it was 101 degrees, so she sent me back to bed and brought me supper later.

'Course laying in bed you'll naturally think, so I thought out of me head a rhyme.

Why Not Be Glad

What's the use of being cranky?
When all the world is bright and gay
Why not do like other folks do
Just have your own way.
'Course to some things the Government
Momma and Mr. Conscience say, No!
But that only to the bad things
That you want to do.
And when to bad places you want to go.
But let me tell you just one thing
You can always have your own sweet way,
If you pick out just the good things
And do them all each day.

Pearl E. Tooley

Friday Nov. 1, 1918

I had to stay in bed again today, I guess I must have a poetic streak in me because I made up another poem this morning.

November

Jack Frost he is 'er comin' 'round on dark and chilly nights,
To paint the windows and the ground all a silvery frosty white.
We'll see pictures on the window panes
And we'll freeze our noses most nigh off
If we should chance to get out.
For Jack Frost is ready waiting there of that we should not doubt.
Grandfather winter's a thinkin' about drawing near,

180

While Jolly Old Thanksgiving knows it's about time he was here.
Old Turkey Gobbler is looking mighty sad,
For I guess he must know he'll be used
To make some youngsters glad.
The leaves have been changing colors
And have been dancing all around
The air is getting chilly
Which tells that snow will soon be falling down.
Autumn days are flying fast
With all their merry fun and cheer
But all of nature's heralds tell us
Dear Old November is already here.

P.E.T.

The older girls at the home loved to read stories. Many times they would read out loud to each other, making noises and actions to go along with the reading. One of their favorite stories was about a very rich and "uppity" family called "The Bowsers."

There was a room above the barn that was used to store old furniture and bedding. Laura, Hazel, and Pearl found it be a great place for reenacting the story they liked.

Monday Nov. 3, 1918
. . . In the afternoon I went up to the wonderful "Bowser Mansion" to visit my daughter and son-in-law, Mr. and Mrs. Bowser (Hazel and Laura), for I am the latter's mother, Madame La Vovic. My daughter's former name was Gwendolyn Xerna La Vovic.

They have in their home (a room in the upper part of the barn) a couch with a couch cover over it of rather dull orange (the couch is made of about three sacks of rags and a mattress for the bottom and a piece of a bed for the back to hold the cover on), a stool with a velvet cushion on it, a wonderful phonograph (fixed up the same way), a table, a cupboard, a wheelchair, a stand for books, and a chair, and rugs on the floor. They also have an electric light and I heard the phonograph play (Hazel sang).

Wednesday Nov. 6, 1918
The quarantine has been lifted and we can start school again. After dinner we did our work, put on our caps and sweaters and then dared Elizabeth to ask Mrs. Waters if we could have an apple. We were afraid she would say No!, but she said we could, so we all got one and went up to the "Bowser Manion." The wonderful phonograph was playing for us (Hazel sang again) and I swept the "mansion" for my daughter and son-in-law.

Monday Nov. 11, 1918

Peace, Peace sweet Peace, the paper announced this morning. The World War ended at six A.M. Kaiser, Von Hindenburg, the crown prince fleeing to Holland for refuge.

. . . While we were in the sewing room mending, a auto load of people passed with flags on the car and tin cans tied to the back of it, they were out celebrating Peace.

. . . Mrs. Howland took Viola and I up to the attic, we got some doll bodies and heads and took them down to the sewing room. We fixed the heads on and made dresses and stockings for them and gave them to the little girls.

The Soldier

The wind rustled noisily by the little brown house at the end of the lane,
And something in its dampness, brought news of coming rain.
Inside was a mother young and fair, two children knelt beside her knee,
Her hair was of a ruddy brown, but her face was worn with care.
A tiny gold star in the window told the story, sad but true,
Of a soldier who'd been fighting, "Over There," for me and you.
Fighting for this dear good land of ours, amid German shot and shell,
Fighting, that there might be worldwide peace, instead of Prussian hell.
One day came the sad news of his death, to that poor but happy home
    of three,
Their heads were all bowed down with grief, but the mother felt as if it
    could not be.
Peace sweet peace was soon declared, the armistice was signed,
The boys would be returning home, from the trenches and front lines.
The usual train came into the station, its shrill whistle loudly blew,
While on to the platform stepped many khaki clad figures, and some in
    navy blue.
Each took his own direction, homeward bound they came,
Some chased the wealthy avenues and streets, but one went down the lane.
A drizzle of rain was then coming down, in the window the light so
    dimly shone,
But, to him 'twas a cheery welcome, to his poor, yet sorrowful, home.
But he knew nought of the sorrowing, or of the tears those three had shed,
Or that they had knelt down that very night asking God to provide the
    next day's bread.
He knocked at the little door, the mother heard from within,
But she thought, 'tis only a neighbor callin' after finishing her nightly
    chore.

She softly crossed the floor, with a footstep firm but light,
And opened the door, but grew very pale, and drew back at the sight.
"Why Mary it is only I, you know" said the figure from without,
Then he drew her close unto his side and asked her what she was so
frightened about.
"Oh, John," she cried. "Can it be true I scarcely dare believe."
Then she told him of the letter they had gotten, and of the message they
had received.
After all the letter was only a mistake, and the message a false alarm.
But to that poor and humble cottage they brought sorrowing and harm.

P.E.T.

That Christmas was full of fun and excitement as the girls sewed hair ribbons and handkerchiefs and made candies to give as gifts to each other. A large tree was decorated and nightly caroling before bed made for a wonderful time for Pearl and her friends.

A few days before Christmas, Pearl received a very special surprise. Mr. and Mrs. Lewis had come to the home with Helen and Robert Earl. It was the first time the siblings had seen each other in four years, and the reunion was splendid. Helen was now eleven and still as feisty as ever. Robert Earl was seven and had truly been *spoiled* by the Lewises. He really didn't remember Pearl very well, as he was only three when they were separated, but that didn't make any difference to the oldest sister; she was still overjoyed to see him.

The two girls quickly ran toward each other and hugged tightly. It was a reunion each had waited four years to have. Four hard and sad years waiting for another embrace from each other.

"This is the best Christmas present," Pearl whispered to her sister as they hugged.

"When Mrs. Lewis told me we were coming to the home today and that you were here, I was so excited. I could hardly believe we would see each other again," Helen responded with joyful tones and expressions.

Pearl saw the young boy holding onto Mrs. Lewis's skirt, almost afraid to show himself. She let loose of Helen and turned to address the lad. "Earl?" she questioned the brown-haired boy.

"No. My name is Robert, not Earl," he responded with a pouting face and attitude.

"Oh, excuse me," Pearl apologetically stated. "I forgot. The last time I saw you, your name was still Earl." She made sure she had corrected her mistake before addressing her little brother again. "Robert, do you remember me? I'm your big sister Pearl."

He studied her face and tried to remember the thirteen-year-old girl who now stood in front of him.

"I'm the one who used to hold and rock you a lot when you would cry. You might not remember me, but I'll never forget you," the sister remarked.

A glimmer of recollection seemed to come forward in his mind, and Robert Earl responded with a tender squeeze to his sister's big hug.

"We brought you presents," the boy blurted out. "I got to help Mother wrap them. Helen didn't get to because she had been naughty to me and had to stay in her room."

Pearl looked at her younger sister with a gleam in her eyes. Helen responded with a dagger stare aimed at her youngest brother. Robert Earl ducked behind his mother's skirt, then peeked around and stuck his tongue out at Helen. Pearl stepped in front of her sister. She knew if she didn't, Helen would "sock" the boy with her fist that was now doubled up, ready to strike.

"I've got some things I want the two of you to have for Christmas. I just need to go upstairs to get them. Do either of you want to come with me?" Pearl asked.

"I'll come," Helen quickly responded as she grabbed her sister by the arm.

"Do you want to come, too?" Pearl asked her brother.

"No! I want to stay with Momma. I don't like this place," Robert Earl commented as he stayed near Mrs. Lewis. "I've had bad dreams about a house like this one."

As they climbed the stairs together, Helen explained to her sister just how spoiled their youngest brother was. "He gets everything he wants. If he doesn't, he just throws a temper tantrum until he does. It's going to take Mother a long time to tame this rotten behavior when we're all together again," Helen reported.

Pearl selected two appropriate gifts, and the girls went back down to the visitors' room to exchange Christmas gifts with each other. The siblings gave hugs and promises before separating again.

Both sisters were now old enough to write letters and keep in touch. Each promised the other she would do it. Mrs. Howland pledged to forward any mail that might come to the home if the girls' placement changed. The girls each got Roy's address in Canada and promised to keep in touch with their now nine-year-old brother also.

Pearl felt happiness and security at the home, even though there had been so much sickness the past few months. It didn't matter because she had several good friends and the staff were pleasant to be around. She felt like people really cared about her this time at the children's home.

Mr. and Mrs. Howland had put off the terrible task as long as they could, knowing how teens need close friendships, but finally called Elizabeth, Florence, and Pearl into the office on Sunday afternoon to break the bad news.

Trying to be upbeat and positive about the situation, Mr. Howland stated, "I have some wonderful news for you three girls. We have found placements for you. You'll be leaving on Tuesday for your new homes."

The announcement hit Pearl like a "ton of bricks" had been dropped from the sky. Florence and Elizabeth both started to cry, but Pearl held the tears as numbness took over her countenance.

"I'll work harder and try not to be sick so much, if you let me stay here," Pearl announced in a solemn voice. "I'll try to be a better person, if I've done something wrong. Please let me stay."

"Girls, please understand," Mr. Howland said, trying to console the heartbroken girls. "If we had our choice, we would have you stay here at the home until you are eighteen, but we can't. Our jobs are to find you families to live with. People who will help prepare you to live on your own someday. We are just trying to do what we feel is best."

"But I don't want another family. You are my family and I want to stay here!" Elizabeth cried.

"I'm sorry, girls, if this hurts you, but it just has to be this way," stated Mr. Howland. "Try to look on the bright side and you will be better off."

Pearl lay in her bed staring into the darkness. Why had her life been so unstable? She felt like a seed that had been tossed into the air, with no control over the winds of fate. She had been tossed to and fro by the prevailing winds of placement and the home. She never had enough time to grow roots in one good spot long enough to become a stable tree. One that could be firm and something to hold onto.

Her thoughts drifted to her torn-apart family. Where were her parents? What had she done to make them not want her anymore? Nobody seemed to want her, she thought. The tears finely welled up in her eyes and rolled down her cheeks.

The next day was extremely difficult as she prepared her clothing for packing. Laura and Hazel followed Pearl around all day. They just didn't want to believe the "three musketeers" were splitting up.

After lunch, they all put on their coats and boots and trekked to the barn. They wanted Pearl to be in the "Bowser Mansion" one last time. They each promised to be friends forever and to write faithfully. After all, the mother (Pearl) could never forget her daughter (Laura) and son-in-law (Hazel).

Twilight

When the day is ending, then comes softly falling night
When night and day are blending, into the shadowy twilight,
I like to sit in my garden, with my thoughts of what might have been,
Of the joy of those fleeting day dreams, but let me forget the pain.

P.E.T.

IN A ONE-HORSE OPEN SLEIGH

When the train pulled into the station and stopped, the big sign read: "WELCOME TO MOSCOW, IDAHO." Pearl took a deep breath when she saw the family she had been sent to live with. The woman was dressed very plainly and wore a strange-type bonnet. The man and three young boys were all dressed in dark clothing. Their clothing looked similar to pictures in Pearl's history book of what people of the Quaker and Mennonite religions wore.

They greeted her cordially and introduced themselves as Otto and Helen Lyons. The boys were Adam, age seven; Joseph, age five; and Jacob, age two.

Pearl was still unhappy and a bit resentful about leaving the home and her friends. At first she was as cold to the family as the air outside on that wintry day in January 1919.

"Are you Pearl?" Otto Lyons inquired of the young teenage girl.

"Yes, I'm Pearl Tooley," she coldly stated.

"Was the train ride fun?" seven-year-old Adam asked.

"It was very cold inside. I almost froze coming here," Pearl responded with a bitter tone in her voice.

"We're sorry you had a bad train ride. I brought a heavy blanket you can put over yourself for the ride out to the farm," Mrs. Lyons stated.

"You do have a car, don't you? I'm used to riding in a car," Pearl snidely remarked.

"Oh no!" five-year-old Joseph quickly responded. "We have something better than a car. Come with me, I'll show you." The young boy grabbed Pearl by the hand and led her behind the train station. It was there that he revealed the mode of transportation the Lyons family used in the snowy wintertime. The gloom and doom melted from Pearl's countenance as she viewed the husky steed hooked up to the large open sleigh owned by the family. By the time they arrived at the farm, Pearl had warmed up both inside and out.

The Lyons family lived on a farm outside Moscow. Pearl finished the eighth grade in a small one-room country schoolhouse not too far from the farm. The school reminded her of the one so long ago back in Lakeview, where she and her sister would skip or run on their merry way. But those times were gone and only the memories were left behind.

Otto and Helen Lyons were nice to Pearl, and she soon felt a sense of purpose as she helped with the chores and the little boys. She helped

Mrs. Lyons with the meals and the mending that went along with three active boys. Pearl could do laundry, iron, and clean house as well as any grown woman. She was also becoming a pretty efficient cook. Pearl had definitely had plenty of practice in all kinds of domestic work.

During the winter months, the children were taken to school in the horse-drawn sleigh. That experience was always a thrill for the young teenager. But in the spring when the snow melted, they would walk home from school. Pearl loved the beautiful scenery of the area.

The Lyonses had lived in Kansas for a few years before moving to Idaho. They were trying to raise wheat the same way they had there. It was called "dry farming," because the farmers depended on the rain for a successful crop. Pearl resolved that spring and summer she never wanted to depend on dry farming for a living. It never seemed to rain at the right time for the crop. If it didn't rain when the wheat needed it, the family worried. But if it did rain when it was time to harvest, they worried again.

The family were members of a religious group something like he Mennonites. They belonged to the Church of the Brethren and attended the meetings whenever possible. Pearl went with them to church. Before too long, she became a member. She liked the fellowship and the way the members treated each other. It was also a good social gathering place for teenagers. That part really made it attractive to a fourteen-year-old girl who was looking for new friends.

Living full-time with the Lyonses was only temporary for Pearl. The only high school was in Moscow, and horse and buggy or sleigh transportation took too many hours out of a working day for the family. Pearl had become extremely fond of the Lyonses, and they of her. They had accepted her as one of their own. It was the kind of bond she had been desperately seeking. Even though she would not be living with them daily, she had come to call the farm "home" and planned on considering these folk as her people.

When she started high school in the fall of 1919, Pearl again had to move in order to be near a school.

"I'm going to miss you, Pearl," were the words of the sober-faced six-year-old boy.

"Don't worry, Joseph; you'll see me at church each week. I'll come out here and have dinner on Sundays sometimes," Pearl explained to the sad boy.

"I wuve you," three-year-old Jacob added. "Can I come wiff you?"

She picked the youngest boy up and gave him a special squeeze. "If I could take you I would," she remarked, trying to comfort the sad little guy. "Remember, this is not a good-bye forever—believe me, I know what those kind are. This good-bye is only for a short time. You'll see me so much, you'll get sick of me," she laughed.

She gave everyone a hug and a thank-you as they dropped her off at the new house she would stay at in the town of Moscow, Idaho.

The couple she moved in with in the fall of 1919 were the Creetmores. They were middle-aged and had no children. Pearl earned her board and room by doing housework.

Mr. Creetmore was a businessman, and Mrs. Creetmore worked at David's Department Store. They were accustomed to peace and quiet in their home. Keeping track of a busy teenager was not what they wanted to do. They were very pleased with Pearl's work, but the generation gap was just too wide. Pearl only stayed with the Creetmores a few month, before a new family was arranged for her to board with.

The next home was with a prominent family who also lived in Moscow. Their names were William and Madeline Lee. They had three young children, Billy, Richard, and Mary Madeline. Billy was the oldest at age four. Richard was two and a half, and Mary was a year old. Mr. Lee was a lawyer, and Mrs. Lee was involved in social activities and clubs, between having children.

This kind of a life was hard on a teenage girl. It was tough trying to keep up with everything. She was the housekeeper, nanny, student, and church attender. With all her responsibilities, Pearl had very little time left for fun. She learned quickly how to budget her time and tried to find joy wherever she could.

The first year after Pearl left her friends at the home, most of her free time was spent in writing letters. She had a sister and two brothers to keep in touch with and five girlfriends as well. Of course Laura and Hazel got most of the "juicy gossip" about the new people she would meet, so Pearl didn't take time to keep a personal diary in 1919.

It wasn't long, however, before the letters from her friends got further and further apart. Pearl needed a way to remember her adventurers. She got a little notebook from the variety store and began to pen her activities and feelings once again.

Sunday Sept. 19, 1920
Went to church this morn. Pretty good attendance, mostly women though 'cause the men are threshing, even if 'tis Sunday.

189

Came home for dinner and in the afternoon read some of Edger Allan Poe's stories. They are awfully gruesome and it's a wonder my dreams weren't composed of Black Cats, Amontillado, Pit and Pendulum, and so forth.

I went to church tonight, pretty good attendance. I sat by Floyd, rather he sat down by me when he came in 'cause I got there first.

The Church of the Brethren meetinghouse was located about a mile from the Lees' home, just on the outskirts of the main part of town. Many of the members lived in town, unlike those like the Lyonses, who lived in the country. It was a sacrifice for Pearl to attend the meetings because of the distance. She often had to walk by herself to and from the church building. Because she looked forward to seeing and meeting interesting young men, she was willing to travel the miles to be there.

Being a sophomore in high school, Pearl was, like most other girls her age, more interested in the older boys than the ones her own age. Of course the infatuations she had were not always shared by the one she was intrigued with, but at her age that fact wasn't too important. What did seem to matter, however, was her ability to just be near certain young men if she went to church.

Her first big crush on a boy was with Floyd Yearout. Floyd was a senior in high school, and Pearl enjoyed any opportunity she had to be around him. Even if he only thought of her as a friend and was more interested in a girl named Kathryn Sanders, Pearl wanted to be where she thought he would be.

Monday Sept. 20, 1920

Went to school as usual, my cap in sewing is all ready for the lace now . . .

I told Kathryn that Floyd asked how she was yesterday and about the picture Millard took of Floyd and her, she was *real interested* to hear about them. I made her blush too.

Billy Lee is five years old today, so of course we had a party. The kids made an awful lot of noise but I guess they had a good time.

The age of transportation advances was changing lifestyles in the West, and Moscow, Idaho, was no exception. Some folk still had the horse-drawn wagons and carriages, but many people also had automobiles. The Lee family, whom Pearl was living with, had two cars, and some of the members of her church also had automobiles. The Yearouts had a car, and Pearl savored the times when Floyd gave her rides in his mother's vehicle.

Friday Sept. 24, 1920

Finished my cap in sewing today, going to give it to Rosie for a wedding present, and it's pretty cute. (You shouldn't brag on your own handiwork).

The sixth period was taken out this afternoon. Mr. Hulme talked to us on "Books." I liked his lecture fine. He told about the greetings of different nationalities and the way they spoke, of their manners of living and ideas. For instance, the Italian says "coma es sta" (or something of the sort) meaning "How do you *stand*." The Italian youth thinks a great deal about his appearance and doesn't work or do anything in the summer, because it might spoil his hands, and in the evening he's accompanied by his cane. He takes a little walk for exercise instead of playing tennis or baseball or something like that for recreation for he "Wishes to make the gentleman" as they say.

The Frenchman, who likes to have "white hands" also but who doesn't go quite the extreme the Italian does, says, "How do you *carry* yourself."

The German who is always getting things mixed up and living a sort of "topsy turvy" life says, "Vie befindex du" "How do you *find* yourself."

And the active, full of life English and Americans say, "How do you *do*."

Sunday, September 26, 1920

"Floyd, psst . . . Floyd." Pearl whispered, trying to get the dreamy boy's attention. "Kathryn wants to see the picture you have most awfully bad."

"Is that so," the confident young man responded. "Tell her if she wants to see it so bad, then she'll have to come to church."

"You are so cruel," the infatuated Pearl commented.

"Do you need a ride home?" Floyd asked. "We'll drive down through town and see what's going on if you want to."

Pearl didn't really care that she wasn't the center of his thoughts or attentions; she was just happy to be a part of Floyd's activities.

191

Friday, Oct. 1, 1920

. . . I went to our class party to-night. Floyd was the only boy there, but after the business meeting we played games and had a pretty good time. Floyd brought me home in his car. It's now 12:30 A.M. so Adieu and sweet dreams to you all.

Sunday Oct. 3, 1920

Went to Sunday School this morning, came back home for dinner and read most of the afternoon. Went to Church again tonight. Kathryn and Earl, her brother, were there. We played nearly all the time. (Naughty weren't we?) Floyd showed us some pictures after church.

Moscow, Idaho, had two movie houses that played the wonderful silent films of the day. The teens took every opportunity to go and view this great form of entertainment.

Monday Oct. 4, 1920

Washed the kitchen walls today. "Birth of a Nation" was on at the "Kenworthy" tonight so I went down but there wasn't any sitting or standing room. I then went down to the "Liberty" to see Margarita Clark in "All of the Sudden, Peggy." That was awfully crowded too but met Irene Barber, so we waited in the hall (or whatever you call it) until the first show was over, then went in. I liked it pretty well. 'Twas about spiders and Peggy trying to marry her mother off to the bugologist" etc. Irene was awfully sleepy when we came out so she leaned her head on my shoulder. When we were going up Washington Street, Russell Wittes over-took us. Irene was shivering a little so he took off his coat and made her put it on and said he wasn't cold (Gallant Knight). I left them at Second Street and Irene asked me if I wasn't afraid and I told her no! That I didn't believe in ghosts or something of the sort. Au Revoir.

The young woman who occupied most of Floyd Yearout's attentions was not allowed to go on dates unless she had other people with her. Kathryn's brother Earl was more than happy to go with his sister and cover for her if he could also get a date. Pearl was often chosen as a date for Earl.

Saturday Oct. 9, 1920

. . . Earl came about 10:00 P.M. and called for me. He wanted to know if I could go out car riding with them. I told him I'd ask Mrs. Lee. (I knew Kathryn was in there but I'd forgotten to ask what car they were in). I asked Mrs. Lee and she didn't know whether I should go out so late or not. When she found out that it was some kids who lived up our way, she asked if there was an older person with them. I told her I supposed there must be 'cause Earl didn't have a car. Well I finally went but she told me not to stay out very late.

I don't know just where we went but out near the Burns place and around, we sat in the car for about an hour I guess and talked etc. About a million cars passed us and one had the nerve to turn the spotlight on.

Coming home Floyd hit a bump in the road and I thought for sure I was going to have a chance to visit Mars. I have a bump on my head to remember the ride by. Earl got a swollen lip. Floyd and Kathryn shouldn't have been so preoccupied, should they?

I got home at 12:00 midnight. Hope awfully that isn't *very late*. Au revoir.' '

Sunday Oct. 10, 1920

Mrs. Lee asked me this morning if we had a chaperone last night and I told her that Floyd was there. She said that was alright then. I thought perhaps it wouldn't be very good for my "health" if I mentioned that I thought the chaperone needed chaperoning. I let good enough alone.

Went to church this morning and went home with the folks (the Lyonses). There were a lot of other people there also including the Year-outs. We ate and ate and ate watermelon. Auntie Lillie Yearout said she believed she had enough for once. After dinner, we ate some more melon, then Aunt Lillie and I washed the dishes.

We went to church or rather to town and rode around until church time. The boys got some candy at Wittes. Then we went to church. Church let out at five after eight and I came home just as soon as I could give Floyd's watch back to him and get my handkerchief from Arnold.

Lees didn't go out, but I hope it's not 'cause I didn't get home just at eight sharp. (If it is, I may get a scolding and I just hate them, *Most Terribly*. I'd rather be licked, wouldn't you?) Au revoir.

Southern Drawl

I've got a gal from Dixie Land, she's the cutest little thing you ever saw
When she smiles she shows her pearly teeth, and she's got that Southern
    Drawl.
She's a ray of Southern sunshine, her hands are white and small
But the thing that made me love her, is her dreamy Southern Drawl.
My gal she's got that Southern' Drawl, she comes from old Virginie here
Her hair is black and curly, she surely is a dear.

P.E.T.

William and Madeline Lee had lived in Moscow for several years before getting married. Madeline's maiden name was Shields, and she had a brother named Thomas. William Lee and Thomas Shields had played football together at the University of Idaho at Moscow before Mr. Lee studied law.

After Madeline and William married, Thomas Shields also married and moved to Spokane, Washington, a distance that had been made easier to travel with modern roads and the motorcar.

Thursday Oct. 14, 1920

Mrs. Lee's brother and sister came tonight. I went down to the rally and pajama parade this evening, it was sure good. Mr. Lee made a speech.

I saw Floyd on the street and spoke to him. He looked awfully funny 'cause he hadn't shaved and had on an old sweater. (Every day isn't Sunday though is it?)

Saturday Oct. 16, 1920

Did up the work this morning and went to the football game this afternoon. It was an awfully good game even if we did get beat. Our boys worked awfully hard anyway but the Lewis and Clark boys were a lot bigger than our boys.

One of the Lewis and Clark boys got his shoulder broken. The score was twenty to thirteen in favor of Spokane.

Somebody said "hello" to me when I was going down to the game and I turned around just in time to see Earl Sanders beating it for some place. Au revoir.

Sunday Oct. 17, 1920

Mrs. Lee and the boys went to Spokane this morning with her brother. I didn't go to church until after they left, which was about 11:30 A.M.

Miss Talbot came home about 5:30 P.M. to take baby Mary Madeline home with her while Mrs. Lee was away. We had lunch, then I went to church.

Earl and the kids that stay at Humpheries were there. Floyd took me down to the post office to mail my letter, then brought me up home. Au revoir.

Thursday Oct. 21, 1920

Mrs. Lee came home tonight. She got a "New Edison" in Spokane and we spent quite a bit of time unpacking it. After supper I went down to the rally with Ellen Cornwall. We had a dandy one. We had speeches and yelled in the assembly, then we went to the gymnasium and had a wrestling match and a boxing match. Floyd and John were dressed up as "cowpunchers" and they "rustled" too.

After the rally we were going to church but Ellen wanted to go to the show because "The Price of Redemption" was on at the Kenworthy, so she finally persuaded me. I got home about quarter after ten and went to the rally at seven. My dishes weren't washed yet, so I'll probably get "Hail Columbia Happy Land" in the morning.

Well here's hopin' for luck. Au revoir.

Friday Oct. 22, 1920

Went to school at eight this morning and got out at twelve. This afternoon went to Pullman to the game, with Mildred Gilbertson, and we had a dandy time.

We beat Pullman thirty-three to zero (some score), an awfully large crowd went over, the "bug" was jammed full.

The game didn't let out in time for us to go back on the "bug" so after the game we went uptown and got some cocoa, sandwiches, and pie to eat. Then we bought some candy and found some other kids and walked around town. Just before train time, we went over to the depot. The train was full, a lot of them Moscownians. We yelled and sang all the way up home. Au revoir.

Monday Oct. 25, 1920

Went to school this morning. Kathryn is mad at Floyd because he didn't stay and watch them dance Friday night after church. She said Earl called Floyd "Necktie." I don't think that's a bit nice. Kathryn used to dislike Ester and Ruth Henderson too, but now as far as she is concerned they're all "Honey and Pie." I don't know them, though, of course, only what I've heard, and I don't care to repeat it.

Funny, isn't it, how some people can change their minds so suddenly. Grief, I hope Kathryn never gets a hold of this diary, 'cause if she does wowee!! She won't speak to me again. But a person has to give her thoughts to somebody or something, so the best thing I could do was to put them down here. Well we have two tests tomorrow, Geometry and General Science, so I'd better get busy and study them or I'll flunk flat as a pancake I'm afraid. Here's hopin' for everything to turn out right. Au revoir.

The youth of the church planned a big Halloween party in the country at one of the farms. Otto Lyons made sure that Pearl had transportation.

Saturday Oct. 30, 1920

Cleaned up the house this morning. After dinner I went downtown to get a flashlight battery for Otto. I went home (to the Lyons house) before I went to the party. Otto took me over in the wagon. We had a dandy time at the party. We played games, "Skip to Mallou." "Ten Little Indians,"

"Virginia Reel," "Streets and Alleys," "I've Got a New Pig in the Parlor," "Miller Boys," etc. We had pumpkin pie, sandwiches, doughnuts, cakes and pickles (of course). Au revoir.

School let out for the Thanksgiving weekend, and the Lees took their children to Spokane to spend the holiday with the Shieldses.

Pearl was invited home to the Lyonses for a few days, and Helen Lyons went into town with the wagon to get her.

Thursday Nov. 25, 1920

I came out to Otto's last night, Helen came in after me. I fixed my new dress this morning, just had to shorten it. I think it's rather cute, it's made of Mary Blue Tricotine. Cost $21.95, terrible price isn't it? We had roast chicken, cranberry sauce, mashed potatoes, and all sorts of good things for dinner.

SWEET SIXTEEN OR SEVENTEEN

Sunday April 3, 1921

It's supposed to be Spring now but it snowed last night and looked more like Christmas than anything else this morning. I've been out of school for two weeks and oh, but I dread to make up the exams I missed. So many many weeks since I wrote in this diary last, that I believe I'll try to think of some of the things that have happened in between times.

I got all my credits in school last semester, just barely made Geometry though. Went out home Christmas week.

Had the mumps week before last and had to miss the tournament and school too.

Helen Lyons had a new baby boy. Donald Morgan was born Wednesday March 23, at five after twelve, and weighed thirteen pounds.

Otto Lyons' mother came to help, but she had a sore finger and couldn't do anything but take care of the baby, so I had to go out home last Saturday. Arnie and Mel came up and ate Easter dinner with us.

I got all of the meals besides making bread, cookies, and pies, so I think I'm getting to be quite a cook.

Floyd and Aunt Lillie came up home to see Helen and the baby Monday morning.

Otto's mother went home yesterday and Helen got up. Baby is pretty badly spoiled, had to be rocked all of the time.

Otto brought me in town today. I dread to start school tomorrow. I've missed so much. I may have to drop Geometry. Well, Au revoir, for this time. I guess everything's done here. P.E.T.

Monday April 4, 1921

Started back to school this morning, it wasn't so bad after all. If I work hard enough I think I can catch up, but I dread my Geometry test.

Sunday April 10, 1921

Yesterday evening Mr. Williams of Lewiston called me up and told me my sister was coming to see me today. I went to church this morning and this afternoon Helen came. She has grown a lot taller than she was when I saw her last, she is even a little taller than I am and I think she weighs more. She lives with a family named Lyons, strange that we should both live with people of the same name isn't it? He is the President of one of the Lewiston banks.

The two teenage girls were happy when all the introductions and questions by the adult were over so they could go to Pearl's room and be alone. As they climbed the staircase hand in hand, Helen whispered in her sister's ear, ''I know where Mother is.''

The statement caused Pearl to stop in her tracks and look with inquiring eyes at her younger sister.

"Shhhh!" Helen uttered as she pulled her sister's hand to continue upwards. "I'll tell you when we're alone."

They entered the room and closed the door. Pearl made sure the lock was secure so the Lee children wouldn't come snooping around. The two girls were very careful not to discuss shameful matters around certain people. After all, they did have their dignity to maintain. They definitely didn't want anyone to know their parents had broken the law and spent time in jail.

Pearl's curiosity was piqued. "Have you seen Mother?" she quickly asked.

"No, but a man who works for the bank saw her," Helen informed Pearl.

"Go on!" insisted the anxious girl.

"Well, this man took a trip to Spokane three weeks ago. He told me he had seen my mother one night in a restaurant. She was playing the piano, entertaining people while they ate their supper," the informer reported.

"The piano?" Pearl questioned in amazement. "I didn't even know she could lay the piano."

"He told me the woman he saw looks enough like me to be my mother, so it must be her. You remember when we were younger, everyone said I looked just like Mother."

Pearl stopped listening to reflect back long ago.

"Another thing I found out." Helen paused to make sure her sister was listening. "Mrs. Lyons told me that we were one hundred percent Irish."

"Really!" the stunned elder sister replied. "I thought we had other blood in us also."

"No. Mrs. Lyons told me that a person with my coloring and disposition had to be *all Irish*. If I'm all Irish, then you are, too," Helen announced with authority.

As Pearl wrote in her diary that evening, she contemplated all the information Helen had reported. In the last paragraph for the day, she expressed her hidden feelings.

I wish I could see my mother, it's been such a long long time since I've seen her, perhaps I may some day. Well Au revoir.

198

She lay in the still darkness unable to fall asleep. The visit by her sister earlier that day had stirred some deep suppressed feelings. She began to ask the same unanswered questions that troubled her. Was it really possible her mother was in Spokane? If it were true, where was her father? What were they doing? Why, why, why, had they not wanted her back? Why had they not come like her mother had promised? Pearl's head swirled with questions she hoped to find answers to someday.

Friday April 22, 1921

I'm seventeen today (getting aged). I'll soon have to count backwards instead of forwards . . .

Somewhere over the last seven years since she had been in foster care, Pearl had lost track of how old she really was. It must have been way back when she went to live with Miss Jett, because Pearl now thought she was a year older than she actually was.

THE CHARMER

The summer of 1921 was full of hard work and many lonesome days for Pearl. She saw her school friends now and again, but her main social life stemmed around the youth at church.

Her infatuation with Floyd Yearout ended when he became involved with a girl named Alice Reed. By October, the two were married and off to California. There were other fellows around, but none were interesting enough for Pearl to go after.

Pearl became more involved with the churchfolk. They now accepted her as a permanent member of the Lyons family. Otto Lyons had two sisters who lived nearby. Pearl became quite close to those families also that fall and winter. Otto's sister Belle was married to Hirum Hylton. They had a daughter named Ruby and a son named Jewel. Both were a few years older than Pearl. Otto's other sister was Lillie Yearout, Floyd's mother. She was a nurse and traveled around caring for the sick people in the area. Lillie was married to Charles Yearout, who was also the preacher for the church. Their second son was named Paul. He was the same age as Pearl really was; however, she thought he was a year younger than she was.

The families insisted Pearl call them Aunt and Uncle. They wanted her to feel attached to a family. In that regard, they were very compassionate people.

Pearl had kept in touch with Helen as they had promised each other. Helen no longer lived with the bank president's family in Lewiston. She was now living with a woman by the name of Bethmann. Mrs. Bethmann was the same lady Pearl had met when she was with the Moore family in Pardee back in 1918. Mrs. Bethmann was the owner of the beautiful home Pearl went to for a birthday party. Helen really liked this placement. Even though she was not formally adopted by this woman, Helen changed her last name to Bethmann. Mrs. Bethmann now had the red-haired daughter she had always wanted.

Pearl had done well in school her junior year and had almost enough credits to graduate. She had been counseled she would only need to go for one semester of her senior year to graduate. Pearl choose to skip the first semester and wait until after Christmas to finish. By doing this, she could work full-time for the Lees. She wanted to save enough money to get the nice things she would need for graduation.

Pearl also kept in touch with her brothers. She was sad that Roy was having such a terrible life in Canada. He had written to her and told of the things he was required to do for the family he was with.

Roy

In the summer months in Cowley, Roy had to help plow the land. At age nine, he was in charge of driving eight horses on a gang plow. The plow had an iron seat where he rode. Many times he was thrown off when the plow hit a boulder and turned over. He was given the work that was the most undesirable, the jobs Mrs. Sleighter's nephew didn't want to do.

When Roy was ten, he was given the chore of driving a four-horse team and wagon filled with three cows. He had to take the cows from Coleman, a mining town about forty miles from the farm, back to Cowley. He was by himself and started his trip home on a Sunday. When he got about halfway home, the Royal Canadian Mounted Police made him pull over. They informed him it was against the law to do this kind of work on Sunday. The police directed him to a farm and made him wait until the next day to continue. He didn't arrive home until Monday evening. Neither Mrs. Sleighter nor her nephew Victor was the least bit concerned about him. They figured if he had an accident, they would get the team and cattle back in due time. They never once said they cared what happened to him as a person. He was just another body living there to work. He was often told if he couldn't do the job, they would simply get someone else who could.

Pearl was always concerned about her brother and felt bad that he was being treated so poorly. She wished she had the power to rescue him. However, she was in no position to do anything but just survive from day to day herself.

In the spring of 1922, when the workload was heavy on Uncle Hirum Hylton's farm, he hired on his second cousin from Texas to work for him. George Jensen was a man in his mid-thirties and had been around. He had married when he was nineteen and was the father of an eleven-year-old girl. He served in the military for two years. While he was away in the service, his wife divorced him and married someone else.

201

Since leaving the military, George had drifted from place to place looking to find somewhere to put down roots. He had written to Uncle Hirum and Aunt Belle a few times and now was in Moscow working on the farm.

He was about five-ten, with a slender build and dark wavy hair. His brown eyes sparkled when he flirted with the ladies. George had a way of manipulating girls and never lacked for dates.

George took an immediate liking to Pearl and started pursuing her right off. At first she was uninterested and afraid of this older man's attentions. After a few weeks, however, she became giddy and flattered that a fellow of his age and experience would pay her so much attention. Perhaps it was the fact that he was older and she was looking for some attention from a man of his age, never experiencing attention from her father, that caused her to become attracted to him.

In his pursuit of Pearl, George used all the people around to his advantage. With his charm and demeanor he made sure the innocent young woman was invited to picnics and other activities he would be attending. He was good on the telephone and arranged group outings with folks Pearl knew and liked. By August of 1922, George had Pearl pretty well "hooked." He was able to sweet-talk her into doing what he wanted to do and going where he wanted to go. It was hard for the young seventeen-year-old to know she was being "charmed" by this older man.

George lived at the Hyltons' in the back room and liked to hang around with the young people. Ruby and her brother, Jewel, and Paul Yearout were among the teens who allowed George to be a part of their social circle.

Pearl could remember her father was about fifteen years older than her mother. The fact that George was also about that much older than she was just part of a pattern being repeated in her mind.

As Pearl became more and more infatuated with George, she needed someone to express her feeling to. This was an important time in her life, and she began recording her daily activities in a diary again.

Sunday August 27, 1922

Went to church this morning. After church I went home with Ruby. George and I were sort of at outs, but we buried the hatchet and everything's running smoothly. After dinner we sat around and looked at pictures etc. Paul and Jewel were perfect clowns, so they kept us amused.

Went up to Steltzes to call Mrs. Lee but couldn't get her. Then we walked over to the sand pit. The scenery was wonderful, the sunset sky and the mountains were reflected in the water and the wild ducks exhibited their swimming accomplishments for us.

George told me part of a fortune he was told by a palmist, part of which he says has come true nearly exactly as she told it, and the rest—oh well. I accused him of kidding me, but he swore he wasn't. We shall see what we shall see, n'est pas?

Otto is going to get up a bunch and we're planning to go to the mountains Sunday. Went to church, then home and to bed.

Monday Aug. 28, 1922

Washed: cloths, dishes, face, hands, kids, etc.

Wednesday Aug. 30, 1922

Cleaned the living room, and it looks just lovely. I don't mind cleaning so much because everything is so nice when I'm thru.

Jewel came to the door this afternoon with a note from George saying that he was going to leave for Potlatch in the morning and wanted me to come to Hylton's for supper. I asked the boss about it and she said I could go.

After supper the Weeks, Reeds, Yearouts and Joe Hylton came and we had ice cream, cake, watermelon, musk melon, peaches, grapes, and bananas for refreshments.

George and Pearl went out to the back porch area of Hyltons' farmhouse. George wanted to be away from all the other folk to speak to Pearl privately.

"I asked the Hyltons to have everyone out this evening so I could see my special girl." George quietly spoke as he leaned his face close to Pearl's ear.

"Oh, George, you're such a flatterer," the bashful girl replied.

"I have a present for you," the cunning man stated as he put his hand into his pocket. "Would you take a gift from me? I won't show you what it is until you tell me if you'll accept it or not."

Pearl supposed the gift was just some trifle, candy or something of the sort, so she said she would. "Let me see it," the curious young maiden coaxed.

"No. You have to wait until you're ready to go home," he teased.

"That's not fair," she stated. "You can't tell me you have a present for me and not show me right this minute," Pearl insisted as she reached around to find the pocket where the surprise was hidden.

George played hard to get, turning away and laughing quietly, so as not to attract the attention of the other people in the house. "OK, I'll let you take a peek if you give me a kiss first," he instructed.

203

She smiled slightly, then raised her face upward and prepared for the kiss. Her heart seemed to flutter like butterfly wings as the charmer put his lips on hers.

"I guess I'll let you see." He reached in his pocket and pulled out a small paper bag and handed it to the innocent young woman.

Pearl carefully opened the sack and reached inside. As she pulled out the contents, her eyes widened and her mouth dropped open. "Oh, my goodness!" she exclaimed. "They are beautiful. You shouldn't be giving me such expensive things."

"Do you really like them?" George questioned, yet knowing the answer due to Pearl's reaction. He took the lavaliere and put it around her neck. She looked down to admire its beauty as it rested on her chest. He then slipped the ruby ring on her finger as she stood speechless.

"I wanted you to have these and to be my special one and only. I didn't want you to forget me while I'm in Potlatch. I'll probably be there until Christmas. Will you be my girl?" he whispered in her ear.

"Oh yes. I promise I'll be true and not even think of anyone but you," the ardent-minded girl spoke in her most romantic tones. Her heart was all a flutter again as they embraced once more.

It stopped raining long enough for us to get home. George told me something that made my heart go "pit-a-pat" and I didn't want him to go to that old place at all. He said he'd write, so I'll have to exist on his letters until Christmas. Oh Gee! That seems an eternity away.

Saturday Sept. 2, 1922

Cleaned house. Went riding with the Lees after supper. There was just a lovely moon and I wished awfully that somebody was here to look at it with me.

Love's Plea

Pleading, pleading, because I want you dear.
Pleading, pleading, listen and hear.
Star eyes are shining, moon up above
My heart is pining, I want you my love.

P.E.T.

Monday Sept. 4, 1922

Labor day and I labored over the electric washing machine.

First day of school too and I'm not going. I feel sort of out of it when I see all the kids passing by on their way.

204

Toiling On

Toiling on thru countless ages, toiling o'er the wrecks of time,
Toiling on but never faltering, toiling to the heights sublime.
Toiling on but never weary, toiling on thru pain and strife,
Toiling on with hope undaunted, toiling to Eternal Life.
But oh, what rest and peace will be when our toil on Earth is done,
When we're with the King of Glory, and the crown of life we've won.

P.E.T.

Tuesday Sept. 5, 1922

A letter from George. I don't know whether to believe anything he says or not. Also such is the irony of fate—a letter from Helen giving me a "grandmotherly" lecture on a certain subject—the same that the first one dwells upon, but from an altogether different angle.

Wednesday Sept. 6, 1922

Another letter from George. He said he heard I was at a dance with some fellow. It made me laugh and made me mad too. Somebody is trying to stuff him, or he's trying to stuff me, I don't know which.

I had answered his first letter and written some nice things in it too, but I was so provoked I had to add an answer to his second that wasn't so nice.

Met Ruby Hylton downtown. Went up to see Cora Weeks for a few minutes. I hear Aunt Belle has been saying some pretty catty things about George and I getting together, but I shouldn't worry as long as we suit each other, it's none of her business. I don't see why the dickens she can't leave us alone. If I get stuck in the mud, I sure won't call for her to pull me out.

Sunday Sept. 10, 1922

Went to church. Say, but I was sure dumbfounded when I saw George there. Ruby, George and I went down town to get a paper and then out to Hylton's. I don't like to go out there 'cause I know Aunt Belle doesn't like the idea of George and I going together but I wanted to be with my beau most awfully bad.

After dinner Orvil, Ruby, Jewel and George and I went to Troy, and then back to Hylton's to do chores. Orvil milked and so forth and I separated the milk. Then we went to church.

When we came home, Lees hadn't gotten home so George and I strolled around town a while. I love to stroll with him, but I know I said some awfully crazy things. Sometimes I get so provoked at myself for saying things without thinking.

Thursday Sept. 14, 1922

. . . Went down town with the Lees tonight. The kids wanted to see Buster Brown, but his dog got sick, so they weren't performing tonight . . .

Monday Sept. 18, 1922

Washed. Mr. Lee went on a campaign trip to Grangeville, Stites and those places. He's running for Judge of the Supreme Court, you know. Mrs. Lee went to a Delta Gamma meeting tonight. College started today.

Wednesday Sept. 20, 1922

Billy Lee is seven years old today. Mrs. Lee made him a cake and he invited a few of his little friends over. They are out in the back yard now building a pen or something of the sort. I think the kids around this neighborhood will be the future carpenters of the town, they're always hammering on something. Mary Madeline included, in fact I think she's the most energetic of the lot. Mrs. Lee wanted a letter mailed and a book for Richard, so I went down town. On the way back I stopped in to see how Martha Reed was. She is up now but Ruby is still staying there. Cora Weeks was down there too, so we gossiped, looked at the catalog and tried on hats.

When I came home, I ate a piece of Billy's birthday cake and a cone of ice cream.

Friday, Sept. 29, 1922

Did a little bit of everything today. Cleaned up the guest room, my room. Mrs. Lee washed blankets and baby clothes (she's preparing for the stork again) and I hung them up.

Mrs. Lee went to a party this afternoon and I took care of the kids, they were sure a handful too. Mary Madeline was a cry baby, Richard had a grouch on and Billy was in a teasing mood. (And me all nerves.) So you can imagine what sort of a time we had.

Saturday Sept. 30, 1922

Cleaned up the house. George called this afternoon and wanted me to come down tonight. He said he had something to show me. He wouldn't tell me over the phone, said I'd have to see it in person.

When I got out there, I asked George what it was and he told me it was his hat. He had a new one so I admired it. But he told me he was just kidding me and gave me a wrist watch. He said he got one for his daughter too. That guy is too good to me.

Tuesday, Oct. 3, 1922

. . . The wind is blowing a gale outside and the lights went out a few minutes ago so we have to use candles. Wrote a letter to Roy, I haven't heard from him for a coon's age.

The romance continued to flourish through September and into October. George was generous with gifts, and Pearl was falling in love. He told her of his army experiences and other adventures in Texas. The man had the young woman totally in awe of his mystique.

By the middle of October, Pearl and George confided in Aunt Lillie about their future plans.

"I'm going to tell Aunt Lillie about our engagement," George teased the lovesick girl.

"Go ahead, but wait until I'm out of the room. If she gets mad I don't want to be around," Pearl confessed.

"Oh, no, you don't," he said. "You have to be in the room, too. If you try to run out on me, I'll hold on so you can't go." George jokingly gestured.

Pearl was nervous as George started to kid around with her in front of Aunt Lillie. With George being so much older, she wasn't sure how Auntie would react.

"I think I'm going to take this girl and marry her, Auntie. What would you think about that?" George questioned the matronly woman.

"Well, more power to you. Whoever does marry Pearl will surely be getting someone special," Aunt Lillie responded, thinking George was not really serious.

"Did you hear that, Pearl? Auntie believes you would make me a good wife. We're already engaged, Auntie," George chuckled.

"George , stop this kidding. It's not nice to put Pearl on like this," Aunt Lillie retorted as she gave George a frown and shook her finger at him.

"I'm not kidding. Tell her, sweetie; tell Auntie we really are engaged to be married," George prodded.

Mrs. Yearout looked puzzled at George's serious demeanor. "What's going on here? Is he telling the truth, Pearl?"

"Yes. We really are engaged," Pearl said shyly. "What do you think about it?"

Pearl respected Aunt Lillie so much; she had been so nice to her of late. She prayed the nice woman would think it was good.

"Well . . . if the two of you are serious, then I think it is fine." She paused to study the blush coming to Pearl's cheeks. "When are you planning to get married?" Auntie finally asked.

"We are going to wait until I graduate from high school. We were thinking June of next year would be a good time," Pearl answered, now with more confidence.

"We want to keep our plans to ourselves for right now. You are the only one we have told. Please don't tell anyone else. We don't want a lot of talk," he added, "if you know what I mean."

Monday Oct. 16, 1922

Washed. Aunt Lillie called up this noon and wants me to come out tonight. Went out about seven thirty. Aunt Lillie wants me to go to Coeur d'Alene on a fishing trip with them. Gee I don't think I can get off work. I told George I wouldn't ask Mrs. Lee and for him to tell Auntie not to call her up as she had threatened. But say, wouldn't we have a swell time though. I'd love to do it if I could.

Wednesday Oct. 18, 1922

Cleaned upstairs, waxed the stairs. Mrs. Lee's sister and brother and their little boy Frederick are coming tomorrow for the Idaho—Pullman game.

Aunt Lillie called me this afternoon to see if I couldn't go on that trip the first of the week. Start Sunday after church and stay until about Wednesday. I hummed and hawed around about it but she made me promise to ask Mrs. Lee and call her up about seven tonight. So I asked the lady and she was awfully nice about it, but she is going to have bridge club Tuesday night and she needs me until then. She said she'd be glad to let me go Wednesday. I called up Aunt Lillie tonight and told her, she said she'd ask George and "Papa" and let me know tomorrow. Hope things can be arranged so we can go. The biggest difficulty is the weather, we want it to stay nice so we can sleep out in the tent and camp. Here's hopin' things turn out all right.

Friday Oct. 20, 1922

The Lees and Shieldses went to the game this afternoon and I took care of the kids. We sure had a heck of a time too. They wouldn't do anything I told them to. Frederick was pretty good, but Billy was the limit and Mary and Richard were, Oh—just in between.

Mrs. Lee is trying to prevail on her brother's family to stay until Sunday. Heck!! I'm dead tired tonight, so you can guess how bad I want them to stay.

Idaho got licked 17 to 9. Mr. Lee and Mr. Shields were awfully blue about it.

Saturday Oct. 21, 1922

Saw George up town and he walked me home. He said if I could go out tonight to call Aunt Lillie and she'd let him know. He called me again about 7:30 P.M. We'd just gotten thru supper and I had a million things to do, dishes to wash, kitchen and dining room to clean up, etc., and an awful headache to boot. I supposed Lees and Shieldses were going out. He told me to ask them and I said I didn't want to. I know I made him mad and I suppose he's feeling bluer than this ink just now. I just hate to hurt him, but he was so insistent. I knew I couldn't get all thru with everything much before 8:30 P.M. and that's too late to start anywhere. Oh Gee but I was bluer than blue. Everything seems to be going wrong.

Billy was awfully mean tonight. If he keeps on taking his spite out by·hitting me I think I'll pack my bags. The only way to bring him to his senses when he gets started is to "treat him rough" and I'm not going to beat up other people's kids.

The Shieldses are going to stay until tomorrow, Oh heck! I suppose I'll have to stay at home all day.

I'd better take a bath and go to bed, I'm so tired. If I don't I'll be a regular grouch tomorrow, and if I should happen to get to be with my beau, he might take a notion to ditch me.

Pearl was becoming very attached to the Yearout family, especially Aunt Lillie. Lillie was taking on the role of the mother Pearl needed so desperately in her teen years.

Even though Pearl had lived with the Lees for almost three years. Madeline Lee assumed the role of employer instead of mother. Pearl was the live-in housekeeper, not an accepted member of the family. The two roles were very different. The Lees liked her and treated her well, but the young teenager needed an older and wiser female to advise her on personal matters. Mrs. Lee was not a person the young woman could confide in. Lillie Yearout, on the other hand, was compassionate and took Pearl under her protecting wing to listen, to encourage, and counsel whenever the occasion arose.

Pearl wasn't able to go out to the Lyons farm very often anymore, so Mrs. Yearout was taking over the mothering the young woman still needed.

The Yearouts son Paul was only seventeen but was very much his own person. He had the gypsy wanderlust and looked to adventure and excitement anywhere he could find it. He was a constant worry to his parents, sometime getting angry and leaving home for several days.

Paul also had a very sweet side to his personality, and most of the young people liked him. The fact that he was also quite good-looking added to his ability to attract the opposite sex. He never seemed to lack for friends to do activities with.

Pearl liked Paul in a brotherly way now that she was adopting the Yearouts as her new family.

Uncle Charley Yearout was the preacher for the Church of the Brethren where Pearl was a member. He was quite a bit older than Lillie, and the generation gap between him and Paul was definitely a factor in the teenager's rebellion. Uncle Charley had a lot to say across the pulpit, but sometimes at home he was moody and quiet.

Sunday Oct. 22, 1922

Went to church. After church we went home with Aunt Lillie. Paul was home but he was in bed when we got there (12:30), lazy bones. He got up in time for dinner. In the evening Paul put on the frying pan to cook some eggs. I wasn't a bit hungry when I started in, but I ate an egg, some pudding, and a piece of cake at that.

I asked Auntie what she thought of my beau. First time I've gotten to see her in private since last Sunday. She said she thought he was a fine man, and she said Paul thought he was nice and good looking too.

Tuesday Oct. 24, 1922

Stork came about 2:30 A.M. this morning and left a five pound baby girl for Mrs. Lee to take care of. She slipped and fell last night so that hastened the baby's arrival, wasn't expected until next month. Course that knocked our plans for the fishing trip in the head. Aunt Lillie called up this afternoon and asked me if I'd be ready in the morning. She was awfully disappointed when I told her I couldn't go. They had everything ready you know, and now we'll have to give it up for good.

Ellen said she'd take my place here, but Mr. Lee wouldn't consider it at all. I didn't care so much, but I hated to disappoint Aunt Lillie so.

Wednesday Oct. 25, 1922

Cleaned up the upstairs thoroughly and the rest of the house just straightened up. Mrs. Shields is expected today. Miss Talbot stays here nights, comes up in the afternoon and keeps Mary in the morning.

George said last night that he wouldn't work here now for five dollars a week, but I told him he wasn't me. It probably will be heck, but I'm going some place else when second semester of school starts anyway. (At least those are my intentions.) I think I've stayed here long enough anyway. The kids won't mind me, and the grown-ups aren't much more than strangers to me although I have stayed here nearly three years. Aunt Lillie says there are better days ahead!! Let's hope so!!

Saturday Oct. 28, 1922

George gave me a nice gold pencil. I love it because—well you know, "The Giver." Got me a hat. George doesn't like it very well. Says it's too "kiddish." I said something that hurt him and it made me feel so badly.

Went to the show after I finished my shopping. George said he and Uncle Charley talked over our "case" and Uncle Charley said he thought it perfectly all right.

Monday Oct. 30, 1922

Washed. Mr. Lee started for Coeur d'Alene, Sandpoint and some of those places this morning. Doing a little more campaigning before election.

Tuesday Oct. 31, 1922

Ironed. Went down to the hospital to take some things to the baby and get a Jack O' Lantern for Mary Madeline. Miss Talbot and I went Halloweening with the kids.

George and I went out to Aunt Lillie's later and played Rook until about 11:30 P.M. George doesn't want me to stay at the Lees' this winter, but if he really doesn't want me to, he'll have to explain to Mrs. Lee I'm not going to.

Tuesday Nov. 7 1922

Election day. Mr. Lee is awfully busy. Hope he gets elected. Got a letter from Helen and one from Roy today.

Wednesday Nov. 8, 1922

Paper said Mr. Lee was elected but they haven't all the returns yet and he isn't quite sure.

Thursday Nov. 9, 1922

...Mr. Lee is sure he was elected now and they're making plans for going to Boise to live, so that will relieve me of the necessity of telling them I'm not going to stay here after Christmas. All winds blow together to make fair weather if we don't meddle with them too much. But just let them take their own course, n'est pas? (I'm going to be a Socrates when I get big.)

Friday Nov. 10, 1922

... Phone rings about every two seconds for Mr. Lee, people wanting to congratulate him I s'pose.

George and I decided to go to the show, pretty good one at the Kenworthy. He told me something that made me despise him for just a minute. I practically asked him though and I admired him for telling me but it made me a wee bit disappointed. I guess I'd put him on too high a pedestal and it hurt me, you know. To find out that he wasn't quite what I'd thought he was. In fact, I'd really rather he hadn't told me the truth. Oh Gee! I shouldn't be writing this but I had to get it out of my system someway. I've been thinking about it all day.

Saturday Nov. 11, 1922

... Took the kids down to the Armistice Day Parade. Saw George, walked home with him. Left the kids down at their dad's office.

211

George called up this evening and wanted me to come down and see our pictures. I was so blooming tired to do anything so I told him I didn't want to come and I think it made him mad. I'm awfully sorry, but I wish he wouldn't be so insistent . . .''

Sunday Nov. 12, 1922

Went to church. Evil spirits must be at large. Didn't get to arrange with George about this afternoon. But I'm not going to have people thinking I'm simply crazy about him and he doesn't care a thing about me. Maybe he'll call up. Lovely way for engaged people to act isn't it? Maybe we'll have a calm ending, the beginning has sure been blustery enough. Here's hopin'.

Tuesday Nov. 14, 1922

. . . Lees went to Bridge Club tonight. Baby woke up about eight, and stayed awake until they came home about nine thirty. Gee it makes me nervous to have a baby cry. Did everything for her I knew to do, but I think she was hungry and I couldn't appease that you know.

Sunday Nov. 19, 1922

Went to Auntie's for dinner. It snowed tonight so I stayed at Auntie's all night.

Monday Nov. 20, 1922

Got home this morning at 5:30 A.M., did yesterday's dishes and started washing. Mrs. Lee heard me come in this morning and she said she didn't like to have me stay all night, so guess I'd better swear off.

With Mr. Lee being elected to Supreme Court Judge of Idaho, it meant he would have to move his family to Boise. They planned to leave in January and really wanted Pearl to go with them. It was just before Thanksgiving that Mr. Lee talked to his live-in working girl about the move.

"Pearl, we would like to invite you to go to Boise with us when we move," the judge announced.

"What do you want me down there for?" Pearl replied, trying to make light of the invitation rather than come right out and say she didn't want to move. She still had a hard time communicating with Mr. Lee, even though she had lived under his roof for several years. She always considered him the dictating master of the house, not a father or friend.

"You can go to school down in Boise just as well as you can here, and anyway, it would be a nice trip for you." Mr. Lee added. "Of course you would have to be away from that fellow of yours for a while."

Pearl blushed scarlet and didn't know what to say.

212

Mr. Lee picked up the teasing. "Maybe if you and your beau had a falling out, you would take a notion to go with us," he continued. "Mrs. Lee decided she'd better do all of her traveling before she was married. Maybe that would be a good idea for you to follow the same plan."

Pearl giggled a little as she cleaned up the dishes from the table and took them to the kitchen. Mr. Lee had hit really close to the reason Pearl was confused about moving, and she wanted to avoid giving the judge her answer. She hoped they wouldn't press too hard for her to go. She couldn't possibly leave Moscow and George now they were engaged.

Friday Nov. 24, 1922
. . . Got a letter from Mrs. Bethmann today (the woman my sister Helen is living with). Can't understand what she's trying to get at unless it's something about Uncle Clarence's "Will."

Sunday Nov. 26, 1922
Went to church. Ruby wanted me to go home with her so I did. Showed George the letter from Mrs. Bethmann and asked his advice. He told me to consult Mr. Lee and have him investigate the matter because it might mean quite a lot to me. Gee I hate to do it, it's such a muddled up affair. I'm afraid I'll never be able to explain it to him clearly, but I guess I'd better try or I'll get "Hail Columbia" from George.

We went over to Aunt Lillie's and she thinks it's advisable to get Mr. Lee to see about that Will too. I may (small chance) be an heiress.

SNOW BLIND

Tuesday Nov. 28, 1922

... First real snow of the season fell last night and this morning and something in the soft whiteness of the landscape or something about the air caused me to have a poetic streak. (Almost like paralytic stroke, n'est-pas?) So as I was a a-sweepin' an' dustin' I made a wee sonnet centered around that age old theme of a departed loved one. The theme that has been sung thru the ages and probably will continue to be sung until the Messiah comes again and Heaven and Earth are merged into one and there is no more parting of loves and friends.

The City of Lights

When the weeping willows sigh and the birds make sweet melody,
Where the brook melancholy murmers by, flowing solemnly to the sea,
It is there that my footsteps stray when I pine for the love that is fled,
For the spring time when you were near and the dream things are dead.
Then somehow my spirit arises out of its gloom and sight and soars,
From my heart's sad brooding. To you in the City of Lights.

P.E.T.

Rather silly disjointed affair N'est-ce-pas? But I "kinda" like the last part. Me thinks it savors a wee bit of Milton (wouldn't he be scandalized if he could read this?). Gee!! I'd better get out of this sentimental mood, at least not put any more of it on paper. 'Cause anybody happening to read this would think I was a complex of some old Celtic philosopher or somethin' of a sort what with me brogue an' all that is.

Wednesday Nov. 29, 1922

Invited out to Yearouts' for a four day holiday leave of absence. ... Auntie advised me about my legal problems and I think what she suggested is what I'll do.

"Pearl, I've been thinking about that letter and your legal matter with the will," Auntie remarked while she and the young woman were working in the kitchen getting ready for Thanksgiving. "I know you're afraid to bring up your family history with Mr. Lee. Why don't you write to Mrs. Bethmann and find out what she is doing for your sister about it? Perhaps you can simply send for some papers to fill out and it can all be handled through the mail."

214

"That's a good idea," Pearl responded as she heaved a sigh of relief. "Maybe I can handle everything myself and won't have to say anything to Mr. Lee. I just hate telling people about my past. It's so shameful having criminals for parents. I hope no one that doesn't really love me ever finds out my terrible hidden secrets," Pearl confessed to this woman she trusted with all her heart.

"If by some chance you can't handle the matter by yourself, I suggest you go and see Judge Forney. He's a good man and probably easier to talk to than Mr. Lee," Auntie advised.

Pearl took her suggestion and wrote a letter that very day.

Answered Mrs. Bethmann's letter today, and learned to swear over my sewin', naughty child, but Gee, it's provokin' when those threads won't behave. Guess I'd better get to bed, goin' to see my beau tomorrow and better get my beauty nap. (I sure need it. Not the nap so much as the other.)

Thursday Nov. 30, 1922

... Went to Thanksgiving service and then to Auntie's for dinner.

Paul came home from Potlatch about 10:30 P.M. Auntie didn't know he was coming.

Otto and Aunt Belle tried to talk me into going to Boise. (Good way to get George and I to bust up) but I said "Nix."

Sunday Dec. 3, 1922

"Snowed an awful lot last night, so Auntie called up and said there would be no church. Read to Richard until dinner time. Auntie called again and wanted me to come out this afternoon. Paul said he was awfully lonesome and for me to get George and come out. But I haven't heard a peep from that child, must be snowed under. Hope he calls pretty soon, if he don't I'm going out there anyway, too darned lonesome for any use around here. Here's hopin'.

Went down to the post office to mail a letter, met Billy and Mrs. Lee on the way, so coasted with Billy down First Street. Got a paper to take to Auntie, then walked out there.

George came and the group of us played Rook and Pit all evening. George and I had to come home in the snow storm. He said I didn't have any nerve and made me promise to ask Mr. Lee about that "Will" if I got a chance. Auntie wants me to see Judge Forney.

George constantly pressed Pearl about the "will" matter. It seemed of late that was all he could talk about. He was very interested to find out if his fiancée would be coming into money or property in the near future. Even though he knew she didn't want to discuss certain past problems with her employer, George was more interested in finding out the information than Pearl's feelings.

Tuesday Dec. 5, 1922

. . . Mrs. Lee went to a Delta Gamma meeting tonight. Best chance in the world to consult the Judge and finally did. Oh Gee! I simply had to force myself to do it, but knew if I didn't then I never would. I wanted to be able to tell George I had some nerve after all. Mr. Lee said he would look after it for me. Oh, but I sure felt as if the responsibility of the whole kingdom had been lifted from my shoulders. That thing had been a dead weight to me ever since I told George about it. Not so much because I was so terribly interested in it but because every time I saw George he would bawl me out about not asking Mr. Lee about it.

Friday Dec. 8, 1922

Richard had his tonsils out today. Too deep snow for Miss Talbot to come after the children, so I took them over in a taxi. Sewed this afternoon. Everybody gone, awfully lonesome.

Saturday Dec. 9, 1922

Woke up with an awfully sore throat and a headache. Cleaned up the house and ironed some of the baby's things. Mrs. Lee went to club. Billy came home sick from Miss Talbot's this morning, so he's in bed and Richard's on the couch. Mary ate some toothpaste and nail white, so she's puffy under the eyes and pretty pale, but she's not sick. Regular hospital around this place.

George called up this afternoon. I was so hoarse I could scarcely talk and I was so tired. Mrs. Lee could hear all I said so I just answered in one syllables and he accused me of being mad. Wants me to go out to Auntie's tomorrow. Will if I can, I'm most awfully blue an' tired 'n' everything.

When the sick young woman received the telephone call from Auntie on Sunday morning announcing there would be no church this morning because of the blizzard outside, Pearl not only felt sick from the flu symptoms; she also felt heartsick. The thought of not being with her friends at least one day a week brought the ailing girl to her feet.

Aunt Lillie had invited her to come out to the house for dinner, but with all the snow and wind no one was willing to take a car or team out in the storm.

216

Sunday Dec. 10, 1922

Snow, snow, snow, snow!!! Oh yes and some wind, is all around this place.

Mr. Lee is trying to make Boise attractive to me by telling me of its wonders. It believe I'd go if it wasn't for George. Hope I can go to Auntie's this afternoon.

No on can take me out, so if I go I'll have to wade thru drifts, but I'm blue enough that I'm afraid wading the Pacific to get to see some of my friends, as Billy says, would be inviting.

Walked out to Aunt Lillie's. Had an awful cold and felt dizzy, but just couldn't stay at home, too awfully blue. Got an ear ache and felt just awfully punk. George, Auntie and Paul hadn't realized I was so sick. Combined, they persuaded me not to go home tonight.

Monday Dec. 11, 1922

Auntie didn't call me so slept until 10:30 A.M. Still feeling pretty punk. Auntie called Mrs. Lee and told her I was sick.

Paul made some cookies this afternoon. They were good too.

Tuesday Dec. 12, 1922

Mr. Lee called up this morning to find out when I'd be home, but Gee, I sure don't feel much like workin', still dizzy and have a temperature.

Thursday Dec. 14, 1922

Lees getting pretty cross, wants me to walk in, but darned if I'm going to do it.

Friday Dec. 15, 1922

Mrs. Lee called up and said they couldn't get out with the car, but for me to try and find some way to come in. Tried to get the neighbor, but no one is out and about much. No one even passed by this afternoon.

The telephone rang three times before Auntie was able to dry her hands and answer it. The woman on the other and spoke firmly and gruffly as she asked to speak to Pearl.

Auntie covered the microphone end of the phone and softly spoke to the nervous young woman. "It's Mrs. Lee, and she doesn't sound very pleasant," she quietly stated. "Remember what I told you. The offer stands firm."

"Hello." Pearl spoke meekly in her still-hoarse voice.

The woman on the other end was neither meek nor patient. "Pearl, this is Madeline Lee. I thought I told you I needed you to come home for sure tonight. Mr. Lee was gone and I had to cancel my meeting because you didn't show up. This is very irresponsible of you, and I cannot tolerate your absence any longer."

"I'm sorry," Pearl responded. "I was not able to find anyone to bring me in."

"Well, young lady," Mrs. Lee continued, "when you want to go out to the Yearouts' you don't seem to mind walking. You still have two feet, don't you? If you don't come back here this evening, then you needn't come back at all."

Pearl listened as the woman on the other end of the line hung up the telephone without even saying good-bye. The sensitive young woman's eyes began to fill with tears at the harsh words spoken by this person whom she had lived with and worked for nearly four years. Pearl had never wanted to leave the Lees' this way. She had hoped the family cared enough about her heath and would be understanding, but she now realized they only cared about her as an employee who wasn't doing her job.

The weather outside was still freezing, and Auntie couldn't get her car started. It would be morning before they could get a wagon or sleigh to take Pearl back into town.

After much discussion, it was decided what Pearl would do in the morning.

Saturday Dec. 16, 1922

Called Mrs. Lee up this morning' and told her I'd be in after my clothes today. George called up so Auntie told him and he said he'd be able to get Tom's sleigh and take me to get my things. Gee, I hate facing them.

Mrs. Lee asked me to stay, but I told her I'd already made my plans. I'd just as well go now as later when they go to Boise.

Billy's sick and Richard's just getting over having his tonsils removed. I feel sorry for them, but I wouldn't face the Judge for anything right now. Just as soon stand in front of a loaded cannon with a man behind it just ready to fire 'cause what he wouldn't say and look, wouldn't be worth saying and looking.

The boys about froze while I was getting my things ready and it took me an age. I didn't suppose I'd be over three quarters of an hour.

I had a letter from Roy and one from Robert Earl there. Robert sent me a picture.

Tuesday Dec. 19, 1922

Felt much better today. Auntie and I went to town to do some shoppin', mailed Robert and Roy a tie and Helen a pair of silk stockings.

Thursday Dec. 21, 1922

Auntie went to club this morning. George called up and said he'd be up this afternoon so I changed my dress and sat down on the lounge to sew. Paul was reading and he began teasing me to tell him whether I was engaged or not. I wouldn't tell him, so be coaxed and threatened and everything to try to get me to tell.

I asked George if I could tell Paul and he said no at first and then that he didn't care. Paul began to tease me again just after George went and I told him no, until he swore that George had already told him we were. So I told him we were, but then Paul was really surprised, 'cause he was just kidding me. Say, but I was mad at that kid, and I felt like a fool. He swore he wouldn't tell anybody and he'd better not either.

Paul and his mother had words tonight. Gee! But he has a temper and when he once gets started there's no stopping until he gets cooled down.

Paul said he'd tell me something some time, I'd like to know what it is.

Sunday Dec. 24, 1922

Too muddy for Auntie and I to go to church, so stayed at home and got ready for tomorrow. Paul and I got into a snow fight this morning and Auntie felt like giving us both a spanking.

Paul is cross this afternoon because he found out Auntie didn't get him a coat.

Monday Dec. 25, 1922

MERRY CHRISTMAS!! Santa brought me a leather purse and a Kodak (from George), a appliqued apron from Auntie, and a collar and cuff set from my sister Helen.

Tuesday Dec. 26, 1922

Auntie and I went on a strike today, too blamed tired to do anything. Paul and I had planned to go to the show, but it was raining too much.

Aunt Belle called up and wanted us to come down. Dick said we could use his team and hack, so we went. We finally persuaded Paul to go along, that kid is developing an awful disposition, tries to go contrary to his mother and dad every time.

We had a good time, the girls helped me with my basket for the auction Thursday night. Paul made me peeved tonight, of course I brought it on myself, but I got rather "Hostile," as he says.

Thursday Dec. 27, 1922

Rained most of the day. Auntie and I worked like troopers to get the house cleaned up for the activity here tonight. Had a regular H—— of a time around here this morning. Paul is cross etc. etc., nearly called off the basket social, but Marceys, Harts, Lyonses and some of the rest said they were coming so we didn't.

George didn't come this evening. I was in the dumps the first part of the evening, but we got to playing games etc. so I got out of them.

After the games the bidding started for the baskets of food.

219

"OK, men!" Uncle Charley started. "What do you bid for this next basket with the lavender-striped paper and the big white bow?"

Pearl's stomach began to develop butterflies as Uncle Charley described her basket. She had so wished George was here; he would have for sure paid a big price for it if he had too. He wouldn't let any other guy eat a basket supper prepared by his girl, Pearl reassured herself. However, he wasn't here and she was afraid Warren or Ed would buy it. Both of them were always making eyes at her when George wasn't around.

"One dollar!" Lloyd Fisher spoke up.

"Two dollars!" the voice of Warren Trout yelled from the kitchen doorway.

"Two fifty!" the third voice joined in the bidding.

Pearl turned around and spotted Paul raising his hand with the bid. She starred at him with desperate eyes and pleaded with young Yearout through her expression to buy the basket.

"Three dollars!" Lloyd barked out before the bidding could stop.

"Three fifty!" Warren called out.

"Five dollars!" Paul stated with firmness. "Ahs" and "ohs" came from the other people in the room as Paul stopped the bidding with the five-dollar amount.

"Going once . . . twice . . . sold to Paul for five dollars!"

Pearl heaved a sigh of relief as the sheepish grin took over her face. Several of the couples gathered together in various rooms of the Yearouts' home to eat their purchased meals. Three couples ate in Paul's room, and they had a great time. Pearl saw a new fun side of Paul exhibited that night, and she wished he were her real brother.

Aunt Belle said that George had a woman down in Troy he went to see tonight. They'll tell anything. That's probably one of George's stories he made up to fool them.

With Pearl now living with the Yearouts the house was very crowded. Aunt Lillie and Uncle Charley had a bedroom upstairs, and Paul had a room downstairs. There was a small cubbyhole room also upstairs; however, it was not large enough for a bedroom. A small cot was there in case someone needed to stay overnight.

Pearl was given a small closet near the bathroom for her clothing, and the living room couch was designated as her bed. It wasn't very

220

private and she had to endure all the traffic of the household coming and going, yet the young maiden was just happy to be near her friends.

Saturday Dec. 30, 1922

George came home from Troy today and was pretty sick. Paul and I went down to see him this afternoon. That kid really is sick. His throat is swollen terribly. I played nurse for a while.

Paul went down town tonight. Had a run-in with his mother and father first though. He came back about 10:30 P.M. I couldn't persuade him to go to bed, he wanted me to let him sleep on the couch, and me sleep in his room. I knew Auntie wouldn't like that, so I stayed up and read and talked until after two.

Sunday Dec. 31, 1922

Went to church. After church went to Hylton's for dinner.

George feels better today, but he has an awful color. We persuaded him to come up here so we could doctor him up. We watched the old year out and the New Year in.

Monday Jan. 1, 1923

Paul was terribly out of sorts today, said last night he was going to make a New Year's resolution not to speak a kind word to a woman for a year. He sure is living up to it. Auntie had some Cherry Wine for medicinal purposes and Paul happened to find it today. Auntie hid it from him but he found it again, so she gave him and George some.

Tuesday Jan. 2, 1923

George went home this afternoon. Paul still in a bad humor. Auntie and I are trying to persuade George to go to a doctor, but he won't. Auntie's awfully afraid he has Tuberculosis. Grief I hope he hasn't.

Sunday Jan, 7, 1923

Auntie and Uncle Charley went to Reed's for dinner. George came home from church with me and I got dinner for him and Paul.

George is getting to be awfully different, he's so irritable and cross lately, everybody notices it. Maybe it's because he doesn't feel well, but you know, if I had met him now instead of when I did, I'm afraid I wouldn't have fallen in love with him so easily. As it is of course I love him yet, but it hurts me to have him act the way he does. George simply won't listen to reason, he goes coyote hunting nearly every day and he doesn't feel like it at all. If he doesn't be careful. Oh Gee, I'd better quit—lay off or something of the sort.

George went home early, didn't feel well. Paul got mad and went down to Hylton's for a while.

Tuesday Jan. 9, 1923

George came up this evening. We started playing Rook, but George and Paul got mad. George went home without saying good-bye. I felt like bawling for a minute. I hope George acquires a better disposition before we get married, and I sure pity the girl that gets Paul. He's like the little girl with the curl right in the middle of her forehead. When he's good, he's very very good, but when he's bad he's "Horrid."

Saturday Jan. 13, 1923

Auntie went down town his afternoon to get Paul some shoes and an overcoat. Overcoat too small, so Paul and I went down tonight and changed it. I like the one he got just awfully well.

Sunday, January 16, 1923

George and Paul were sitting at the kitchen table playing Rook when Auntie came in.

"I think you should stay the night again, George. With you still being in poor health the cold night air won't do your illness any good. You can use the cot upstairs again," Auntie instructed. "I sure hope Paul comes home soon," the mother remarked as she looked out the front window in hopes of seeing her rebellious son coming.

"I'm sure he'll be home within the hour. The town pretty much closes down after the movies are over," Pearl commented in an effort to put the worried woman's mind at ease.

About thirty minutes after Uncle Charley and Aunt Lillie went to bed, Paul came home. He had been downtown, and as soon as Pearl saw him she knew something was the matter. He had a strange look in his eyes and staggered ever so slightly as he walked into his bedroom and closed the door.

George had his back to the front entrance and hadn't seen Paul, only heard him come in.

"Where did Paul go?" George asked Pearl as he turned to look for young Yearout.

"He went straight to his bedroom and closed the door. He must be mad about something again," she responded.

"Well, now that I know Paul is in bed and won't be out here nosin' around, I guess I'll go to bed, too. I'm pretty tired," George remarked.

Pearl had just made her bed on the couch and was preparing to settle down for the night when Paul got up and went into the living room. He sat down in the big chair and lit up a cigarette.

"So, did you and lover boy have a romantic evening?" Paul asked in a slurred and garbled voice. "If you were my girl . . ." He paused, losing his train of thought. "I had a girlfriend once."

Pearl was sure now of what she had only suspected when Paul first came home. He was drunk. Somewhere he had got hold of hard cider. He was now in an amorous mood.

"I think you had better go to bed and get some sleep," Pearl strongly suggested to the intoxicated boy.

He pulled himself out of the chair and weaved over to the couch and started to sit down. Pearl was able to get to her feet in time to push him back to a standing position.

"Oh, no, you don't. You need to go to your own bed." she said again.

"I was just going to have you sit on my lap," he blubbered. "Don't you want to sit on my lap?"

"No! I want you to go to your room and get some sleep. It's late." Pearl pushed him from behind and guided the stumbling young man back toward his bedroom.

George had heard the commotion and went downstairs again, just in time to see Paul go back to his room. George was angry because Paul had been out in the living room when Pearl was already in bed. George didn't like any other guy being around his girl, and especially not Paul.

Pearl could see the fire in George's eyes as he entered the room. "What's the matter?" Pearl asked the angry-faced man.

"I don't like this whole situation. It's a damned zoo around here. I don't want you to live here anymore," George cursed. "I'm leaving, and if you want to be my girl, then you had better leave, too."

He started for the front door, where his coat and shoes were, and intended to leave the house.

"Wait!" Pearl pleaded. "What's wrong? You're acting as if I've done something wrong. You at least owe me an explanation. I can't undo something if I don't know what I've done." She was confused by his actions, but she took hold of his arm and pulled him back toward the couch. "Come on, tell me why you are so angry all of a sudden."

George sat pouting for a few minutes before Pearl finally broke the deadening silence.

"Is it something about Paul?" she finally asked.

"He's starting to get on my nerves," George immediately responded. "I don't like the way he looks and talks to you. I don't want you around him anymore."

"Are you jealous of Paul?" the stunned girl questioned in amazement. "You don't need to be jealous of him. We are like brother and sister, nothing more."

"I don't like you and him living under the same roof," George replied in a possessive tone. "Paul thinks he's such a ladies' man."

"Well, I can't just leave here. I don't have anywhere else to go. Anyway, I start school tomorrow and I can't offend Auntie. She had promised to help me get ready for graduation and our wedding in the spring. I really need her help. Please understand." Pearl continued her logic and pleading, "It's hard on me not having my own mother to help me. Auntie is now like a mother to me." She spoke in soft tones, hoping to calm the fuming man. George finally mellowed and went back upstairs to bed.

The young woman was confused and worried about this new side of her finances that was coming to the surface. She felt she still loved George, yet she didn't like the way his once-sweet personality was changing into that of a possessive, controlling creature.

METAMORPHOSIS: FROM CHARMER TO SNAKE

Monday Jan. 15, 1923

Started school today. Registered.

George came up this evening, walked downtown with him to get some cigarettes. Talked matters over. Bawled him out for getting so mad over nothing. He said if I hadn't made him stay last night and reason things out with him, he would have left town the next morning, he was so mad. Lovely way for him to act, he's liable to do something like that after we're married.''

Wednesday Jan. 17, 1923

Paul and George sawed wood today. George had a babyish streak on tonight and accused me of not treating him like I used to. He expects me to mush around him all the time I guess, but believe me, I'm not going to do it. He makes me tired, blames me for everything and thinks he is a perfect saint who could never do anything wrong.

Auntie met me downtown after school tonight and we went to see Judge Forney. I told him about the estate and he said he'd tend to it for me.

Friday Jan. 19, 1923

Auntie and I washed this evening after I came home from school.

George came up and talked for a while. Paul came home just as Auntie was going to bed. She thought he went to bed also, but he got a jug of cider and he and Lyle went out and had a spree.

George left to go home just as the now-drunken Paul was coming home. The two passed each other on the road.

Paul stomped in the front door and immediately began ranting and raving about George. ''That lying son-of-a-gun was telling all sorts of things about me, wasn't he?'' Paul yelled. ''Lyle and I heard him tell you about where I go and what I do. Well, he's a big liar, and anyway, it's none of his business. I waited at the end of the road until he left here. If I would have come in while he was here I'm afraid I would have killed him,'' Paul continued to rant on.

''Please calm down, Paul,'' Pearl pleaded. ''George is gone now. The two of you are at odds right now; I'm sure neither one of you really means what you say about the other.''

''Well, who does he think he is anyway? He's no angel himself, you know. I know what he does and who he goes to see in Troy,'' Paul slurred out. ''I could tell you . . . a few . . . things that would . . . make you hate him. . . .'' Paul calmed as the intoxication clouded his mind

225

and he started to doze off. He slumped his rubberlike body down onto the couch.

Pearl knew he couldn't stay on the sofa or she wouldn't be able to go to bed. She took his hand and tried to encourage him to get up and go to bed. The limp body was impossible to move as Paul seemed to have passed out.

The sound of a thud outside the window turned Pearl's attention from the drunk on her bed to the noise she had just heard. She went to the window and looked into the darkness. All she could see was the frozen snow that was caked on the ground. Her inner soul felt there was someone outside the window hiding from her sight. Her intuition sensed George was still near the house, watching and listening.

She went back to the drowsy young man on the couch and tried to get him conscious enough to leave her bed. Paul came to just long enough to yell some garbled profanity and take a swing with his arm in Pearl's direction.

It took almost two hours of trying before she was able to get Paul off the couch and into his room. The whole time, Pearl felt in her bones that George was outside waiting and listening.

Sunday Jan. 21, 1923

George came up to go to church with me. On the way to church we had it out. He's been so different and everything that I just can't like him as well as I used to. Auntie thinks he's jealous of Paul. You know, if he'd be jealous now, what would he be after we were married? I couldn't look at another man without him flying in a rage and making home a perfect inferno or something equally as awful. So I thought I'd just let things drift and if he kept on developing a disagreeable disposition and everything the best thing we could do would be to call it quits. Gee!!! but this life is sure heck sometimes.

George and I got talking and I told him just how things stood. He promised everything under the sun, even to giving up his lodges and joining my church, if I wanted him to.

Tuesday Jan. 23, 1923

Paul started to walk to school with me this morning. George met us by Brummunda's and Paul went on with Ted. George told me not to think hard of him for coming, because he was going to the doctor and just wanted to see me. He asked me if I thought Paul would think he was jealous and I told him that was the only logical thing he could think. He swore he wasn't. I wish George wouldn't be so perfectly silly about me, it makes me sort of disgusted.

226

Friday Jan. 26, 1923

Woke up with a cold, but went to school anyway.

George came up this evening and we went to the show. Auntie thought I shouldn't 'cause I didn't feel well, but we went anyway.

George went home about eleven, Auntie and Uncle Charley got home about two. Paul didn't come home at all tonight.

Saturday Jan. 27, 1923

Everybody sort of on the "lazy list" today.

Paul came home this evening. Had some girl's watch and told me a wild tale about going to Troy etc.

Play the Game

Play the game my brother, play it hard and fast.
For the numbered days you're given, this may be your last.
Play the game my brother, of good times get your share.
Play the game my brother, but play it on the square.

P.E.T.

Monday Jan. 29, 1923

Auntie said I'd better not go to school today, because I felt so sick. George called up to see how I was. Said he'd be up after a while with Paul. The two of them are on speaking terms again. The guys all stayed at Hylton's last night after going sleigh riding.

You know, I should hate Paul, but some ways I can't. I so want him to be my brother, but Oh Gee—life is a terribly mixed up affair, at best.

Thursday Feb. 1, 1923

. . . Washed dishes and straightened up the house. Had just laid down when George came. . . .

She struggled to get off the couch and answer the door because she felt so "punk" from the flu bug that was in her body. As she opened the door, a cold blast of air rushed in, causing the shawl on her shivering shoulders to be swept off and fall to the floor.

George was waiting to come inside and into the warmth of his fiancée's arms. He expected a more romantic reception than the ailing girl was in a mind to give. The man could sense the tenderness and awe he had once received each time he saw Pearl was no longer being displayed by her.

227

"Oh, hi [sniffle, sniffle]. . . . Come in before you let all the warm air out," Pearl instructed.

"That was a pretty chilly greeting. A guy certainly expects more than that from his special girl," George expressed.

"I'm sorry." Pearl explained, "I guess this darn cold has really got me feeling blue."

"Come here," he insisted as he pulled the sniffling young woman down beside him on the sofa. "It's not the sickness that's got you blue; it's me. I can tell by the way you have been acting the past week you just don't love me anymore."

"You're just being silly," she said, trying to hide her real feelings.

George was not fooled one bit and could see right through Pearl's empty words. "That's it. I guessed it, didn't I?" he questioned.

"It's not that I don't still love you; it's . . . ," she stammered, trying to find a easy way to say what she felt. "It's just since that Sunday night when you got so mad about Paul and wouldn't listen to reason . . . well, I simply don't like the way you acted then and since about Paul."

George immediately went on the defensive and started to lay blame on everyone and everything except himself. "Well, it's not my fault things are the way they are around here. It's more your fault than mine," he reasoned. "This is not a good place for you to be living. If Paul was not living at home right now it would be all right. With him around getting drunk and wandering around your sleeping place at night, well, I just don't like it."

"Paul isn't interested in me," Pearl stated. "Anyway, I can handle him. Your are worrying about something that isn't worth fretting over."

"Well, it does worry me. You have to either go someplace else to stay while you're going to school or quit me," George demanded. "If you won't leave, then I'll . . ." He stopped before he finished.

"You'll what?" Pearl asked with a concerned wrinkle in her brow.

"If you quit me, I'll tell people that I had to dump you because you and Paul were sneaking around here nights doing things. You know folks will believe it because of the way Paul is. It sure could cause a stir at church. Might even get Uncle Charley in hot water for letting it happen right under his roof," George threatened.

Pearl was so angry and dumbfounded she couldn't even respond. All she could do was open her mouth in amazement. Yet she was also scared and unsure what might happen if rumors started circulating through the community. It was at that moment she realized how much power George held over her. She had witnessed the transformation of a once-sweet, charming man to a vindictive snake that was capable of causing some real trouble, even if what he would say would be lies. People seem to want to believe the worst about what they hear. It would take a lot of time proving the lies wrong for them to stop being suspicious. Pearl didn't want the Yearouts to be hurt over something George might say.

"Would you really spread such vicious trash about me if I don't move from here?" Pearl questioned with fear in her voice.

"I'm your fiancé I think I know what is best," he stated firmly. George was a stubborn man and would not listen to any of Pearl's reasons why she felt she should stay at the Yearouts'.

She finally gave up trying to reason with him and conceded defeat. "You need to give me a little time to think things over. It might not be easy to find another place to live," the intimidated girl stated.

"OK, I'll give you a few days," he agreed.

When Auntie came back from town, George went home. Pearl was left to support this heavy burden on her weak shoulders. She was scared and didn't have the heart to tell Aunt Lillie what George was threatening. Pearl could hardly believe the words herself. She hoped George would cool down and see things more clearly tomorrow.

Friday Feb. 2, 1923
. . . George called up to see how I was, and said he'd be up this afternoon. . . .

That afternoon when George came to see Pearl, Paul was sitting on the edge of the couch talking to her. After inviting George to come in, Paul got his hat and coat and went outside. By the time Paul was out the door, George was so angry he was about to explode.

"I can't stand this any longer!" George yelled. "Either you get out of here today or else."

"George, be reasonable. I don't have anywhere else to go," the frightened girl responded.

"Then we'll get married right now, today. You and I can get a place together," he growled out like a maniac.

"What about school, and having money to live on? You'll have to spend your savings for us just to live." She was trying to stall in making the commitment.

229

"Are you trying to tell me you don't want to marry me now?" he confronted the shaking young woman. "If you don't go away with me tonight so we can be married, you won't be able to show your face outside this house for a very long time," he began to threaten.

"Oh, please don't threaten those things," she pleaded.

"I have some other things I could say, too, about your real parents being criminals and so forth," the snake added. "It's up to you. Marry me tonight or face the shame."

Pearl realized the man meant what he said, and he had her scared silly. "OK. What do you want me to do?" she responded to the madman.

"Pack your things in my travel bag and be ready to go about eleven tonight," he instructed. "I'll get the marriage license and have everything all ready. We'll leave after everyone has gone to bed."

"I'll be ready by eleven," Pearl replied. She didn't know what else she could do or say.

"I love you so much, Pearl. I just get crazy when I see another man around you. We'll be happy together; you'll see." He kissed her and headed toward town to get the license.

She sank into the sofa and began to cry. George was like a lunatic, so demanding and beastly. Yet Pearl was afraid of what he would do and say if she didn't do what he wanted.

"Pearl!" Auntie called as she came in the back door. "How are you feeling?" She entered the living room and put her hat and coat in the entry closet.

"I feel just terrible," the sick-at-heart-and-body girl responded.

"Well, honey, I have something to tell you that will probably make you feel even worse," Aunt Lillie voiced as she sat down in a motherly fashion. "I'm not trying to spread rumors or anything. This information must be kept confidential. I'm only telling you for your own good, because I think you have a right to know."

"I don't think anything could make me feel any worse than I do right now," Pearl responded. "So go ahead and tell me."

"I went to see Dr. Clark and I asked him about George's condition. He wouldn't come right out and say what he is suffering from, but he did say he had advised George that he shouldn't marry. He said it would be hard on him and the girl both."

"Oh, no!" Pearl gasped. "What do you think he has?"

"Like I said, Dr. Clark wouldn't come right out and say, but he inferred that George has tuberculosis."

"Oh gee!!I don't know what to do now," Pearl responded as she began to cry.

Aunt Lillie put her arms around the sobbing girl to comfort her. "I know this is a shock, but everything will be all right."

"No, it won't," Pearl stated. "I'm so confused. Everything is so horrible."

"What do you mean?" Auntie questioned.

Pearl couldn't stand the misery any longer. She spilled the whole story about the threats and planned elopement. Aunt Lillie was so angry if George were in reaching distance at that moment, she probably would have taken her rolling pin to his head.

"I don't want to get married right now," Pearl declared. "I want to wait until spring, after I have graduated. Why are men so unreasonable?"

"Well, if you're sure you don't want to get married right now, I'll just fix things so you can't go out tonight," Auntie responded as she went to the medicine cabinet and took out her thermometer and a hot water bottle. "You're already sick, but when Mr. George Jensen comes to get you tonight, you'll be far too sick to go out," the nurse explained as she filled the water bottle with hot liquid.

The patient already had a little fever, but by the time the nurse had finished carrying out her plan, the future bride would have to wait for another day to get married. By holding the thermometer on the hot water bottle for a few minutes before putting it in Pearl's mouth, Auntie was able to up the fever to 102 degrees.

George came up about six thirty to show me the license. Of course you know, I was too sick to go out that night. George just "ding donged" at me and argued with Auntie for me to marry him Sunday, until I had an awful headache. I tried to reason with him to wait until I'd finished school, but just as well try to argue with a house afire, as with him.

He finally went home but told me he'd be up at nine in the morning to get my answer and I had decided which I would do.

Saturday Feb. 3, 1923

George came up this morning. I felt just awfully sick, but he kept harping on me. I tried to persuade him to wait a month to give me time to decide. I simply couldn't make up my mind in so short a time. He finally said he would, then he changed his mind all of the sudden and said, no, he couldn't do that. I had to decide today whether I'd marry him or not and if we got married it had to be tomorrow. I finally told him I'd marry him but I positively would not do it before next Sunday. He just wouldn't hardly take no for an answer. Anyway he told me he loved me so much and I'd just as well shoot him as to go back on him and all that sort of stuff.

George went home and I went to bed. You know, I couldn't help but hate George tonight. He had been so beastly unreasonable and wouldn't see anything my way.

Sunday Feb. 4, 1923

George came up about nine thirty this morning. We talked things out in a calm way and I saw his side a little bit and I like him a lot better when I'm with him than when he's away.

Paul got up about eleven thirty and went downtown. Grief but I was scared while Paul was in the room here where George and I were. I was so afraid there would be trouble.

Monday Feb. 5, 1923

George came up this afternoon. We decided to go to Portland instead of staying here until after our business with the "Will" is settled up. George promised to let me go to school after we got there (Auntie's suggestion).

Tuesday Feb. 6, 1923

Paul slept all day. George came up this evening and said he'd bring his trunk up in the morning so I could get my clothes packed.

Wednesday Feb. 7, 1923

Tom brought George's trunk up, and Auntie and I went downtown with them. Did some shopping. Auntie got a new dress. Saw the school principal about transferring my credits to Portland High School. George and I walked home.

George came up for supper. Just before going back to the Hyltons' for the night, George went into the kitchen to talk to Pearl privately. "Pearl, if you're not completely satisfied with our new plans, maybe we should just split up and forget everything," he stated out of the blue.

"If you want to get married and go to Portland, I'm ready. Everything is set with the school; that's what I was mostly worried about. My transcript can be sent as soon as we get there." Pearl spoke calmly. "I'll go along with anything you want."

By the time George left the house, everything was fine between the couple.

Auntie was out milking when George called.

"Pearl, I've changed my mind," the voice on the other end announced. "I'm going to send the dray up after my trunk. I've decided it would be best for me to go away in the morning by myself."

232

She paused for a few seconds before responding. The last comments had come as a total surprise. Pearl was too tired from all the stress of the past few days to keep up the fight. "All right, if that's what you really think is best," the stunned young woman replied. "I wish you would stop by before you leave so we can talk things over."

"OK," George agreed. "I'll be over in a hour."

Auntie and Paul hadn't gone to bed yet when George came over. Pearl didn't open the subject at all but just left it for him. George was as nice as pie and said he had thought better of his plans to go away. He stated that he would wait and they would get married. He just made oceans of promises.

Auntie invited George to stay all night because it was late. George declined the offer and said he would go home pretty soon. Pearl was feeling terrible, so George had her lie down on the lounge, and she went to sleep for a short while. A few minutes after she woke up George announced he would stay all night after all. George said that Paul had come and challenged him by saying that he wasn't going to stay because he was afraid. Pearl looked at George with a bewildered smirk on her face.

"I don't believe Paul said you were afraid," she teased.

George had been caught in a fib, and he knew it. He immediately became defensive, however, and flew into a rage. "Why do you always take Paul's side and not mine?" he spouted.

"I'm not taking sides," Pearl explained.

"Yes, you are. You're always sticking up for him. Paul is just a no-good hell-raising kid who should be slapped around and knocked down a peg or two," the jealous man responded. "If I stay around this town any longer, I'm afraid I will beat that kid to a bloody stump."

Pearl had finally had enough. This last outburst was the "straw that broke the camel's back." She was not about to put up with George's temper tantrums any longer. This time he had gone too far. "That's it! I've had enough!!" Pearl announced as she went to the small drawer of the writing table. All the things George had ever given her were stored there waiting to be packed. She took out the pen, the watch, the camera, and the lavaliere, then slipped the ring off her finger and gave everything back to him.

George was stunned at the realization that his girl was breaking off their engagement. He was now hurt to think she would really go through with breaking up. Giving back all his gifts was a pretty final gesture and meant serious business.

"You'll look back on this day and remember me as the best friend you ever had," George gushed. "I love you better than anything in the whole world. I'll always love you. I just don't see how I'll ever be able to give you up."

"Good-bye, George!" the courageous young woman stated as she walked to the front door and started to open it, inviting George to leave.

"Honey, I'm sorry. Please let's get married on Sunday. Everything will be different after we're married," the lovesick man pleaded.

Pearl stood her ground. She was tired of all this nonsense. She felt she had a right to make this huge decision, and she wasn't going to listen to any more "bunk." "Do you really expect me to agree to marry you after everything you have said and threatened to say about me?" she responded as she stood with her hands on her hips and a disgusted look on her face.

"I just can't give you up," he repeated. "Maybe I'll just go and blow my brains out."

"You fool!" Pearl blurted out. "It's only cowards who resort to that kind of talk and action. I think you had better leave now, before I lose my temper and start throwing things," the now-angry young woman spouted as she opened the door completely.

The clock on the wall read 5:00 A.M. as she closed the door and became a single, unpromised girl once again.

Thursday Feb. 8, 1923
Earnest and Junior came after George's trunk at six-thirty A.M. George called up about seven-thirty and told Auntie and I good-bye.

Paul just happened to ask me if I was going to get married and I said no. When he began to question me I just couldn't hold my tears any longer. When they began to spill over, I told him au revoir and adjourned to the other room.

Got through today better than I thought I could.
Friday Feb. 9, 1923
Cleaned up the house and made a cake this morning.

Aunt Belle and Jewel came up this afternoon. Auntie and she had a long quiet talk in the kitchen. (Discussing George's pro's and con's I guess.)

After they had gone Auntie told me what Mrs. Hylton had been telling her about the things George was saying down there. He sure told some awful tales.

"I suppose all the quiet talk between you and Aunt Belle was centered around me and George?" Pearl asked after Mrs. Hylton was in her wagon and headed toward home.

"Well, Miss Tooley, you ought to thank your luck stars that you didn't marry that man," Aunt Lillie reported before sitting on the couch to be near the still-ailing girl.

"I'm still so confused, Auntie. One side of me wants George back the way he was a few months ago, not the way he's been of late, while the other side of me is somehow relieved of the stressful pressure he was adding to my life. I will miss having a man to love, though," the heartbroken maiden confessed.

"I don't think George was really the good man we all thought he was and he pretended to be," Auntie said, trying to break the news that had just been reported by Aunt Belle.

"What do you mean?" Pearl questioned. She could sense that Auntie wanted to tell her what the conversation between her and Mrs. Hylton had been about.

"Didn't George tell you he had quite a bit of money saved in the bank?" Auntie asked.

"At one time he said he had about twenty-eight thousand dollars. He was saving it for us to buy a house and things with," the young woman answered.

"I'm sure he was lying about that. Belle said that George was flat broke. He had to pawn his revolver to Joe Hylton to get enough money to go away on," Auntie continued, "and at Christmas, he borrowed the money from Jewel to buy your present with."

Pearl was shocked. Why would he tell her such a story? "Are you sure?" Pearl gasped. "I was never really interested in him for the money."

Well, I think he was interested in the money that you might inherit," Lillie added. "He told everyone that he would pay them back when his 'woman' got her money."

"No wonder he pestered me so much about it," Pearl commented. "I can see now why I felt sometimes he was more interested in the inheritance than he was in me."

"That's not all," Auntie reported. "I guess there really is a woman in Troy who George would go and see. In fact, he told Jewel that he dumped you because he couldn't stand to be away from his girlfriend in Troy. He was moving over there to be with her."

Even though she was glad to be out from under her relationship, Pearl was sick to her stomach at the fact that there had been another woman. She knew, however, that was not the real reason George was going to Troy. He had just said that to save face. Tears came to her eyes at the thought of him two-timing behind her back, just before the anger took over.

"I can't believe he was such a liar," Pearl lashed out. "Why do men have to be so awful sometimes?"

"Another thing," the informer continued. "He also said another reason he was leaving was because he had caught you and Paul in bed together."

"Oh, Auntie, you know that isn't true," Pearl gasped again. "He told me if I didn't marry him he was going to spread rumors like that. How can one person be so vindictive to someone they claim to be in love with?'

"I guess it's all a matter of 'pride.' Some people can never accept the blame for their behavior. They always want to place the cause of their wrongdoings on someone else," Auntie responded. "No one with any sense is going to believe that lie about you. Even Belle knew he was lying when he said that.

"Belle said that Ruby had told her several times that he would quit you if she would be his girl. Ruby also reported that George told her as soon as he got your money he would leave you and come to get her. Ruby told him to stop playing games and leave her alone.

Pearl had a hard time sleeping that night even though she still didn't feel well physically. She contemplated all the things she could remember about George's behavior over the last several months, and she realized how cunning and deceitful the man had been.

Saturday Feb. 10, 1923

Washed out some handkerchiefs and Paul's shirts. Ironed them this evening.

This was to be my wedding day you know, seven P.M. this evening. I can sure thank my lucky stars that it wasn't. I can hardly conceive how George could play such a game as he was playing though. Some men must be little more than beasts to do the things they do. This one must have been St. Lucifer in disguise. (Blessing him off proper eh?)

George is the gayest deceiver and most awful liar I've happened on to yet. Some merciful fate must have kept me from marrying him. (They say there's a guiding influence that protects drunkards and "fools.")

236

Tuesday Feb. 13, 1923

Finally started back to school today. Wanted to drop Algebra but the Principal wouldn't let me.

Got a letter from George today. Grief! I didn't have the least idea he'd write after all the things he said about me. I'm of the opinion that he's half nuts. He said he felt so bad and all he did was gaze on my picture. Gee! He sure is strong on dramatics. I didn't suppose people said such things and acted the way he does outside of dime novels and movies. I guess there's a lot of things I don't know though. I learn something new 'most every day. George said he might come back to Moscow. He had better not if he knows what's good for him.

I read the letter to everybody in the family and we had a laugh over his slush. He's undoubtedly the biggest hypocrite I ever saw or heard tell of.

Wednesday Feb. 14, 1923

Auntie said she didn't have another surprise for me this evening when I came home (meaning another letter from George). I hadn't been home but a little while when Aunt Belle called up and said Uncle Hirum had seen George get off the train. Auntie couldn't believe her ears for a minute, but when Belle had convinced her that he had come back she was awfully mad and so was I when she told me.

If that fellow's fool enough to come back in the face of everything he's said, he's fool enough to do most anything. Here's hopin' he won't cause too much trouble though.

I told Paul that George was back, when he came home tonight, and say but he was mad. Paul was for beating up on him the first time he saw him. I told Paul he'd better be careful though, because George wouldn't fight fair.

Thursday Feb. 15, 1923

Saw George this morning on the way to school, but I was with the other girls so he didn't stop me. I'm confident that was his intention if I had been alone, and he thought I would be.

Auntie told me this evening that Grandma Hylton had been up here this morning and from the things she said, she'd been siding with George. He denied saying anything about Ruby and she believed what he had said about me.

George had Uncle Charley come down to Hylton's this afternoon and he told him a lot of stuff, thinking he would turn against me, but Uncle Charley just discredited the things George said.

Sunday Feb. 18, 1923

Went to church this morning. George came in time for church, I acted just like I always have, only I treated him like a stranger. Say, but he was awfully mad. I don't know what about, but he looked just like he did that Sunday night he got so mad at Paul.

George walked with Uncle Charley to where he was to turn off to go to Hylton's. I think he wanted a chance to talk to me but I sure didn't give him any encouragement.

Got dinner. Paul got some cider and that dope he made and had some other fellows come out. They got the truck stuck in the mud and had an awful time getting it out. Had to get a team to pull them out.

I'm awfully afraid Paul will come home drunk tonight and I wish he wouldn't. It makes me so nervous I can't see straight.

After George Jensen was out of her hopes and dreams, Pearl turned her attentions to the only other fellow she cared about. Not even realizing it herself, she was wanting Paul in her life more and more. The brotherly love she felt for him was slowly turning into a different kind of love. Paul, however, was too footloose and fancy free to even notice. He simply regarded Pearl as a nice girl and good friend.

Friday Feb. 23, 1923

Got a letter from George. Wants me to meet him someplace and talk with him. Nothing I want to discuss with that snake.

Paul took the car out tonight. Uncle Charley discovered it was gone when he went down to milk. Probably be one heck of a row in the morning.

Paul came home at three-thirty in the morning. He woke me to ask me what time it was. He was awfully drunk, I should say "sick." I told him to go to bed, and for a wonder, he did as I said.

Tuesday Feb. 27, 1923

Paul went to Clarka this morning. Gee! It'll seem lonesome without him around. He's a pretty good kid in spite of his faults. We all have faults you know. Maybe when he comes back it'll be different. Here's hopin' any how.

Aunt Belle called Auntie today and said Jewel had run off some place. He told his mother that him and another kid are going to bum their way. She was awfully worried. I guess he got the wanderlust feelin'.

If I was a boy I'd start too. I feel like I want to go and go until I come to the end of the trail. But we girls can't just go when we want to. We're held down more or less by convention etc. "I wish I was a boy."

Saturday March 3, 1923

Baked a cake and cleaned the house. Paul came back today, didn't expect to see him for an age. Camp at Clarka not open yet.

Sunday March 4, 1923

. . .Went to church this evening, George was there. Grief but I hate that fellow.

Wednesday March 7, 1923

Got a letter from George today. My note to him evidently made him peeved, because he gave me a heck of a bawling out. Lot I care how much he bawls me out, but I do wish he wouldn't accuse me of things I don't do.

Paul went to Lewiston tonight.

COLOR MY WORLD BLUE

The next week went by slowly as Pearl concentrated on school. Paul was away and she missed having him around, even if he wasn't always pleasant. There was just something about knowing he was there that made her now-dull life brighter.

The flu bug that had attacked her body never fully went away. She felt well enough to go to school and work around the house, but she coughed quite often, warning her the bug was still around.

Monday March 12, 1923
Went to school this morning. Didn't feel so bad until after I got there, and then I sure felt punk. I must have looked it too, because everybody asked me what was the matter. I just told them I had an awful headache. Felt like coming home at noon but I stuck it out until three. I had one awful time getting home, it never seemed so far away and it sure looked good when I got there.

Didn't eat supper, temperature was 102.3 degrees. Went to bed. Paul came home from Lewiston tonight.

Tuesday March 13, 1923
Auntie had Doctor Clarke come up to see me this morning. He said I had pneumonia pleurisy. Put a plaster on my back and gave me some little red pills.

The next two weeks were touch-and-go as Pearl's temperature went up and down. Some days it was as high as 105 degrees, and others 101. Staying in bed and feeling so weak was miserable for a girl in her senior year of high school. She worried that she would fall so far behind in her studies that she wouldn't have enough credits to graduate in May. She was also missing out on many fun activities that seniors got to do, and that made the thought of staying at home in bed even tougher.

Friday March 23, 1923
Auntie let me sit up a little while today. I felt awfully strong in bed, but it was all I could do to walk across the room when I got up. Then I had to lean on Auntie to stay up. Paul brought some good books home from the library for me so started reading one of them, Zane Grey's "Desert of Meat."

Monday March 26, 1923
Felt much better today. Auntie left to go take care of a very sick man in Grangeville. She said she will probably be gone for a few weeks. Oh

240

Gee!! I miss her already. Made a cake this morning that was tough as leather. Guess I didn't beat it enough or something. Uncle Charley got me some medicine today. Awfully bitter stuff but it's supposed to make me strong so I guess I'll have to take it. Awfully tired tonight.

Got a letter from Mr. Lee, enclosed was a letter from the War Department about the insurance. My mother has gotten remarried again. Her new name is Myrtle Broughton. That was more interesting to me than the information about the insurance. I wish I knew more about my people. It's awful to be like this. Knowing you have relatives in the world but not knowing anything about them or anything.

Tuesday March 27, 1923

Wrote three letters today, one to Mr. Lee, one to Mrs. Moore, and one to Roy. Paul took them to mail for me when he went downtown.

Wednesday March 28, 1923

Paul was horrid this morning. A few months ago I didn't know life was like this. I certainly wish I hadn't found out. They say it's what you make it, but others have a lot to do with the making of it too. I'm not going to take all the blame. Oh, but I wish things were different.

Friday March 30, 1923

Made some cookies this morning, they were awful. I'm getting so I can't cook a thing half decent. Washed out Paul's shirts. Paul is trying to coax his dad to let him get the batteries for the car, but he won't do it. Afraid Paul will bust it up I guess. But Paul promises he wouldn't run it, only when his dad wanted him to. Paul would probably forget this promise pretty quick though if he happened to want to go someplace real bad.

Got a letter from Auntie, she said she'd probably be home in a few days. I sure hope so. We all miss her a lot.

Sunday April 1, 1923

Raining this morning so didn't go to church. Paul got up about eleven, had an awful grouch on. Paul and I are getting so we quarrel all the time, and I believe he gets mad. I do half the time, fly off the handle before I know it. I don't know why I do it. It used to be that he could say things to me and I wouldn't get peeved. I guess I'm developing nerves or something. I have a case of the blues every evening, everything so lonely and quiet around her. Uncle Charley never says anything to me. I guess it doesn't agree with him to have Auntie gone. Hope she comes back pretty soon.

Twelve-thirty and Paul is gone and Uncle Charley hasn't come home from church yet. Wish he'd hurry up, this quiet is getting on my nerves. Played the phonograph and read a little this afternoon.

Uncle Charley called up Estes's this afternoon and asked how Auntie's patient was. They reported that he had gotten over the pneumonia, but the flu had settled in his intestines and he was pretty bad again. Guess that means another week or so for Auntie. Wish he'd hurry up and get well so Auntie could come home.

Paul came home awfully "sick" (drunk) tonight. Got me up to get him something to throw up in, but he couldn't throw up. I asked him if he'd take some Soda if I fixed it for him and he said he'd take anything. Took the Soda and that did the work. His head quit whirling and he began to talk more sensible. He asked me while he was so sick if I didn't think he had pneumonia and if it was very serious. I told him yes, I thought he was going to die. I felt sorry for him, but it was funny too.

Thursday April 19, 1923

Went to school today. First time since I got sick. It will be hard to catch up on everything I missed, but the teachers feel I can do it okay. Had class meeting after school to decide about class day and "Senior Sneak."

I did some Algebra tonight and doctored Paul's cold. He had a streak on and was pretty grouchy. I felt sorry for him, at one time he about coughed his head off.

Saw Auntie for a few minutes today. She is in town now but is out at Estes's with the sick man. I was just awfully glad to see her. She's awfully thin and doesn't look at all well though. I guess she's been working too hard. We tried to coax her to stay at home longer but she said she couldn't. I think I'll have to tack a "WHAT'S A HOME WITHOUT A MOTHER?" sign on the wall. I think both Uncle Charley and Paul's answer would be the same. "It's————." Oh well maybe I'd better not say it. Things don't go right at all around here when she's gone. Uncle Charley's cross, Paul's cross and I'm cross. Even the birds seem to fight.

Saturday April 21, 1923

Cleaned up the house and baked a cake. Auntie came home for a while and we went downtown to see Judge Forney. He handled the "situation" under consideration better than I'd hoped for. Didn't have those affidavits ready so have to go back next Saturday to sign them.

Took a notion to bake some cookies after I got home. Paul came home about seven this evening, brought his friend Oron up with him. He changed his clothes and they went downtown. Gave them a piece of cake (Paul's orders) but he growled at me because I'd put chocolate icing on it.

Sunday April 22, 1923

I'm getting terribly ancient, nineteen today. . . .

Went to church tonight. They're going to operate on Auntie's patient tomorrow and she thinks she'll be home in a few days. Won't it be gr-r-rand an' glorious feelin' though. Everything will run along smooth again I guess. Au revoir.

A TIME TO WALK

Monday April 23, 1923

Went to school. Group pictures of Senior Class taken in front of the High School. Senior Sneak tomorrow. I'll bet we have oceans of fun.

Had to make some sandwiches tonight for the picnic tomorrow. Paul came in while I was making them and we had an awful time to keep him from calling several friends. If he had, I'd sure get in bad for letting him find it out. Auntie came home tonight.

Tuesday April 24, 1923

Got down to the High School a few minutes before five-thirty this morning, we left for the mountains at six. Went to Dew Drop Inn, a little picnic place.

Took a hike to the top of the mountain before dinner, had awfully good eats.

The Junior boys and Paul came up in the afternoon. They weren't supposed to be there. When they came, they said they were there to camp, Ha Ha. We had a wiener roast about five in the evening. The boys teased one of the lady teachers and she got awfully mad. Came home about seven-thirty.

Climb High

Don't stop when nearly to the summit
To gaze upon some folly or fascinating fancy
Of the world below, tho it seems to be so fair.
But keep steadily plodding upward
And behold the glorious sunrise
That awaits you there.
Don't mingle in nor be a part
Of every little trifle
But make your aim high
And work steadily towards the end.
But blend harmoniously with those about you
And don't be a discord
To your fellow men.

P.E.T.

Wednesday April 25, 1923

. . . Paul shook his head for me not to tell Auntie about him being with the boys that came up the mountains yesterday for "Sneak Day."

243

But I came awfully near it once before I thought. Started to tell something Miss Jensen said about him when we were coming home, and had to change the subject all of the sudden.

Judge Forney came up to see Auntie about our legal matters.

Friday May 4, 1923

. . . Met Auntie downtown after school. Went up to see Judge Forney. I'm only eighteen, I was born in 1905 instead 1904, as I had gotten it into my head. Judge Forney got it from Mr. Convington at the Children's Home, and he got it from my birth record at Thompson Falls, where I was born.

Got the material for my baccalaureate dress and say it's going to be pretty, dark brown crepe de chine, with a sort of a paisley design lace Bertha in blue, red, green and silver, and the sleeve piping in blue crepe de chine. Also some of the blue wound in with the girdle.

Auntie has my commencement dress nearly made. White silk jersey trimmed with silver ribbon.

Sunday May 13, 1923

. . . Baccalaureate tonight. The girls all had pretty dresses. Mr. Gale decided to have us march in at the last minute. He had told us Friday to just go in informally instead of formally.

Mr. Chenowith gave a good talk, his text being the first verse of Genesis. "And God created the Heavens and the earth." Said that man created the world in which he lived. Each one gave to the world what he had taken out of it. Byron's poetry portraying the baseness in mankind is not so much of a tragedy in the effect it has on other people, but the tragedy lies in the fact that a life was ruined. Byron only saw the base and low things in the world, so consequently that was all he had to give back to it.

Tuesday May 15, 1923

Went to the University at four to get our places on the stage for Commencement.

Got a check today from Mrs. Covington and a hankie from Mrs. Moore. My brother Robert Earl sent me a string of beads, and Helen a silk handkerchief.

Wednesday May 16, 1923

Commencement tonight. Girls all had pretty dresses, most of them white or light silks, and a few organdies and voiles.

Professor Dale of the Department of Economics gave the address. His subject was, "The Handicap of an Education." Not in the sense it seems at first glance, but that an education is a handicap because it gives us a later start in the business world, and places the responsibility of higher things on the shoulder of the educated, instead of those with just a grammar school education or even a High School education. One must have a college education to accomplish the real big things and be sure of success. He said there were two Universities in this State. The University of Idaho, and The University of "Hard Knocks."

Paul left for Potlatch today to see about Summer work.

Sunday May 20, 1923

Went to church this evening. George was there. He had two girls with him, but they all left after song service. He probably thinks he can spite me, but I don't bother about him any more. Wrote some letters today, Auntie wrote to Paul.

Tuesday May 22, 1923

... Went to the barber shop. Bunnie not busy so had him cut my hair.

I look funny, more like a boy. If I put on pants I think I could pass for a Shakespearean youth very easily. (If I wasn't so fat.) I know Aunt Belle will rave about it, but it was coming out so awfully from my illness, I had to do something.

IS THERE A GOOD JOB OUT THERE?

Now that school was over, Pearl knew it was time to look for a job. The only talent she thought she had was housekeeping. She started asking around trying to get on with someone who had the financial ability to pay a housekeeper.

Sunday May 27, 1923

. . . Mrs. Estes told me about a lady, Mrs. Miller, wife of one of the University Professors who wants me to work for her. But according to her description of the woman and her ways, she seems awfully peculiar. If I can't do better I guess I'll go. I sure want to get a job someplace pretty soon so I can earn some money.

Monday May 28, 1923

Went to see Mrs. Miller this afternoon. Don't like her appearance very well. Acts like she considers herself better than anyone else . . .

Monday June 4, 1923

Went to Mrs. Willis today, she wants me to work for her. They have a lovely house, but they say Mrs. Willis has an awful temper. She shot at her son-in-law because she didn't want her daughter to marry him. Her daughter Belle has a little baby now and is going to come and stay with her mother for a few weeks. Guess I'll start tomorrow in the morning. It will probably be all right if she doesn't happen to fly into a rage and beat up on me for something or other.

Tuesday June 5, 1923

Went to Willis's today. Washed windows, cleaned bathroom and sun porch while Mrs. Willis cleaned the rest of the house. Getting ready for her daughter Belle and the new baby tomorrow.

Wednesday June 6, 1923

Belle came home to her mother's today about noon. Ironed some of the baby's things and got bawled out about it. Every wrinkle has to be out and things here have to be done in double quick hurry. So blue tonight I can't see straight, everything has an azure hue.

Thursday June 7, 1923

Straightened up downstairs and rinsed and hung out some of Belle's baby's things.

Came home after dinner. Got a letter from Mrs. Lee, one from my sister Helen, and one from George. George sent some pictures of me he took one Sunday, and said I might want to give them to someone else. He said he didn't know where those handkerchiefs were that I made for him, but if I'd tell him how much they cost he would send me the money for

246

them. Just to show him that he can't get the best of me, I'm going to write him a little note and tell him how much they cost and also cut his picture from one of those he sent me and send it back to him. Needn't think he can put one over on me.

I guess Mrs. Hylton is the news carrier. Auntie told her a long time ago that George hadn't given my things back, but I'd given all of his to him. Well so much for that, I start raving every time I think of that old goose, he's got about as much sense as one.

Auntie told me to tell Mrs. Willis to get that other girl from Troy she got a letter from, and for me to go to work for Mrs. Miller. Mrs. Estes had told her that Mrs. Miller's place was far better than Mrs. Willis's. Anyway, Mrs. Willis is such a high strung person she flies off the handle so easily and just works herself and everyone else around her to death, except Belle of course. But I sort of like Belle, she seemed awfully nice. Mrs. Willis worships her and that baby, but the baby is a doll. She had the prettiest hair and eyes. They call her Phyllis.

Friday June 8, 1923

Cleaned upstairs and finished the ironing. Mrs. Willis bragged awfully about it. Told her about getting that other girl from Troy and she made more of a fuss than I thought she would. I didn't tell her I was going to Mrs. Miller's but that Auntie was going to have a case and wanted me home, which is the truth.

Monday June 11, 1923

Went back to Willis's this morning. We got the washing out by noon. After dinner the girl from Troy came so I went home. Mrs. Willis wants me to come back after Belle goes and works half days, and I can be home nights and afternoons. I told her I would if I had nothing else by that time. She seemed to have taken quite a fancy to me for some reason or other.

Saturday June 16, 1923

... Went to Judge Forney's office and filled out those affidavits. He thinks his wife is looking for a housekeeper.

Monday June 18, 1923

Mrs. Forney called up yesterday and wanted me to come and see her about working there. Ethel, her current housekeeper, is going to Oregon. I went to see her, only one thing in the way was Mrs. Miller, so Auntie and I went up there and she wasn't in. Mrs. Forney wanted to know by noon, so called her and told her I'd come. May said she would go to the Millers', so Mrs. Miller can work out her own salvation I guess.

Wednesday June 20, 1923

Went to work for Forneys this morning. Ethel showed me how things went. Mrs. Harrison, Mrs. Forney's mother, also lives there, and she is the only drawback. But she has a little Scottie dog named ''Jack'' that occupies most of her time. She's trying to train him. He really is a cute dog. She calls him her ''little brown Doggie.'' Mrs. Forney is in poor health, so she needs someone to help with the housework.

Mrs. Willis called up this evening and wanted me. She fired the girl from Troy I guess.

Thursday June 21, 1923

Everything has a place, so I get a little mixed up and suppose I'll continue to until I find out where everything goes.

Go to work at seven-thirty in the mornings and stay until after dinner. I come home for a few hours, then go back at five-thirty to get supper, and stay home nights. I'm trying hard to reduce by climbing hills.

Tom Weeks called Auntie up and said George had skipped and he's afraid he's going to Spokane. Has an axe to grind and would like awfully well for us to do the grinding.

Saturday June 23, 1923

Baked bread today. Mrs. Forney has a special recipe and it will be a wonder if it's any good.

Heard Mrs. Harrison talking over the phone today while I was cleaning off the table. The way she puts on is the limit. It's ''Oh my dear,'' ''Now isn't that disgusting'' . . . etc. All in that horrid English accent. She was trying to get out of playing bridge at Mrs. Day's I think. She's a lot nicer when she doesn't exaggerate so and try to be so awfully English.

Monday June 25, 1923

Made pancakes this morning, Mr. Forney ate ten. He laughed and told Mrs. Harrison about it.

Auntie told me tonight that the proprietor of the Moscow Hotel called up this morning and wanted me at twelve dollars a week. That's over double what I am making now but I can't possibly quit at Forney's, I'd be sure to offend Mrs. Forney. I certainly don't want to do that because of my legal matter. ''Such is life'' though just one darn thing after another makes a fellow feel like helping some poor soul, and especially yourself, n'est-ce-pas?

Wednesday June 27, 1923

Baked. Awfully hot today. Guess Mrs. Harrison smokes, saw a cigarette steel that was still smokey in the ashtray in Mrs. Forney's room just after Mrs. Harrison had gone out.

Was a thinking away as I was working and here's what came into my head, just a little jingle:

Day unto day is shadow

Night after night is pain
When I'm longin' for you
To be home again.

P.E.T.

Auntie got a letter from Paul. She says she knows the kid's getting home sick because his letters come more often and he just writes about everything. She'll have to number the answers 1, 2, 3, 4—if she answers all the questions he asked this time. I wonder what it's like where he's working?

Friday June 29, 1923
Mrs. Harrison went to Lewiston today to spend a few days with some friends of her's. Auntie gave me my first lesson in driving today.

Saturday June 30, 1923
. . . Went downtown tonight and got me a hat. Had an awful time finding one that would suit my hair. I got to drive home.

Thursday July 5, 1923
Paul came home today, it was sure good to see him again. He's going back tomorrow on the train. I miss him a lot.

Friday July 13, 1923
The day when all the wicked fairies are supposed to do their worst.

I drove the car downtown. Auntie wanted to stop there on Main Street in front of Huff's Cafe, so she could go to the bakery. I didn't get her directions soon enough, turned too fast and couldn't get stopped. Ran the front wheels up on the side walk. My first accident, but you know this is Friday the 13th so I'd have to have some bad luck.

Paul came home from Potlatch the middle of July. The construction job he was working on ended. Floyd Yearout had called his mother and told her of work in California where he was living and that he knew he could get Paul on if he would go there.

The young man had been homesick while he was away in Potlatch, but he knew he shouldn't pass up such a good opportunity just because he missed home. By the first week of August Paul had left Moscow to start a new adventure in central California.

His letters indicated he was very homesick, after two months away, so Auntie sent him some extra money to take the train home when the job had a break in mid-September.

This time when he came home he seemed different somehow. Pearl especially noticed his more mellow disposition and commented on it one evening when they were alone in the living room. "You must have really been homesick this time or struck by lightning," she teased. "I expected you to be out with your friends tonight with a jug of cider."

"I know, it's not like me to be happy just staying at home. I guess a person never appreciates what he has until he is away from it," Paul commented. "I haven't been a very good son to my parents the last few years. I didn't realize just how rebellious I was until I saw Floyd and his family out in California. It wasn't easy being the second son of a preacher when the first son was so good of a church boy. You know, Floyd was pretty crazy sometimes, but he was never disrespectful or wild like me. I guess I was always a little jealous of him and wanted to make my own place in the community. Well, I succeeded in being different from my brother, but after working alongside him for the last few weeks I now appreciate the kind of a person he is. I really want to be more like him. I love my mom and dad and I didn't know how much until I was away this time."

Pearl listened intently to this changed young man before speaking. "You just don't know how lucky you are to have good parents like yours. I never . . ." Her voice trailed off as the tears welled in her eyes. She wanted to run and hide, but Paul took hold of her arm and waited until she had regained her composure.

"You never talk about what happened to your parents, Pearl. Why?" he questioned.

"It's hard for me to admit what happened to myself, let alone anyone else. I guess it's because everything about my parents is still so confusing to me," Pearl responded. "I can tell you this, however; it was a living hell growing up and feeling so alone sometimes. I would have given anything to have had your mother as my own. I always felt so bad when I saw you not appreciating her. You have no idea what it's like being shuffled from home to home and having no real roots."

Paul contemplated the words of this sincere young woman and began to feel a new compassion for her. She was becoming a gracious, caring person, and he sensed her real beauty was more on the inside than on the outside. "You're quite a girl," he remarked. "I didn't know quite what to think about you when you and old George were engaged. Since you dumped him, you have become more and more . . . Well, I guess . . ." He paused, not wanting to come right and say it, but he just did anyway. "Attractive."

Pearl blushed red and couldn't even respond. Had Paul just paid her a real compliment? She had only hoped and dreamed of this moment but never felt it would actually be happening.

"Are you blushing?" the young man teased. "Yes, you are." He laughed and got up from the couch. "Hey, what do you say we go downtown and see what's playing at the Kenworthy?"

The two of them seemed inseparable the next few days of Paul's time at home. They went for rides and hikes and even baked cookies together one afternoon. The two young people were developing a special bond that Pearl hoped would continue to grow.

The Sunday that he left to go back to California was a terrible day for the young woman. She had a sick feeling deep inside that he shouldn't go.

"I'll be back before Christmas. They said we won't be working over the holidays, so plan some fun things for us to do," Paul instructed his new best friend. "Make sure you get me a nice gift; you know I deserve it," he laughed.

"You better be good while you're away, then, if you don't want Santa to leave you a lump of coal instead of a present," Pearl joked back.

Paul was tempted to give Pearl a kiss good-bye but opted for just a quick hug in front of his parents. He didn't want them to know how he was starting to feel about the girl whom he had once considered a sister.

SUPPLICATION

Sunday October 14, 1923

Lots of things have happened since I wrote in here last. Will try to fill in the most important things. Paul is still working in California, but his letters indicate that he is homesick.

President Harding died August 11. Dean Little and Mr. Creighton died about that time too.

... I finally got away from working at Forney's and started in at David's Department Store. Mrs. Forney got a college girl but Mrs. Harrison doesn't like her very well and I'm afraid the girl will have a pretty tough time of it. Forneys wanted me to stay there and go to college, with ten dollars a month wages. Not so bad, but I'd rather have a little more to go on before I start.

Homer at the department store started me at six dollars per week, and raised me to eight dollars yesterday. I get balled up once in a while, but I guess I'll learn the trade sometime. Here's hopin'.

We hear from Paul about twice a week. He's homesick as the deuce. He can't stay away from home a week without wanting to rush back.

Saturday, October 20, 1923

It was nine at night, and Pearl was in the kitchen ironing. She paused for a minute, thinking Aunt Lillie or Uncle Charley would answer the door. Neither one seemed to be paying attention, so Pearl spoke out.

"Somebody's at the door, Auntie. Didn't you hear the knocking?" Pearl questioned.

"No. I didn't hear it," Auntie responded as she rose to her feet. She went to the entryway and turned on the porch light. She opened the door and was met by a fragrant breeze that smelled similar to the cologne her son Paul wore. Lillie Yearout looked all around, but no one was there.

"Hello!" she called out to the darkness, hoping someone would appear from the shadows. A quick thought passed through her mind, and she somehow expected Paul to be hiding, to tease her. "Is someone out there?" she called again, but only the quiet sound of crickets chirping in the grass responded. "Paul," she muttered almost to herself before turning back to talk to Pearl. "Are you sure you heard someone knock?" Auntie questioned the young woman behind the ironing board.

252

"I thought I heard a knock," Pearl answered. "Maybe it was only my imagination." A little flutter of butterflies stirred in her soul, yet Pearl passed the incident off as a mistake.

Monday Oct. 22, 1923

We got a telegram last night about five-thirty from Floyd that Paul was killed in an automobile accident Saturday night at Mercedes, California, about thirty miles from Floyd's.

Lord it will be terrible never to see him again, but my world doesn't seem much emptier than the Sunday he went back to California. I had an awful feeling then that I'd never see him again. It's an awful shock to Auntie, she is nearly wild with grief.

Just think of his beautiful youth, crushed to mangled nothingness.

He's the fourth person who has gone to California to die within the last three months. The Saturday night we got news of Mr. Little's death was the night before Paul left. I happened to remark to Auntie in a joking way that Paul had better reconsider before he decided to go or he might meet with a like fate.

Such is the irony of fate. Lord we don't know what hour life will be snatched away. Oh, there are so many things we know nothing about. Let us hope that Paul's soul is with his maker and that we may all live right so we can be with him by and by. In that eternal realm where the life can't be crushed out of bodies and where there is no sorrow.

My heart is sore and unhappy and I'm afraid of life.
The winds of fate have buffeted me to the shores of the river of despair.
My God in Heaven lead my feet from the inky waters,
Guide them to the fields of Hope where wild flowers bloom
And the waving grass is bathed in the morning sun.
Then my mind may be freed of this pounding fear and can live in peace
   again.

P.E.T.

WOMANHOOD

Pearl lay in her room alone crying for a lost love. Her love for Paul had extended over the last year from that of brotherly love to a deeper, more romantic love. She had hoped someday he might have the same feelings for her. But now everything was gone. It had been crushed and mangled so far away. There was nothing she or anyone else could do.

Something else had also changed with Paul's death. A silent robber had come and snatched away Pearl's youth. She was somehow transformed as if overnight from a whimsical girl to a grown woman. It was time to put away the frivolities of a teen and enter the world of adulthood. She didn't know if she was ready for the responsibilities, but she knew she had to be strong, as least for Aunt Lillie and Uncle Charley, who were so devastated by their son's death.

The next few months were so hard living at the Yearouts', with the hope of Paul's homecomings never to be again. Everywhere Pearl turned there was a memory of him. It was so hard to come home after a long day at the store to sad memories and unfulfilled dreams.

To make life even worse, right after Christmas Helen Lyons got sick with pneumonia. She waited too long to get proper treatment. By the time Auntie was called to nurse her it was too late. On a cold January morning of 1924, Helen Lyons died. Her death left Otto to manage the farm and children by himself. His sister Belle helped him a lot with the children, but it just wasn't the same wonderful home without his wife. Pearl had grown to love Helen, and her loss was another blow to the young woman's tender heart.

Little Donald was only three and sorely missed his loving momma. The tears of the little guy brought back memories of another three-year-old boy so long ago, when his mother was taken from him.

Why was this life so cruel? Why were the ones Pearl loved always being taken away? Would she ever be able to have a stable, lasting relationship with anyone? These were questions she asked herself over and over many times.

In the summer of 1924, Auntie bought a brand-new Chevrolet. Ruby Hylton and Pearl went with her on a trip to California. They followed the map, going across to Portland and down the coast of Oregon and California. They went to see Floyd and his family, but the underlying goal was to make sure Paul had a proper resting place. Auntie had to see for herself that his body was resting in an appropriate spot. They could never bring him back, but they could make sure he had a marker stone and some fresh flowers.

The travelers spent about three weeks touring the surrounding area before heading back to Idaho. The trip was long but worthwhile. Pearl got to see some beautiful sights on the trip. She was also able to bring closure to a portion of her life. She now could put Paul to rest in her heart and move on with her life once again.

When the fall of 1924 came around, several of Pearl's church friends were off on their own. Pearl made friends with the people who worked with her at David's Department Store. She especially liked the Penwell girls, Doris, Ione, and their married sister, Mary Green.

Even though Pearl wasn't enrolled at the university, she was invited to many of the activities. Doris and Ione made sure Pearl had transportation to and from the Yearouts' so she could go places with them. She attended parties at the Penwells' home and went to several football games.

On the afternoons of the football games the store would close down and everyone would go and cheer for the home team. Pearl never really understood the rules or strategies of the game. She just loved being with her friends and cheering when a touchdown by the Moscow team was made.

Pearl received a letter from Roy in April of 1925. He was no longer living with Mrs. Sleighter and her family but had been out on his own for almost a year. He explained in the letter the reason he had finally left.

. . . Mrs. Sleighter informed me that if I couldn't get along with her daughter, Uldine, I would have to move out. I took her advice and went to work for Mr. Tom Hammond.

After the harvest was over, I had accumulated approximately $40.00 in wages. Unfortunately, when I went to collect my pay, Mr. Hammond told me that Mrs. Sleighter had already collected it. In order to avoid her collecting my wages in the future, I saddled up my horse and rode up into the Porcupine Hills. Last Fall and Winter I worked for Mr. Gus Schambourn. I earned $25.00 per month plus board. Unfortunately, when Spring arrived, Gus didn't have any money to pay me. Instead, he gave me a horse and good saddle for my wages. At this point in time, I now have two horses and two saddles.*

*Letters in this book from Roy to Pearl are actual letters, published here compliments of Roy Tooley.

255

In May of 1925, Pearl's sister, Helen, graduated from high school. By the first week of September she had moved to Spokane, Washington. Helen was now enrolled in the nursing program at St. Luke's Hospital. Helen had taken on the last name of the people she had been living with the last few years and now went by the name of Helen Bethmann. Mrs. Bethmann had helped Helen get enrolled in the school and was paying out of her own pocket for Helen to become a nurse.

Pearl's brother Roy, though only sixteen years old, was on his own. He was free from the feeling of being enslaved by the Sleighter family. Roy was now about six feet tall. Pearl wondered why he was so big when she and Helen were only five-two. She could vaguely remember one of her uncles, and he had seemed very tall. But to a seven-year-old, all grown-ups were tall.

The letter Pearl received from Roy just after her twenty-first birthday came from a little place in Alberta, Canada.

North Fork April 29, 1926

Dear Pearl,

I received the ties, and thank you very much for them. You bet I'll wear them, they are just fine.

We are having a little warmer weather now and hope it will keep up for a while.

I am working on a ranch on Heath Creek, have been since last fall, and like it pretty good. I am running a plough at present and resting up a little. The boss had a little saw mill, and we worked in the timber last winter. I guess that's the reason I am so big, from swinging an axe all day long.

I have three saddle horses and a fairly good saddle. All the boys are getting cars now, but I'd sooner stick to the old way and climb a "cayuse" when I want to go anywhere.

I don't think I can possibly come down there this summer, but I sure can thank you for your offer, but you know how a big brother feels. I think you could come out to Alberta instead as it would be a good outing for you, and it would be more reasonable if I was to help you instead.

You asked me if I ever like girls, well sometimes, but generally steer clear of them because they are queer little mortals "Ha, Ha."

Well here's wishing you a happy birthday.

With lots of love,
Roy

256

REMEMBERING MOTHER

Pearl received a letter from Helen in the middle of May. She wanted to make plans to do something with her during her summer break.

Spokane, May 17, 1926

Dear Pearl,

Naughty girl—what do you mean by going out on a party? You should know better than to have accidents. Francis is the only one who is allowed that stunt.

You will be surprised and no doubt not believe it when I tell you I have cut parties out of my diet list, as it isn't so very healthy and you always feel like "hell" the morning after. So am off wine and men for life and am ready to settle down and be a forlorn old maid.

What have you been doing with yourself, be sure you don't do any thing I wouldn't.

By the By, my vacation is the 19th of June—let's plan to do something interesting. I wish you could get your vacation the same time, unless you have other plans. I have until July 9th.

Roy wants us to come up to Canada and see him this summer, but that would take a lot of cash, but let's think it over and you find out what the expense would be, will you, and maybe it can be managed some way. Stranger things have happened.

Oh gee I'm sleepy, but just had to write and tell you this and you let me know what you think of it eh? But I want to do something this summer so nite nite.

"Swell dreams"
Love, Helen

In June of 1926 after Helen's first year in Spokane, she took the train to Moscow to visit with Pearl. They had such a wonderful time together. It was the first time in twelve years the two sisters had more than just an hour or two to visit with each other.

Pearl introduced Helen to everyone, and they liked her right away. Ione and Doris gave a party at their parents' house and invited everyone of "importance" from the store and college.

Helen was so cute with her long dark auburn hair and fading freckles. She was easy to spot in a crowd. The boys flirted with her enough to build her ego and danced with her every dance.

257

Aunt Lillie and Uncle Charley were so nice to Helen. They invited the two girls out to the house after church and made the best dinner. In the evening, Aunt Lillie took the girls for a ride out to the farm to meet Otto and the boys who were still at home.

Pearl had arranged for vacation time off from the store. Auntie Lillie trusted Pearl enough to let her take her new Chevrolet. Pearl and Helen wanted to drive to Orofino to visit the Lewises.

Florence Mills, a girl from Pearl's work, went with the two sisters to Orofino. The three of them gossiped and laughed the whole way. The only time they got serious was when the car would start to heat up climbing the steep hills.

The Lewises were happy to see Helen and Pearl again. Pearl was the happiest, however. It was a chance to finally see her youngest brother again, after so many years.

At first, the warmth Pearl had hoped for from her brother was not evident. He put on airs of being negative to everyone. It wasn't until later the first evening after supper, when the others were inside, that Pearl was finally able to talk to her fifteen-year-old sibling. She tried to express some of her deep feelings to him.

Pearl found Robert Earl in the backyard, sanding down a bench he had been assigned to repaint.

"What are you doing?" Pearl inquired of the young man.

"Sanding this old bench I have to paint," was Robert's snappy reply.

"Why do you need to sand it?" she questioned, hoping to start a conversation with him. "Why don't you just paint it and be done?" Pearl added.

" 'Cause if you don't sand it first then you'll just have splinters or peeling paint," he remarked.

"It seems to me you have been taught well. You are probably going to be a knowledgeable, self-sufficient gentleman one of these day," Pearl encouragingly stated.

"They work me to death around this place," Robert grouched. "You would think I was a just the handyman instead of a son."

"Well, little brother, I know exactly how you feel. Life has not been easy for any of us," Pearl continued. "But I have learned to look at work in a much more positive way the last few years. It's hard while you're doing it. However, when you finish and stand back to admire the fruits of your labors, you can feel good about the end product." She

258

paused for a few seconds before adding, "I know it's hard to see it that way at your age. When you get old like me, you'll see what I mean." She smiled at him, then sat back to watch him work.

"I don't remember you very well," Robert said softly. "I read the letters you sent, and sent you things when Mother said we should, but I can only remember seeing you one time a long time ago."

"I know, Robert. You were only three years old when we were separated," Pearl replied as the tears began to come to her eyes.

Robert could tell his sister was trying to keep from crying by the sound of her voice. "What were our real mother and father like?" the fifteen-year-old questioned.

"Robert, I was only nine years old when we were taken from our parents. I remember a stern father but a patient, loving mother. I remember her reading us stories and making sure we were fed and clothed properly. I remember her making sure our faces and hands were clean before she would let us go anyplace. I remember her taking the time to brush, curl, and comb my hair before I was allowed out of the house each day. I remember her nursing us when we were sick and taking us on walks and picnics when we were well. I can remember a lot of things about her. Most of all, I can remember the love I knew she had for all of us." Pearl paused to clear her choking throat.

"Well, if she loved us so much, why in hell's name did she do bad things and give us away?" questioned the confused youth.

"Robert, I've asked myself the same question over and over. But I can tell you this: I remember very clearly our mother hated letting that man from the children's home take us away from her. I can still remember that hurt and aching in her face as we rode off that terrible day. I remember her promise to come and get us. I don't know why she didn't." Pearl paused to reflect before continuing. "To me, Robert, it's like a puzzle with missing pieces. You can't tell what the real picture is until all the pieces are put in. You know, you and I are only pieces of our family puzzle. Someday I hope to have all the pieces, so I can put my own mind to rest over this whole mystery. Something must have stopped Mother from keeping her promise. I simply don't have all the answers. Maybe someday we will all know. For now, Robert, just believe me when I tell you that our mother loved us. She would have raised us if the choice was hers," Pearl finished her speaking, and the two of them sat silently together for a long time.

259

When Pearl and Helen got back to Moscow there was a note from Judge Forney. He had some more information about the business he was handling for Pearl. Auntie went with the two sisters to see the judge. He had some interesting news, but neither girl could understand exactly what it meant.

Thompson Falls, Mont. January 10, 1925

Clarence Knowles first being duly sworn an oath deposes and says that he is a brother of John W. Knowles Pvt.1/c co. 22, 20th engrs. And to Mrs Myrtle Broughton named as beneficiary in an insurance policy issued to him as a soldier by the United States Government, and that his sister was married to O.B. Tooley and that her oldest child Pearl Tooley was born in Thompson Falls and her second child Helen Tooley was born at Thompson Falls. The dates respectively being according to his belief and best recollection April 22, 1905 and Feb. 12, 1907.

Subscribed and sworn to before me this 10th day of December 1925.

Mrs. Frank Larson Belknop Mint

Both girls read this statement but were quite confused. They had been under the impression that their Uncle Clarence had been the one who had died and left them money. But now they realized it was their Uncle John and their mother was the beneficiary. Why wasn't she the one getting the money?

Pearl had decided when she returned from seeing her brother it was time for some big changes in her life. The trip back and forth to the Yearouts' every day was getting very tiresome. Even though she still loved Auntie and Uncle Charley, Pearl felt restricted in her ability to go and do as she pleased. After all, she was twenty-one and making enough money to support herself. It was time to move from the farm and be on her own.

She had a special spring in her step and a lump in her throat at the same time. Pearl wondered how she could be so happy and excited yet be carrying a certain sadness also. Together with Florence and Ione, Pearl had just paid her share of the fifteen dollars a month rent on their very own apartment in town. It would be so wonderful to finally be her own boss and out from under the critical eyes of Aunt Lillie and Uncle Charley. But inspite of the restrictions of living at the Yearouts' the past few years, Peal loved the couple as if they were her own parents.

Living with a reverend of the church had its own drawbacks. Pearl had been expected to live by all the rules and standards of the church and to be an example to other members. She had played the role well because that type of behavior seemed to come natural to her. She always wanted to do what was right. Pearl was required to dress rather simply and never allowed to wear makeup. The church insisted their members be humble people. Pearl had not minded; it was such a small price to pay for Auntie's help and love. Pearl had been treated like a real daughter and considered Aunt Lillie as a substitute mother. The twenty-one-year-old young woman would miss that close relationship.

Even though she and Auntie had discussed the possibility of Pearl moving into town, it was going to be difficult to tell Auntie she had actually made the move. She hated the thoughts of giving up the security of a family who cared about her, but it would be so much more convenient for everyone with her living in town.

Auntie was chopping vegetables for a salad when Pearl entered the house after work.

"Oh, good, you're home," Auntie greeted Pearl, "You're just in time to mix up a cake for dessert. I know how you love making them."

"I can do that," Pearl responded. "I'll go wash up and change my clothes."

When Pearl returned to the kitchen to help with supper Auntie started up the conversation.

"You know, I've been thinking. Why don't we paint the kitchen this fall? What color do you think it should be?"

"I think you should be the one to make that decision, Auntie...." Pearl paused, not knowing quite how to break the news about the apartment. "This is your kitchen. You should make the choice of color you want it to be."

"It's your kitchen, too. You spend as much time cooking here as I do," Auntie responded.

"Auntie, you know how we have been talking about the possibility of me sharing an apartment in town with some of the girls from the store. Well..." The words seemed to choke in her throat as Auntie looked at her with a wrinkle forming in her brow. "... Florence, Ione, and I found this great four-room place with a porch and bathroom for only five dollars a month each. It will be much more convenient for all of us. I won't have to be imposing on your for rides back and forth, and it will also free up the downstairs bedroom for a sewing or guest room." Pearl babbled on trying to point out all the positive aspects of her decision before Auntie could express her thoughts.

Pearl had caught the motherly woman off guard. Auntie seemed almost dumbfounded at what she was hearing. Pearl waited through the deadening silence before speaking.

"What do you think, Auntie? I know this action was quite sudden, but when the apartment owner called Ione today we had to make our minds up in a hurry. He said if we wanted it we would need to give him the money today, or he would let someone else rent it. We went right over after work, and now we can move in tomorrow." Peal continued to be happy and upbeat, in an effort to bring Auntie around with the enthusiasm.

"My, my," Aunt Lillie stammered. "I guess I wasn't quite prepared to have you say you were moving."

Pearl could see the tears forming in the woman's eyes. "Auntie, please don't be upset with me," Pearl pleaded. "You know I'll still come out here all the time. How could I stay away from you? You've become my mom." The tears gushed to the surface as Pearl finally admitted out loud the words she had felt in her heart for several year. Auntie was her mentor, her role model, and her confidante, all the things a good mother is to a maturing young woman.

"God gave me a wonderful gift when you became my friend," Pearl said as she took Auntie's hand in hers. "You have been here to help me through some rough times. What would I have ever done without you?" Pearl resounded.

"You have been the daughter I prayed for many years ago," Auntie confessed. "I settled with the thought that having my two boys would fulfill all the mothering instincts I had. When you came along, Pearl, with your special quiet qualities, I just wanted to be around and help you grow and mature into the woman I knew was inside you. I'm so delighted you came into our lives. What would I have done when Paul was killed if you hadn't been here to give me support and strength?"

The two women held tight to each other's hands for several minutes until they could stop the tears.

"Pearl, you have my blessings," Auntie sincerely spoke. "It's time for you to spread your wings and fly from the nest, my dear. I know you will lift and soar to great heights as you journey through your life. As long as I'm alive, you can count on me, just as if I were your own mother."

"Oh, Auntie," Pearl sniffled. "You will receive a glorious crown in heaven for the service you have given to me and all the other people you have helped around here. I love you."

The cake never got baked, yet the two women were able to part the next day with a sweet taste in their souls. The bond between them would never be broken.

Pearl moved into the four-room apartment with a sunporch and an indoor bathroom, sharing the place with the two other girls who also worked at the department store. Pearl really felt grown-up and self-sufficient now. She wrote to Helen the first week of August and received a letter in return on the fourteenth.

Spokane, Wa. 8-11-26 2:30 A.M.

Dear Pearl,

Read your letter this last P.M. and am surprising myself by answering it P.D.Q. I'm glad you left Yearouts and have an apartment, it is so much nicer and you are free to do as you want to without any razzing from the side lines.

I bet you are all dolled and frilled up—if you were here a four room apartment with porch and bath would cost you at least $30 or $40 a month and then maybe not as good.

My recreation since I came back has consisted of working nights, sleeping in the day—at intervals—and spending two or three hours in the dentist chair. My dates have gone to smash as I can't keep them. Oh I get calls but never go out as they work of days and I of nights, pretty keen huh. Harry calls about every evening, sends candy etc., but I'm tired of him and think I'll be off men for life unless he is sixty and has long white whiskers and walks with a cane.

How are Florence and Walter, tell them hello for me. I bet Florence thinks I am a stump, from the way I acted on the trip.

Guess how much I weighed when I got here after my vacation, 144 lbs., can you feature it? Believe me I reduced in a hurry. I am down to 126 lbs. now and am going to hit 115lbs. if I have the nerve but I'm afraid it is pretty hard and the doctors are bawling me out right and left. Dr. T.M. said he would spank me if I didn't quit as it is too hard on my heart. I should worry, but guess I'll let up on it for a while 'cause every one is saying "Oh how pale you are," it makes me sick. I'll send you a list next time I write, but you won't reduce as quick as I did because it is foolish

263

and I took medicine that nearly knocked me out. If Dr. T.M. knew it he would kill me.

If you'll send me your height and weight I'll figure out your tolerance and I bet you'll lose 2 lbs. per week if you follow it, or more. So much for Obesity!!

I bet you had a good time up in the mountains, it has been three or four years since I was there, Waffles—yum yum—they are black listed for me Boo Hoo.

Francis is having maternity cases, she was up all night tonight and is about all in. Morva is head nurse on 2 H so we don't see much of each other.

I have just written to Robert and hope he answers as I haven't had a letter from him since our trip. Guess I'll have to write to Roy and I surely am sorry that we didn't get to see him, but perhaps we can next year.

Write when you haven't anything else to do as a letter is always welcome.

> With Love,
> Helen

LOST AND FOUND

The warm rays of the afternoon sun made reflecting sparkles in the gray ringed puddles that had collected on the streets from rain the night before. The black soil of the roads and the small white wildflowers growing along the edges made a sharp contrast in color in the small Utah town.

Sigurd, located in central Utah, lay right on the only road into Fish Lake, the best fishing hole in the state according to some folks. There was also some mining going on not too far away, making this little spot the perfect place for a few stores, a pool hall, and a gas station. Pretty quiet place in the winter. As soon as locals and tourists could get back to the lake in the spring, the townspeople could make a fair living.

Ten-year-old Susan May took out her old, worn skipping rope and looked for a dry place to start her jumping. It didn't matter to her the man sitting in the big wooden chair on his porch was taking a nap. She just needed a good place to play.

"Yellow, yellow, who's my fellow? Rich man, poor man, beggar man, thief, doctor, lawyer, merchant, chief, tinker, taylor, cowboy, sailor," the girl repeated over and over as she jumped in rhythm.

"Pearl!" the drowsy man in the chair called out. "Go somewhere else to do that," he mumbled.

"Mr. Tooley!" the young girl responded. "My name isn't Pearl. You know, it's Susan May." She chuckled at the man, who knew her real name.

The girl's response woke him up. He focused on the familiar face of the Nebeker girl who lived next door.

Susan walked up close to Obe. She sat down on his knee, as she did with all the neighbors. "Why did you call me Pearl?" she inquired.

"I was just dreaming of long ago, I guess."

"Long ago?" she questioned. "Did you know a little girl named Pearl long ago?"

"Yes. One of my little girl's name is Pearl," he confessed.

"You have kids?" Susan May asked with a puzzled look on her face. "Where are they now?"

With each new question and answer Susan May's excitement heightened. Obe Tooley knew he might as well satisfy her curiosity or she would "hound him to death."

Well, many years ago I had a wife and four little kids. But they went away and I haven't been able to find them," Obe stated.

"Your children are lost?" Susan questioned with a sad look on her face. "Did you try real hard to find them?" she continued. "I would be so afraid if I were lost from my daddy."

Obe pondered the question in silence.

"Did you try real hard to find them?" she asked again, not willing to give up the questioning until she had the answer she was trying to get.

"Well, I tried one time," Obe slowly said. "I couldn't get any information. The man at the home where my children went said I would have to wait until they were bigger before he could tell me where they were," he remarked.

"Are they bigger now?" the girl relentlessly questioned.

"Hmm . . . I guess they are," he replied as he did some simple math in his head. "At least my oldest girl is big enough."

"Well, if they are bigger now, then you need to go find them," Susan May insisted. "If I was lost, I'd want my daddy to look for me. Even if I was bigger when he found me."

"You would, huh?" Obe gave the little girl a nudge and lifted her off his knee before standing. "Why don't you go back to your jumping and stop bothering the old folks around here?" He gave her a quick wink and smile.

"OK, Mr. Tooley. You need to go and find your children!" she yelled at him and started her jumping again.

Obe went to his dresser drawer and took out the rectangular box that held his precious memories. There were some pictures, letters, and a gold band. The items were all that was left of a past life. The things brought back a lot of "if" questions he had tried to forget. He took out the letter from the Lewiston Children's Home and reread it to make sure he remembered the contents.

. . . all information concerning the whereabouts of the Tooley children is confidential for their safety. It can not be released until they are twenty-one years of age . . .

He looked at the calendar on the wall, and found today's date. "May 2, 1926," he said out loud. "Well, what do you know? Pearl turned twenty-one ten days ago."

The trip from Sigurd, Utah, to Lewiston, Idaho, took several days even in the 1923 Ford pickup Obe Tooley was driving. He recalled the same trip years earlier taking much longer by horse and wagon.

Many things had changed in the modernization of the country especially in the West, since he had last lived in Idaho. There were now trains, cars, and telephones nearly everywhere a person went.

He hoped he had remembered to bring all the things he would need to get the information from the children's home. He knew he had to try again to find his children if he was ever going to have peace of mind in this life. If not for his own conscience, at least to get away from the eternal nagging of little Susan May. She had been reminding him every day for the past two months about finding his kids.

Obe knocked at the large front door of the Lewiston Children's Home the morning of August 14, 1926. He could only imagine his four youngsters living here. He wondered what this big house could tell of their experiences, if it could talk. Obe remembered how he had felt as he listened to Myrtle screaming at him twelve years ago. He questioned in his mind why that darned money had meant so much to him.

This is a real nice place, he rationalized to himself as he waited for the door to be opened. *The kids were probably OK here,* he thought. *More so than they would have been living in the odd places I've lived in since Sandpoint.*

Obe Tooley knocked again. This time a matronly woman answered.

"Yes?" she asked of the man standing on the porch.

"Good day, madame." Obe graciously tipped his hat and made his introduction and request. "I'm Mr. Tooley. I've come to find out about my children who were brought here some twelve years ago."

"You will need to talk to Reverend Covington, the superintendent, about the matter, sir. Please have a seat and I'll get him," the woman responded.

Obe looked around the room at the pictures of children on the walls. He wondered if any of the faces of the girls were those of Pearl or Helen or the ones of the boys were those of Roy or Earl. Maybe he could look closer later.

Reverend Covington entered the room with a stern look on his face. He had dealt with aggressive parents before and was prepared to throw this man out if he was here to make trouble.

"Good morning," the reverend greeted Obe unconvincingly. "What can I do for you today?"

Obe reached in his jacket pocket and retrieved the letter. He opened it up for the reverend to read. "I have a letter here that I received from this home in 1922. It says I can find out about my girl Pearl Tooley when she turns twenty-one. Is that the truth?" Obe asked.

"Yes, it's true. The state of Idaho will allow us to reveal information about a child who has been in this home, to the parents, when the child has turned twenty-one. We have to have positive proof you are the parent," the reverend explained. "We can't just give out that kind of personal information without proof of identification."

"Yes, sir. I understand how important that would be. What kind of identification do you need?" Obe inquired as he opened up a big envelope he had carried in with him. He dumped the contents on the desk in front of the reverend and spread the documents apart. There were pictures, licenses, and stamped and certified papers with a picture and a judge's signature. Affidavits of identity and everything Obe could think of to prove who he was. Even the superintendent was amazed at the lengths this man had gone to in order to identify himself.

"Well, Mr. Tooley, I'll have my secretary check our files. We'll see if we can give you any information," Mr. Covington remarked after reading the documents.

Obe gathered his papers and returned them back to the envelope. The reverend left the father alone in the room. It seemed like forever before the reverend came back in the office with a folder in his hand.

"I see, Mr. Tooley, you had several children who came to use in 1914," the reverend stated as he thumbed through the folder. "Well, we won't be able to give you information."

Obe cut the man off abruptly. "I'm not here to have you tell me what you can't do. I heard that years ago. The only one I want to know about is my daughter Pearl. She is now twenty-one and can make her own adult decisions about her real father. I just want to know where to start lookin'."

"Uh-hum," the Reverend Covington cleared his throat. "Yes, you're right. Pearl did turn twenty-one on April 22 of this year. OK, Mr. Tooley. If you would like, I can make a telephone call. I'll see if I can find out from her last family if they have been in contact with her recently."

"I'd be obliged if you would do that, sir," Obe replied in a more humble tone. "It's been such a long time and all."

"Operator," the reverend addressed the voice in the telephone, "can you connect me to Moscow, Idaho? Lincoln 5–7–2–8–0 please. Thank you; I'll wait."

Obe sat nervously as the man behind the desk listened to the unanswered rings.

"Hello," he finally said. "This is Reverend Covington from the children's home in Lewiston. Is this Mrs. Yearout?" He paused while the person on the other end of the line responded. "Oh, I'm just fine, and yourself?" the man continued his pleasantries to the person he was conversing with. "Is Pearl Tooley still living with you folks?" he questioned. Then he listened patiently for the explanation. "Oh, I see. Yes . . . Yes . . . OK. Thank you so much, I appreciate the information. . . . No, no, she's not in any trouble. We just like to know where are youngsters go when they are all grown-up. Yes, thanks again. Good-bye."

The reverend hung up the telephone and wrote something down on a blank sheet of paper. When he was finished he looked up at the fidgeting man across the desk. "I was talking to the woman of the house where Pearl has been living for the last few years. She reported Pearl has just recently moved from her place into town. The woman couldn't remember the exact address of her apartment. She did say, however, that Pearl is working at a business in town called David's Department Store. Mrs. Yearout said most anyone there would know where she is living and how to get in touch with her," Mr. Covington remarked.

"Thank you for the information," Obe replied as he took the paper full of directions from the outstretched hand of the reverend.

"Mr. Tooley," the superintendent inquired, "just one question. Why, after all these years, do you *now* want to see your kids?"

There was a long pause. A quiet, humble answer came from the now fifty-eight-year-old man. "I guess I just have to tell each one that I'm sorry." Obe said no more. He left the Lewiston Children's Home that day and headed north to Moscow, Idaho.

STRANGE SURPRISE

David's Department Store had been bustling with people the morning of August 16, 1926. Women were taking advantage of the "Sale on Fabrics" that was being advertised in the newspaper and around the outside of the store. Mothers who sewed were looking for bargains on material. It was the time of year to make school apparel for their youngsters. Pearl had sold yards and yards of fabric that morning. By the time three o'clock had rolled around, most of the shoppers were gone. Only a few people were sorting through the remaining goods.

Pearl was putting away some yardage she had been showing a lady when the gray-haired man came to the counter. As she looked his way, the man asked her a question.

"Are you Pearl Tooley?" he asked the girl behind the counter.

Pearl looked in amazement at the stranger. She wondered how the man knew her name. Thinking this might be some sort of trouble, judging by the man's appearance, she studied his face for a clue to his inquiry. She very cautiously gave the stranger her answer. "Yes, I'm Pearl," the curious young woman replied.

Without hesitation or pregreeting, the man on the other side of the counter blurted out, "Well, if you're Pearl Tooley, I'm your father."

Pearl was shocked by the boldness of this pronouncement. She had been so young the last time she had seen her father that she was not sure if this man was him or not. She studied his face for a glimmer of recognition. Her mind couldn't bring forward the right images to connect this aged man with what she could remember of her dad. She wasn't even sure this person was telling her the truth.

"Uh, uh," she stammered. She felt so awkward not knowing what to say or do. She finally got out the word: "Hello."

"I can come back later when you get off work," he suggested. "If you tell me where you live, I'll stop by and we can talk."

The trembling young woman was still in a state of shock. She didn't know exactly what to think about the claims this old man was making. "How did you find me?" Pearl questioned.

"I talked to a man at the children's home in Lewiston," he answered.

"Oh," she responded. "Well, let me see," she said as she fumbled to find a clean piece of writing paper. "I live at Three twenty-five Wicker Street, Apartment Two. You can come at seven o'clock this evening. We can talk then.'' She gave the man the instructions, and he turned to walk away. He stopped and looked back at the young woman.

"You're grown up to be a nice-looking lady, Pearl," he remarked. He then turned again and walked out of the store.

Pearl watched his every movement until he had exited the store and was out of her sight. She stood motionless as her mind and heart tried to sort through all the emotions. She was trying to pick the ones she was feeling. Was she happy or angry? Did she care or not care? Was there love or hate? Maybe the blankness and confusion stemmed from the fact that she really didn't know if the man was truly her father or not. Perhaps he was just some sinister person trying to manipulate her for unthinkable reasons.

"Pearl. Are you all right?" Mary Green questioned the shaking girl. "You look like you've just seen a ghost."

"I think I have," she replied while still holding onto the counter to steady herself.

"Mary, did you see the man who was just here at the counter talking to me?" Pearl inquired.

"Yes. Didn't we have the fabric he wanted?" Mary jokingly asked.

Pearl looked at her friend with glazed eyes. "What he wanted was me," she remarked. "I mean, the man said he was my father."

"Mary looked at Pearl with a puzzled stare. "Was he your father?"

"I don't know. It's been so long since I last saw my father. I was only nine years old then. I just don't know if he's really my father or not," Pearl stated. "Mary, I need a big favor. Would you come over to the apartment a little before seven o'clock tonight? That man is coming back to see me then. I don't want to be alone with this guy until I find out what his motives are for coming here. If he's not my father, then no telling what the man has up his sleeve. If he is my father, I still would like some company until I'm sure just what he's doing here," Pearl pleaded.

"Oh, you poor thing," Mary responded in sympathy for her friend's dilemma. "Of course I'll come. Should I bring my rolling pin just in case he wants trouble?" Mary was serious and expressed her determination to help. The way she made her eyebrows lift and her mouth twist made a little smile come to Pearl's worried face.

"OK," Pearl snickered. "But be sure to keep it hidden under your skirt, so we can attack by surprise if we need to."

Pearl paced back and forth around the living room of her small shared apartment. She rearranged the cushions of the couch and dusted the little table at least ten times when she returned home from work. She prayed her friend Mary would get here before the old man arrived. Pearl had been rehearsing in her mind what she would do and say if the man proved to be her father and what she might do if he wasn't who he claimed to be. She worried he might be some fraud trying to flimflam her in some way.

When the knock came at the door, she braced herself before opening it.

"Thank goodness it's you, Mary." Pearl said as she heaved a big sigh of relief.

"Hi, Pearl. I just dropped by to see how you're doing," the girl said in an artificial voice, in case the man had arrived before she had.

"It's all right, Mary. He hasn't come yet. I'm so glad you got here first," Pearl expressed with a wide smile.

Mary had just gone to the kitchen to make some coffee when another knock sounded on the front door. Pearl took a deep breath. She opened it to reveal the person on the other side.

"Hello, Pearl," the man greeted her.

"I see you found your way here," she responded.

The man waited for an invitation to enter the house. When he didn't get one, he asked permission himself. "Can I come in?"

"Oh, yes," Pearl stammered. "Come in. This is my neighbor Mary Green. She just stopped by for a cup of coffee," Pearl tried to spit out the words she had been rehearsing.

The man entered and looked at Pearl in a mellow way. "You don't remember me very well, do you girl?"

Pearl shook her head in a negative gesture. "No, I really don't. I'm sorry."

"It's all right," he said. "It's been a long time. Both of us have done a lot of changin'. I could recognize you anywhere, thought. You look just like my sister Elizabeth looked when she was about fifteen," he remarked. "Your mother and I gave you your second name after her. Because I thought you looked like her as a baby."

The information about the name was interesting, but anyone could have made up that story, Pearl thought.

"Do you know anything about the whereabouts of your brothers or sister?" the man asked.

"Yes, I know where all of them are. I promised Mother I would keep track of each of them," Pearl replied without divulging any identifying information.

Does Helen still have her long red curls?" he questioned. "I see you have cut your long hair off."

"Her hair is still quite long," Pearl responded. "As for my hair, I cut it real short a few years ago. It was in such bad shape after I had a bout with pneumonia."

"Well, short hair looks good on you," he said in a complimentary way. "Your sister Helen sure had the coloring of your mother's people. Now you, on the other hand, got the Tooley good looks." He was hoping that declaration and a smile would break the ice that seemed to be present around the girls.

"How about Roy and Earl? I bet they are both all grown-up now?" He paused to do some counting in his head. "Let's see now; Roy must be seventeen, and Earl about fifteen. They're both probably bigger than their old dad."

"I haven't seen Roy. In his last letter, he said he was six-two," Pearl reported.

"My, my, six-two. He takes after his mother's people also. The men in her family were real tall. John Junior and Albert were both at least six foot," Obe commented. "What about Earl?"

"Helen and I saw Earl just a few weeks ago. He's not too awfully tall, but he may have more growing to do. He has more my coloring and looks to be about five-seven," she reported.

"Do you remember your mother at all, Pearl?" Obe asked sincerely.

"Yes, I think I can remember pretty much what she looked like twelve years ago. What happened to her?" was the curious young woman's question.

"Well, it's kind of a long story." the old man replied.

"That's all right," Pearl insisted. "I've waited almost thirteen years to get some answers. Why don't you start back in Lakeview, the night all the trouble started? I'm old enough to understand the truth."

She listened to the old man retell the events of those terrible weeks back in 1914. He recounted the story about the arrests and the sickness she and her siblings had suffered. Pearl could tell this man had been part of that suffering. She could tell by the way he retold the incidents he had also gone through some of the hardships she could remember. Pearl knew this man telling the stories was really her father.

"What happened to us, Daddy?" Pearl asked. "Why did our family get separated and not put back together? We kids tried to wait and keep up hope. We wanted to be back together as it had been before. Why didn't you ever come to get us?''

The old man sat with his head looking down at the floor. He was not able to look the questioning girl in the face, for the shame he was feeling.

"From the day we were taken away from Mother and went with that mean man to the children's home, none of us kids ever got a letter or anything from you or Mother. Why?''

"Now, missy, it was like this." Obe would try to explain part of the truth, in hope's she would understand *his* point of view toward the whole thing. "Your mother and I were not getting along very good when all the trouble came. Both of us were selling the liquor when we were arrested. Your mother thought I should solve the problem one way, and I thought it should be done another. We just didn't agree on much of anything at that time." Obe paused for a moment to reflect on that time so long ago before continuing.

"The sheriff in Lakeview and the Judge in Sandpoint were both a couple of crooks in my opinion. They both wanted me to pay them a bunch of money. They threatened to *make examples of us* if I refused. Well, five hundred dollars was more money than any man in his right mind would pay to those varmints. I just couldn't do it." He paused to see his daughter's reaction, but she sat expressionless listening to his explanation.

"I know your mother tried to write to you while she was still in jail. The man at the home wrote her back and told her not to write anymore. He said it would make you kids unhappy. She got out of jail before I did. She didn't have any money to hire a lawyer to get you back from the home. When your mom would come to visit me, we just fought and fussed at each other every time. She finally got the legal papers together and filed for divorce. She said if I would bring you kids back to her she would remarry me again if I wanted. I guess I was a little hardheaded and waited too long, in her opinion, to try." The man hung his head again as he continued his confession.

"After I got out of jail, I signed the divorce papers. I then shipped out for Alaska and stayed there for six years. It wasn't until I came back to the States that I tried to find out what had happened to everyone. I stopped by the children's home in 1922. They told me I would have to wait until you were twenty-one before they would give me any information about where you were. They also told me all of you had been adopted out. I just figured you were happy and didn't need me around anymore. I wasn't cut out to be a family man, I guess.''

Pearl didn't know how to respond to the story her father was telling. She didn't know if she wanted to give him a hug or a slap. All she knew was since their separation in 1914 all of the Tooley children's lives had been anything but happy.

"Well, Daddy," Pearl stated, "none of us have had very good lives since we were separated. Earl is the only one who has had any stability in his life. However, he had been so spoiled, the woman he lives with can't control him. He basically just runs wild. You may not have been cut out to be a family man, but we children have suffered without our own parents to raise us.''

The old man just hung his head. His eyes began to fill with moisture.

"Would you like a drink or something?" Pearl asked graciously, knowing the disclosure was hard on the aging man.

"OK. Maybe a cup of coffee if you have it," he requested.

"I'll get it," Mary volunteered. She went to the kitchen, letting the man continue with his tale.

"After you came back from Alaska, what did you do then?" Pearl inquired.

"I worked my way down through Idaho and into Salt Lake City. I stayed there for a few months, then headed further south. I didn't know just where I was going. I just hoped to find a place where I could have a place to make a livin' again. When I got to the town of Sigurd, Utah, I took sick with pneumonia and nearly died. If it hadn't been for a good woman who nursed me back to life, I would have died right there. After that experience, I guess I got soft. I sent your momma a letter and told her about you kids being gone. I told her if she wanted to hire a legal man to help us, I'd go back to Sandpoint and get her." Obe paused again as Mary brought him a cup of coffee. He took a few sips of the hot liquid.

"What did Momma say to that?" Pearl asked.

"Nothin', girl. I never heard from your momma again. I don't even know if she got my letter. So I just stayed in Sigurd and opened up a pool hall. I've been there ever since.''

"So you don't know anything more about my mother's where-abouts?" Pearl desperately asked.

"Well, I wrote to her adopted brother, Clarence, a few years back making some inquiries. He wrote back and said she had gone up into Canada. I guess from what he said she married my old business partner,

Nat Broughton. But I never heard from her, so I don't know if that's right or not," Obe explained.

Pearl sat quietly thinking as her father drank his coffee. She felt he was not telling her everything. But at least she now had a few of the missing pieces to the puzzle she had been trying to find. She knew what had happened to her father, and perhaps soon she could find her mother also.

"I'd sure like to see the other kids, too," the graying man stated. "Are they around here somewhere?"

"Earl has been adopted by a family, and he considers them to be his folks. I have only seen him two times in the last twelve years. I don't think it wouldn't be a good idea to try and see him right now. He's still so young and self-centered. Maybe you should wait until he gets a little older to see him. Right now he is quite rebellious and has threatened to run away several times," Pearl reported to her father.

"How about Roy?" Obe asked.

"I have Roy's address. He's way up in Alberta, Canada, working on a ranch. He had a pretty rough time with the family who took him. He left them last year and is now on his own. But, I'll give you his address," the daughter remarked as she got out her pencil and paper.

"And Helen. Where is your sister?" in inquired.

"She's in Spokane, Washington, going to nursing school," Pearl reported. "It's only a day's drive from here, and the roads are real good. Or you can catch a train up and back."

Pearl went to the small cabinet drawer and returned with Helen's last letter. She wanted to make sure the address was correct before writing it down. "There now," she said as she handed the information she had written on the paper to her father. "The apartment is real close to St. Luke's Hospital, where Helen is going to school."

"Well, fancy that. My little girl is goin' to be a real nurse," Obe bragged as if he had something to do with it. "She'll probably be able to make a good livin' doin' nursin' work."

The hour was getting late and Pearl didn't know what to do with her newly reunited relative. But Obe helped her decide what the next move should be.

"Pearl, do you mind if your daddy sleeps here on the couch tonight? I'll wait until mornin' to head on over to Spokane," the father asked.

She wanted to say no. But she had been taught to be a better Christian than that. Not because of anything her father had encouraged her to learn, but by others who also lived that way.

"Sure. I mean OK. I guess it will be all right. I can't offer you a bed, because I have two other girls who live here. We all share the same bedroom," Pearl responded. "I'm sorry for the poor condition of this sofa. We are hoping to get a better one."

"Oh, it's just fine for my old bones," Obe stated. "It'll be better than sleepin' out in the truck. I've been doin' that, when I can't find a better place to rest."

She showed her father where the bathroom was, then went to the linen closet and took out a sheet. She took a blanket and a pillow off her own bed and went back to the living room. She made a bed on the sofa for her dad.

Pearl's two roommates came home about nine that night. She introduced the stranger to them as her father. They graciously greeted the man and told Pearl he was welcome to stay on the sofa for the night.

The young woman was still in a state of shock and disbelief. She contemplated the events that had transpired that day. She knew there was still so many pieces of her life's puzzle missing. However, she felt perhaps this was the first step in finding answers to her parents' abandonment of their children.

Pearl rose early the next morning. She wanted to be up and about before her guest woke up. She had a strong urge to impress upon her father what a competent woman she had grown up to be. She didn't know if he would even notice or care, but she was going to see her dad had a fine meal before he left for Spokane.

The smell of coffee brewing and sausage frying in the small apartment was enough to wake any hungry stomach. Obe's was no exception.

"Smells like someone's rustlin' up some fine grub in here," Obe stated as he entered the kitchen.

"Well, it would be easier if I had a decent knife to cut this bread with," Pearl said as she struggled to cut a loaf of bread with the wobbly knife table.

"I may have a better one out in the car. Would you like me to go and get it?" the hungry man offered.

"Oh, no. You just sit down here and I'll get you a cup of coffee. The rest of your breakfast will be ready in a few minutes," the experienced young woman declared. "How do you like your eggs?"

"Sunny side up," he replied. "Do you know how to cook them that way?" Obe questioned his busy daughter.

"Yes. I've been doing a lot of cooking the last few years. Most of my employment in the past has been cooking and cleaning for rich folks. I've only been working at the department store for about a year," Pearl responded.

"Lookin' to make some man a good wife someday, huh?" the father commented. "Do you have a special beau yet?" he continued to question.

Pearl blushed as she reported to her father, "No, I don't. I swore off men a long time ago. I've found most men are not much better than beasts. They are all right to have as friends, but that's as far it goes for me."

"Sounds like someone has either broken a heart or two, or someone has had her own broken," Obe stated. He chuckled at his confirmed bachelorette daughter.

"No," she lied as she blushed again. "Let's change the subject. Here's your eggs. Just eat your breakfast and stop talking about my non–love life," Pearl jokingly demanded. "What about my other relatives, Daddy? Do you know where any of them are?" Pearl questioned, hoping to find some more missing puzzle pieces. "I can vaguely remember a grandpa. But didn't he die when I was about six or seven?" she asked.

"Your mother's father and brothers lived in Thompson Falls, where you and Helen were born. But you're right: your grandfather John Knowles died while we were living in Sandpoint. Your mother was awfully upset. She didn't find out about it until several weeks after his death. They had been a very close family, and your momma was heartbroken when he died. Your Uncle Albert went to Nevada to do some mining. He was killed in an accident several years ago. He was only in his twenties when he died.

"Now your Uncle John lived with us for a while in Trout Creek and then Sandpoint. He was a good young man, and you kids liked him awfully well. I heard he went into the army and was killed about eight or nine years ago. He was also in his twenties.

"Your grandpa John remarried before he died. He and his second wife adopted a boy by the name of Clarence. He's not your blood, but by law he is considered a brother to your mother. He lives in Thompson Falls still, I think." Obe paused for a few minutes to finish mopping up the egg yolks with his toasted bread.

"Now my people are scattered all over back east. I never hear from any of them," Obe reported.

"Do you ever write to any of them?" Pearl questioned.

"No, not for about twenty years. I don't think I know any of their addresses," he replied.

"Well, how do you expect folks to write to you if you don't write back?" the young woman scolded.

"You're right, missy," he agreed. "When I get back home, I promise I'll write to you, if you'll write back to me."

As soon as the good-byes were said and her father had driven off, Pearl hurried to the telephone to make a long-distance call. She knew a letter would never get to Helen in time, and Pearl wanted to prepare her sister. Pearl didn't want Helen to experience the same shock she had yesterday. She wanted to call and warn her sister about the visitor she would receive tomorrow. Knowing her red-haired sister's temperament, Pearl knew she wouldn't even talk to the stranger. She would simply tell him to go away if she wasn't prepared.

"Hello, Helen, this is Pearl. Have I got something to tell you," the news courier announced. "No, I'm not getting married. Hold onto the wall, or sit down. What I'm going to say will totally shock you." Pearl paused to wait for a comment. "OK. Are you ready? . . . Be prepared to have a visitor come to see you tomorrow."

Pearl listened as her now-curious sister asked, "Who?"

"Our long-lost *father* just left my apartment. He is headed to Spokane to see you," Pearl informed Helen. "No, I'm not joking. He came to the store yesterday and then to my place last evening. I didn't recognize him at first. But after we had talked for a while, I knew he was really our dad." Pearl continued telling Helen everything she could remember about their dad's conversations, then instructed her sister to write and tell her everything that happened when she saw him. "No, you don't have to hide. He's fine," the older sister advised. "I just didn't want you to be caught off guard like I was. And not knowing whether to believe his stories or not. He's driving a Model T pickup and he's wearing a medium brown suit. Anyway, that's what he was wearing when he left here. He might change before he sees you." Pearl paused to listen to her now-nervous little sister. "Helen. It will be OK. Just be yourself. I've got to get to work, so write me. Good-bye."

The letter Pearl had been waiting for was in the mailbox the following week.

Dear Pearl,

I can't begin to thank you for the telephone call prior to Daddy's visit. You were right, I didn't recognize him either. It was good he talked to you first, I would have told him to get out.

I had packed a picnic dinner and had it ready when he arrived. We ate it out in the park. My two roommates were due home at the apartment and I didn't want them to question me about past things. I didn't want them to over hear anything either.

I really didn't know what to talk to him about. But he said one thing I thought was rather interesting. We were talking about our Uncles, John and Clarence. And, he asked me if you or I had gotten any insurance money yet. When I told him no, he dropped the subject. He immediately started talking about the place he is living now, some little town in Utah.

He only stayed for a couple of hours because I had to go back to the hospital. I couldn't invite him to stay over night. We can't have men visitors stay in the dormitory.

He said he would stay in touch and promised to write when he got back home. It was just such a strange visit, talking to my father and having him be like just another stranger.

Well I've got to get back to the hospital,

Love, Helen

The next few months were filled with letters back and forth between family members. Pearl wrote to Roy, and Helen to Robert Earl. Helen received distressing news back from Lottie Lewis, however, about Robert. She reported that Robert had run away from home the week after Helen had visited. Mrs. Lewis hadn't heard a word from him. She hoped if he contacted either of his sisters they would let her know if he was all right.

Pearl received a letter from her father the last day of August.

Aug. 27, 1926

Dear Pearl,

I am sending you a basket of candy and that knife I forgot to bring you. I got home all right but awful tired. Rite to Roy and tell him if he wants to come to me I will send him the money. Any time you want to come let me know.

From your daddy, O. A. Tooley
Sigurd, Utah

Cowley Alba. Nov. 15, 1926

Dear Pearl,

I received your last letter and was very glad to hear from you. I think I will go to Utah about the first of December.

So Robert has run away, hope he gets along alright because it is pretty hard for a boy his age to get along, but I guess he will tough it out alright if he is like me. Ha Ha . . . as I have been working since I was 14 years old, pretty hard at times too. But work makes a person big and strong I guess.

We have all had to work so I needn't kick. I haven't heard from Helen since early in the fall, hope she is getting along alright.

It is pretty cold weather now, think it will snow soon. I am riding horses for a living now for a while, some buck pretty hard but it's lots of fun. One of the boys was bucked off the other day and the horse drug him for about a hundred feet, hurt him pretty bad, but you can expect that when they ride any kind of a horse.

We had to drive the cattle to town the other day to ship them back home, pretty wild ones in the bunch it was a hard time to get them loaded.

I don't know how I will like it down in Utah, do they have much ranching there yet? I'd like to be where I can ride a horse once in a while but I guess it will be cars down there.

Well I must close for this time. Hoping to hear from you soon.

With lots of Love,
Roy

Roy did go to Sigurd, Utah, in December of 1926. He was reunited with a father he hadn't seen since he was five years old, a man he really couldn't remember much about. Roy was only seventeen years old, but he had been working on his own for almost three years. He was at an age when most boys were living at home, doing chores and going to school. Roy, however, was ranching and doing work in the mills. It was no wonder, that after the niceties and pleasant hospitalities wore off, the two men didn't always see eye to eye. The adjustment of a stern old man and a very young independent youth, now living together, became a difficult challenge for both.

Obe wasn't in very good physical condition, and it didn't help his disposition any. He was happy to have a young, healthy youth around to help with all the work, though. Obe was still a typical western character who was ready to fight at the drop of a hat. He continued to carry a concealed handgun in a shoulder holster, under his coat. He felt the need to be in control of his boy, even though he hadn't earned any respect from his son.

Roy, on the other hand, wasn't afraid of working. He had learned quite well how to do that. He did resent, however, this man who had so little to do with his upbringing now expecting to take over the job of father and boss. The tension between the two men was reflected in the letters Pearl received from Roy.

Sigurd, Utah Feb. 28, 1927

Dear Pearl,

I hope you are getting along alright and hope you will write to me some time. How did you like that little cushion cover?

Dad told me to write to you and tell you who sent it because he didn't want the credit, but we cannot give him too much credit though, he sure is a good old dad alright. Ha. Helen has written to me once or twice since I came here.

Dad is feeling fine *now,* and looks much better since I came, than the day I arrived. I am running the pool hall now for him, it is pretty good work.

Don't worry about me Pearl because I can get *along* with dad alright. Wish you was here tho. Well must close for this time. Write soon.

With Love,
Roy

PICKING UP THE PIECES

Pearl worried constantly about Roy and their dad's ability to get along together after so many years of separation. But Sigurd was a long ways away, and she didn't want to just pick up and go there to visit until her legal matters were resolved. She had received news from Judge Forney that the insurance settlement was close to being worked out. Pearl felt she needed to be where she could sign more papers if necessary.

In April of 1927, the insurance matter finally came to closure. Pearl received a check from the U.S. government for $1,000. By the time she paid for all the legal services in order to get the money, she had about $800 for her savings. The other siblings all had to wait until they were twenty-one to get their share. Pearl got from Judge Forney all the papers that Roy needed in order to apply for his share. Mrs. Lewis had what Robert Earl needed if he ever decided to go back to her home.

Helen and Pearl were anxious to see their brother Roy. They decided when Helen graduated from St. Luke's in May of 1927 they would go to Sigurd for the summer. The girls both wrote to the men and told them they were ready to go for a visit, any time after June 5.

Obe and Roy decided the best way to get the young women was to drive to Moscow in the car and pick them up. It was arranged Roy and Obe would go to Moscow to get Pearl and Helen would take the train down from Spokane and meet them there.

Pearl arranged for an extended leave from her job. She didn't know if or when she might ever return to Moscow. She had decided if every thing worked out with her reunited family, she might just stay in Utah for a while. Of course she prayed for everything to be wonderful, like she had dreamed it would be if she was ever back with her real people. But she could tell by Roy's correspondence over the past six months that life with Father was not a "bowl of cherries."

Roy and Obe arrived in Moscow, Idaho, the second week of June 1927. Pearl and Helen's reunion with their brother was one of the biggest events of their lives so far. He was only five years old the last time they had seen him, just a small, scared boy hanging onto Pearl's skirt. But now he was a young man of eighteen. He was tall, handsome, and strong. He reminded Pearl so much of her uncle John Junior Knowles, with his wavy reddish hair and broad shoulders. The memories seemed so vivid once again of those days gone by. She was simply amazed as she looked at the brother who stood at least a foot taller than she and Helen. Had it not been for the letters they had written back and forth over the last thirteen years, the siblings might have lost each other forever. But now they still felt they knew each other. If not in person, at least in spirit.

"Well, my goodness, Pearl, I think you forgot to keep growing since the last time I saw you," the six-two Roy joked. He leaned over and gave his oldest sister a hug.

Tears welled up in her eyes as she held tight to her giant brother. She tried to keep from crying like a baby, so she responded to his height comment with one of her own. "Oh, you think so, huh! What about Helen? She is even shorter than I am."

Before they left Moscow, Pearl insisted they drive out to the Yearouts to meet Aunt Lillie and Uncle Charley. She mostly wanted to show off her handsome brother. She felt she needed to thank her adopted folks and properly say good-bye. These people had been so good to her. She had grown to love and respect them as her family.

The Yearouts insisted they all stay for supper. The women prepared a nice meal while the men toured the yard. They all stayed out at the farm for the night and waited until morning to go back into town and load the girls' belongings.

Helen made a telephone call to Orofino, Idaho, before they left. Robert Earl had not returned home yet after running away. Helen promised to keep in touch with Mrs. Lewis just in case Robert came back or wrote and left the message that his birth family was getting back together and they still cared about him also. If he wanted to write or join them, they would be in Sigurd, Utah.

With the coaxing of his three kids, Obe was persuaded to make a loop back to some of the places in Montana where they had lived. They went over to Thompson Falls, Montana, and stopped by for Obe to talk to Myrtle's adopted brother, Clarence. Most of the conversation was private between Clarence and Obe. The three young folk stayed outside and enjoyed the beautiful area. They could remember playing here as children when they visited their Grandpa Knowles.

They hadn't been there too long before Obe and Clarence started to quarrel about some past trouble between the two of them. Obe invited Clarence to step outside and settle the dispute. When Clarence declined, the Tooleys got in the car and headed for Utah.

On the way, Roy and Obe told the story of learning to drive the new Essex they were currently driving. It seemed this was the first car Obe had ever driven. Before this, he had a Model T pickup. On the

Essex, the foot accelerator was where the brake was on the Model T. Consequently, when he and Roy drove to the train station the first time to pick up the mail in the new car, Obe put his foot on what he thought was the brake and the car accelerated. They went over five railroad tracks before he finally got the car to stop.

The story seemed funny to everyone in the car, and they laughed and told stories all the way to Sigurd.

Just Children

Fond remembrances are thronging in my mind tonight,
Sweet reflections of the days gone by,
When we as children played together beneath an azure sky.
And when tired of our play at twilight we would wander off to dreamland,
In the starlit night.
We were only children then, but our days were gay and bright.
We are now a little older, perhaps with some professional name,
Our faces don't look quite so young, but we're children just the same.
Our hair is turning fast to silver
And we're growing wrinkled, but that is all,
For we're still the merry children of long ago,
Just simply grown up tall.
What if our hair is snowy white, or faces care worn and gray,
Our hearts are still as glad and free as children at their play.
Tho our forms are bent with age,
And death is coming towards the door,
We've nearly reached the heights above
When we'll be children
Evermore.

P.E.T.

After they left Thompson Falls, they continued south to Missoula and Bútte, Montana, then crossed into Idaho. They went down through Idaho Falls and Pocatello, Idaho, and on into Logan Ogden, Salt Lake City, Provo, and all the little places of Utah until they finally reached Sigurd.

It was a long, long trip over some good and bad roads. Obe was quite worn out when they reached Sigurd. The girls were so happy to have some quality time with their own family again. They were both determined to make this the best summer of their lives. This would be

285

the time of hopes and dreams fulfilled after thirteen years of separation. If they only had their brother Earl and their mother with them, it would be perfect. Four out of six would have to do for right now anyway, Pearl thought to herself.

NEW BEGINNINGS

Life in Sigurd, Utah, was very different from the life both Helen and Pearl had been used to. No big stores to shop or people to associate with. The two girls looked for excitement anywhere they could find it.

At first just cleaning the small house they lived in kept them busy. The two experienced working girls made sure the place was scrubbed, polished, and painted. There were several projects of improvement on the place to keep them occupied for several weeks. When the place was clean and polished enough to suit Helen and Pearl, they looked elsewhere for something to do.

One day in early August of 1927, Helen and Pearl borrowed their father's car and drove over to Fish Lake with a picnic supper. Roy was working at the pool hall, so the two girls went by themselves.

As the girls sat enjoying their supper, they had their eyes on some good-looking fellows who were skipping stones over the water's surface. The young men kept glancing their way trying to show off their meager skills. It was obvious to Pearl and Helen the guys were showing their rock talents just to impress them. The girls tried hard to pretend they didn't notice.

Pearl could tell the fellows seemed disappointed when she and Helen gathered up their basket and headed back to their car.

Both girls were unaware as they stopped at the little country store before going home that the two young men had also left the lake and had stopped at the same store. As the girls came out of the market, the fellows were just getting out of their car to go inside. One of the guys took courage and boldly spoke.

"Didn't we just see you nice-looking ladies out at the lake?" he questioned as he tipped his hat in the gesture of a gentleman's greeting.

"I don't know," replied Helen in a sassy but cute way. "We were there, but we didn't notice anyone skipping rocks over the water."

"You did see us!" The other fellow chuckled as he nudged his buddy in the side. "I told you they were looking at us."

"We were not looking at you," Pearl retorted. "We were simply taking in the beauties of nature."

"Are you girls from around these parts?" the first fellow questioned.

"Could be, or maybe not. What do you want to know for?" Helen answered, questioning the men's motives.

"Well, we know of some get-togethers that take place each week over in Richfield. If you girls lived around here, we would invite you to go," he answered.

Thank you anyway, but we couldn't go anywhere with perfect strangers," Pearl piped back.

"Who said anything about going with strangers? My name is Merlin Taylor, and this is my friend Herb Creviston. We work just this side of Richfield on the Baker ranch," he explained. "What names do you lovely creatures go by?"

"Oh, gee! I didn't know these little country towns produced such sweet-talking individuals. Did you, *Helen?*" Pearl stated, emphasizing her sisters' first name.

"No *Pearl,* I didn't. But if these two happen to be in Sigurd and drop in at Tooley's Pool Hall they just might meet up with our big, mean brother. He could wipe up some of that syrup," Helen said.

"Helen and Pearl," stated Herb. "Are you two sisters?" he questioned.

"Well, we both have the same big brother. I guess you can figure it out," Helen responded.

"A pool hall," commented Merlin. "I like to play pool. Don't you, Herb?"

"Oh, yeah. I was just saying the other day, if I only knew where there was a pool hall, I'd sure visit it next *Saturday night* and play a few games of pool," Herb responded, playing the same game the girls were trying to play.

"Saturday night, huh . . . Sigurd . . . Tooley's Pool Hall. Yes, I think that would be a good time to practice some shooting skills," Merlin stated while pretending to have a cue stick and play the game. "Nice meeting you ladies. Maybe we'll see you Saturday night in Sigurd," Merlin said.

Both men gave gentlemanly gestures to the girls as they got in their car and drove away.

The girls giggled about the fellows and made motions of how forward they were. Yet each individually hoped they would show up on Saturday night at the pool hall.

When Saturday came around, the girls just happened to get all cleaned up with freshly washed hair and cleaned and ironed dresses. Roy was suspicious something was going on when they volunteered their services to help him at the business that evening. Pearl suggested they work the cash drawer or serve refreshments. Helen even offered to make sure the tables were brushed between customers.

"Hey, what's up with you two females?" Roy inquired. "You've never shown this kind of interest to working in here before."

"Why do you think something is the matter?" Pearl remarked. "We're just tired of spending Saturday nights home darning socks."

"We're merely interested in seeing what kind of riffraff comes into Sigurd on a Saturday night to play pool," Helen added.

"Riffraff, huh . . . You gals are up to something. I might be your younger brother, but I can spot 'trap bait' when I see it," Roy reported. He studied the coy way his older sisters were moving about the room. They were trying to be nonchalant when the customers began to come in by twos or threes. It wasn't until the two victims came through the doors about half past eight that Roy fully understood why his sisters were acting so strange.

Merlin Taylor was a young man of twenty-two. He was five-eight, dark brown wavy hair and dark eyes. He had already picked the little redhead to make his move on.

Herb Creviston, on the other hand, had thought Pearl was the better of the two girls. He shined up to her right away. Herb was about the same height and build as Merlin. They were both tanned and muscular from working out of doors. Herb had jet black hair but bright blue eyes. They seemed to sparkle even in the smoke-filled pool hall. He was only twenty but had assumed the responsibilities of a older man for the past several years.

It only took about an hour of "cat and mouse games" before they had paired into couples and were ready to go outside for a walk.

The next few weeks the couples attended the mutual activities sponsored by the local church. Even though none of them were members, the activities were open for all the young folk to participate in.

In September there was a big Harvest Party to be held in Richfield and everyone joined in the celebration. Pearl and Herb and Helen and Merlin knew each other well enough to go as dates. Obe even closed the pool hall that night, and he and Roy went to the festivities.

This was the first time in thirteen years Pearl felt the joy families can have when everyone tries to be pleasant and sociable to each other. Before this night she had always felt like a loner, sitting on the outskirts of a family unit. Now she had the feeling of really fitting inside her own circle.

The shindig was held inside a big cleaned-up barn. A group of men from Salina were hired to play their fiddles. Another man who came with them was a dance caller. There were lots of eats and cider. The decorations were autumn leaves and pumpkins, with lights strung everywhere to give a bright glow and a festive atmosphere.

The couples danced until their feet ached and their faces were flushed from all the exercise. Helen and Pearl were so impressed with the fellows trying to be gentlemen and on their best behavior.

Pearl tried to be cautious, however, because of past experiences. She knew first infatuations can blind a girl to the real person who lies underneath. She took all the polite behavior with a "grain of salt." She had learned from her experience with George Jensen that sometimes the real person inside could be totally different from the one acted out on the outside.

Pearl got her first kiss from Herb that September night, and she thought it was the best one she had ever received. Her heart was still going pitter-pat even after the long ride home with her family.

Helen was even more bedazzled than her sister, flying on "cloud nine." When the two girls were alone in their room that night, Helen made her confession to Pearl.

"I know I said I was going to swear off men and be an old-maid nurse. Not anymore, Merlin is so wonderful. If I could get him to ask me to marry him, I'd do it tomorrow," the swooning young red-haired girl blurted out. But with her next breath, she changed her tone to a command. "But don't you dare tell anyone I said that. This is just between you and me." Helen was all of sudden blushing about how giddy she was talking.

"Why, Helen, you're scandalous! You've only known this guy for a few weeks, and you're thinking marriage? I guess that's what a small, boring town can do to a girl," Pearl remarked.

The next few weeks seemed to be consumed with boy talk between the two sisters. Merlin and Helen were getting serious much too fast, in Pearl's opinion. Maybe she was just a little jealous. Perhaps it was the difference in ages between the two fellows, Merlin being twenty-two and Herb only twenty. Merlin seemed ready to take on the responsibilities of adulthood and marriage much more than Herb.

Obe, on the other hand, didn't like either suitor. He advised the girls to wait until they were much older to make marriage decisions. He told them they could find work around these parts if they had a mind to. If they all worked together, they could get into a bigger house and buy some new fancy furnishings. By working together, they could help make life more comfortable for everyone.

Despite their father's warnings and sometimes threats, the two girls continued to see their beaus. Sometimes they had to sneak around so their obstinate dad wouldn't know, but neither sister let this stop her.

Much to the surprise and delight of the family, Robert Earl showed up one day in Sigurd. He had come to join his other brother and sisters in this reunited family experience. He now went by the name of Bob and insisted that's what everyone call him. He was sixteen years old, and the apparent spoiled nature he had grown up with was reflected in his personality. When Bob was growing up and was quite difficult to get along when Mrs. Lewis did not give him enough supervision. He had learned to do what he wanted, when he wanted. He now intended to continue the same behavior with his biological family.

Unlike his other siblings, who had learned they had to work for a living, Bob did not share those same values. He made no attempt to do any of the work the others did or to find employment elsewhere. He just wanted to be footloose and fancy free.

Pearl tried hard to make a bonding family. However, everyone struggled with personalities they hadn't lived with for many years. By the time Thanksgiving came around the Tooleys were pretty much used to each other and tried to have a big family celebration.

Merlin had relatives all over the Utah area. When Thanksgiving came around he traveled south to Loa, Utah, for the holiday. Helen was so awfully blue. She tried to act happy to be with her own family for the first time in thirteen years. She would have been happier if her boyfriend had been closer to share the day with her.

Pearl prepared a wonderful feast for the five Tooleys. She worked for two days making pies, cranberry sauce, turkey, mashed potatoes and gravy, rolls, and vegetables.

Helen tried to be helpful, but her heart was not into making stuffing and candied yams. She hadn't had as much experience in the kitchen as her older sister. Anyway, Helen was pinning much too much for Merlin to concentrate on domestic stuff. The fact that she was always watching her weight made all the food look like extra pounds to her. She was so in love and miserable she couldn't think of anything but Merlin being gone for a whole week.

Thanksgiving dinner was wonderful in spite of the lovesick girl. Pearl's talents were highly praised by her father and brothers. It truly was a memorable feast.

By the time Christmas rolled around, Merlin and Helen had already decided they were getting married. It didn't matter what anyone in Sigurd had to say about it.

On December 27, 1927, with her family around her, Helen became Mrs. Merlin Taylor. In spite of the objections from the man who was her father in blood relationship only, the couple made their vows. They found a little brick house to rent in Sigurd and set up housekeeping as man and wife.

Pearl was so happy for her sister. The two sisters still shared everything with each other except the personal things that went on between a husband and wife. Those things were kept private, and each sister respected that.

Pearl and Herb continued to see each other. Pearl had learned the hard way to be more cautious about men. She wasn't taking the chance of getting mixed up with another "gay deceiver" like George Jensen. This time she would know what she was in for if the relationship with Herb went that far.

Herb was so handsome but definitely not perfect. He was not as educated as Pearl, as he had been forced to give up school and move around with his dad and brothers in order to eke out a living. Herb had been slapped around a lot as he was growing up. He thought fighting was the only way to get results in dealing with people. He had learned to be a scrapper, growing up as the youngest of three boys. Pearl had to clean up his cut face one night when he got into a fight. Another fellow had made what Herb felt was a rude comment about Pearl, and he went about defending his girl, with his fists.

"You shouldn't use your fists to settle differences," Pearl explained as she cleaned up the bleeding defender.

"I just get so mad sometimes. It's like I can't control the anger that builds inside of me," he responded. "If that guy comes near you again, I swear I'll hit him twice as hard next time."

"That's no way for grown men to act," Pearl lectured. "It would be better just to walk away and leave him alone."

"Well, that's not the way I was raised," he spouted back. "If someone gives you the dickens, you need to give it back to them, but harder."

"I don't like it at all, Herb. If you want to see me anymore you need to control your temper," Pearl demanded.

They didn't say much on the way home that evening. Pearl hoped Herb would change his ways because she liked him a lot.

Never Too Late to Mend

Angel forms their vigils keep. All thru the lonely watches wait,
Hope and faith are foremost of them all, but ah, those dark imps.
Jealousy, wrath and despair, have crept up within call.
Could we but know the things that others suffer, silently, oh yes,
We rebuke them for their cowardice, while they are heroes when
It comes to bearing pain.
Could we but know we would strive to do them kindness,
And wish in vain to choose our words again.
But friend, it's never too late to mend and never too early to begin anew
To travel the paths the Great Creator
Has placed here on earth to be tread by you.

P.E.T.

The next time Herb came to see Pearl it was with flowers in hand. "I'm sorry for the way I acted the other night," he said apologetically. "I promise I'll really try to keep my temper under control. I like you so much, Pearl. Please don't be mad any more," Herb begged.

"OK," she said. "The next time you get mad, instead of using your fists, please try and count to ten before you strike out."

"I'll try," he agreed.

SECRETS AND LIES

In April after Bob had turned seventeen he got into some trouble. He was caught taking ten dollars from a cash register at a service station. Rather than go to trial, he was given the option of leaving the state of Utah, which he was advised to do.

His siblings were sorry to see him go. They knew it was better than going to jail at such a young age, but they were just getting to know him. He was definitely a free spirit, and they all hoped someday he would change and be a productive member of society. He promised to keep in touch by letters.

"Maybe someday we can be together again!" Bob shouted from the train as it pulled away from the little station.

It was just after Pearl's twenty-third birthday when Obe purchased the new chest of drawers. It wasn't really new. It had been sold by the family members of the widow Gibbs, who had passed away a few weeks prior. Obe's plan was to clean it up and put it in his room. He would give his old one to Roy to use in his room. Pearl took on the task of cleaning the new one and transferring her dad's things. She was the only one home that day. The men were doing some painting down at the pool hall.

She scrubbed down the inside and outside of the widow's chest and pushed it into her dad's bedroom, then began the job of moving her dad's personal items from the old chest to the newly purchased one. When she got to the bottom left-hand drawer she saw a fairly thin rectangular box. Pearl normally wasn't one to pry; however, the engraved words "Murray's of Sandpoint, Idaho" piqued her curiosity. She opened the lid and there were the pictures her mother had cherished so many years ago. The envelopes and letters quickly caught Pearl's eye. She began to look through everything inside the box.

There were several letters. She began to read them one at a time. As she read, more puzzle pieces of her lost family revealed themselves, as if by magic. The missing pieces about her mother were put in place with each letter.

1914 REPRISE

1914, Bonner County Jail

Mr. Chase, Lewiston, Idaho   July 21, 1914, Sandpoint, Idaho

Dear Sir,

Your kind letter rec'd Sunday. Am so glad the children are well and happy and hope they will continue so.

Am glad they are learning to do things. Hope you will keep them all for me as am going to do all I can to try and get them back again.

Do you think it would make them discontented if they were to write to me? Would like to have them write and write to them but do not wish to do anything to make them unhappy.

Hope to hear from the children again.
Mrs. O. A. Tooley

August 28, 1914

"You have a letter today, Mrs. Tooley," the heavyset woman holding the large stick announced. "If you get all those floors scrubbed and the potatoes peeled in the kitchen on time today, I might just let you take a peek at who it's from before supper. If not, I might just keep it here in my pocket until next week sometime. Now get to work."

The people in charge of the few women prisoners were particularly bad-natured. Especially on hot days, like this one, at the end of August.

She only had a few more days left of her sentence. Myrtle was not sure if she could take much more of the mental and physical abuse the guards had given to the folk who had been incarcerated that summer. She prayed the letter was from one of her children, as she had missed them so terribly the last two months.

Myrtle took up new hope as she hurried with the scrubbing and peeling that afternoon. She didn't want Miss Whitaker to have any excuse to hold back her letter.

"Miss Whitaker," Myrtle spoke meekly. "I finished everything I was assigned. May I please have my letter now?"

"So you did, little Mrs. Mousie," Whitaker mockingly replied. "See what you can accomplish with motivation. Too bad you don't get a letter every day. Then again, if you had anyone who cared about you, you wouldn't be here in the first place, now would you?" Miss Whitaker laughed in a jeering way, trying to intimidate the tired woman who was waiting for her letter. "Here, take your letter and go read it somewhere out of the way."

Children's Home Finding and Aid Society of Idaho

Office North Idaho Receiving Home
S. B. Chase Supt. Lewiston, Idaho   August 24, 1914
Mrs. O. A. Tooley, Sandpoint, Idaho

Dear Madam,

Yours at hand. We are glad to report that the Children are all very well and happy. Only one remains in the Home. The others have gone out to good homes. We had a nice letter from Pearl today.

No, Mrs. Tooley, we do not feel that it is best for the children to write to you or have any word from you. They are to be cared for by others and to be kept in touch with you will only make them unhappy and discontented. You understood this when I talked it over with you in the Sheriff's office. We shall be glad to let you know how they are getting on occasionally, but cannot write often, for we have too much to do in caring for other people's children.

It is a hard thing to say to you, but the children do not ever speak of their former life. They are contented and happy, and you must be as happy as you can without them.

Sincerely yours,
S. B. Chase Superintendent.*

Myrtle was numb. Had she really read the letter correctly or was she misunderstanding the message? As she reread the last part, the words lashed out at her heartstrings. They severed the hope of getting her children back in a few weeks, with painful cutting strokes.

The children were gone to other homes and never spoke of her? That couldn't be true, she thought, or was it? How would she know? The

*This is an actual letter, published here compliments of the Northwest Children's Home.

authorities weren't going to let her communicate with them. The pain and hurt was so strong in her soul, she wasn't even aware she was screaming out loud. "NO, NO, NO, NO!" Two guards grabbed hold of her. Myrtle felt the sharp sting of a slap across her face. Her crying was so violent she could not control herself. She was carried out of the kitchen, screaming and kicking the whole time.

Myrtle woke up the next day in the jail hospital, groggy and limp. The room was spinning, and the task of focusing was just too much trouble. She lay still with her eyes closed until she felt some life returning to her body.

"So you have decided to come back from sleep land," the nurse in charge commented.

"What happened?" Myrtle asked.

"I wasn't here when they brought you in last night. I think it had something to do with that letter." The woman pointed to the paper on the small table by the bed.

Myrtle glanced at the table. The memory of the message flashed to her mind. Tears came to her eyes, and she rolled over to cry silently into the pillow. She had done this same action so many times since being locked up. Just nine more days to go, if she could keep herself together long enough. She didn't want to have days added for misbehavior. She folded the letter and tucked it in her dress. Even though the message was terrible, she felt she needed to keep it to show to Obe.

In mid-September 1914, Myrtle was released from the jail. She was granted a visit with her husband, who still had three weeks left of his sentence.

The emotional drain of the whole legal mess had taken its toll on the once happy, spritely young woman. The ordeal had aged her prematurely. The evidence now remained in her physical countenance. Her long auburn hair had been cut short, not only to identify her as a prisoner, but to ensure she wasn't carrying head lice. Her skin was pale and rough from the harsh soaps of the laundry and kitchen work. The only clothing she had was what she had been wearing when incarcerated. She had mended the moth holes the best she could the day before she was released. Care had been taken in washing and ironing her skirt and blouse so the worn threads would hold up until new ones could be purchased. She had been allowed that much freedom for good behavior. She had removed the scarf that normally was put around the neck of the blouse and draped it over her head to hide her short hair.

Myrtle didn't know if she would ever be able to forgive Obe for this ordeal and all the suffering. She had promised herself, though, she would try to go on with him if they could get their children back.

The guards brought Obe into the small room to face the woman who was waiting for him.

"Hello, Obe," she greeted him in a cold, uncaring manner.

"I see you got out," he stated. "I've only got three weeks left myself. You don't happen to have any smokes, do you?" Obe coldly asked.

"No! I don't have enough money to buy food, let alone cigarettes," Myrtle snapped. "I came to talk to you about family matters." She paused before she took the letter out of her skirt pocket and handed it to Obe. "I received this letter from the home where they took our children. They said in the letter . . ." She stopped as the tears filled in her eyes and a lump began to enlarge in her throat. "They said I could not even write to the children. They have put them in other people's homes." Myrtle tried to control herself before speaking clearly, so her husband would know she was dead serious. "Obe! I want my children back! Unfortunately, I need your help to do it," she firmly stated.

"Well, I can't do anything until I get out of this place," Obe retorted.

"The nurse at the jail told me the only way to get our children away from that state home would be to hire a lawyer to help us," Myrtle informed him. "She told me the children's home gets a large sum of money for each child placed there. The folks in charge don't want to give the kids back. Unless we get legal help to fight them, they won't give us back our children."

"That's a lot of bunk," Obe growled. "When I get out of here, we'll just go down to that home and make them give our kids back," he continued with his tough, authoritarian manner.

"Obe. It's not that simple. We signed papers that made what the home is doing legal. The only way to get the kids back now is through the court system. I want to hire a lawyer to get the paperwork started immediately," Myrtle continued. "You know I don't have any money. You will have to agree to pay for the services or—"

Obe cut her off sharply. "So that's it, huh?" he snapped. "The crooks have convinced you of another scheme to get my money. Well, they ain't goin' to get it. You'll see; when I get out of here I'll go down to Lewiston and get the kids. They have to give them back; I'm their father. Parents have a right to get their own kids back.''

Myrtle just looked at her husband in disbelief as he finished his declaration. ''Crooks! Schemes!'' she stated. ''What on earth are you talking about? I truly believe that money has driven you *mad*, Obe Tooley.'' She shook her head in disgust.

''I spent one hundred and six days in jail,'' Myrtle stated. ''Because you refused to pay a fine. Now you still think someone is trying to cheat you out of that precious money. Well, I will tell you, Obe Tooley . . . No, I'm begging you.'' She paused to rephrase the statement. ''Use whatever money it takes to undo this hell you have put your family through. I just want us to be a whole family unit again. If there is any decency left in you, I'm begging you prove it to me now.''

''I told you. I'll go get the kids when I get out of here. But I'm not going to pay any crooked lawyer to do what I can do myself,'' he firmly stated.

Myrtle just stared in shock at this man she had once loved so much. She wondered where he was hiding in that shell. ''So, you're telling me you won't pay for a lawyer to help me get the children?'' she questioned one last time. She wanted to give the man one more chance to change his mind.

''No! If you want a damn lawyer, then find some way to pay for him yourself,'' Obe answered.

''OK. If that's your decision . . .'' She stopped her remarks to Obe. ''Guard, I want to leave now.''

As the door closed behind her, Myrtle knew what her next step would be.

Myrtle went to the hotel across from the nightclub Mr. Broughton and her husband use to operate. Mrs. Hendricks, the woman who owned and operated the place, had always been so kind to Myrtle and the children. The woman was not snooty, like some of Myrtle's old club people had been. She prayed Grace Hendricks still had her kind disposition and would fine some compassion for her humble situation.

Myrtle went around to the side door she knew the hotel workers used and knocked. She waited for a few minutes before knocking the second and third times.

''Hold on!'' she heard a voice from inside yell. ''I'm coming.''

''Hello, Mrs. Hendricks,'' Myrtle quietly greeted her.

The woman paused and studied the frail Myrtle in disbelief. "Mrs. Tooley?" she finally questioned. "I barely recognized you."

"Mrs. Hendricks, I need . . ." The words wouldn't come, as her throat got choked up. Tears began to roll down her checks like they had been accustomed to doing the last several months.

"It's all right, honey," the kind woman stated as she wrapped Myrtle in her comforting arms. "You just come in and sit yourself down. "Tell Grace what you need." She poured Myrtle a cup of hot tea and waited until she had regained her composure and could speak.

"Now there. Do you feel better?" Grace Hendricks inquired.

Myrtle nodded in the affirmative and took one more swallow of the refreshing brew.

"You tell me what you need," Grace kindly told the shaken woman.

"Mrs. Hendricks, I need a job and a place to stay," Myrtle stated most humbly. "I can clean, cook, mend, anything. I'll work hard and stay out of the way. You'll never be sorry I'm around," the desperate woman pleaded.

Mrs. Hendricks just looked at the broken woman before remarking, "I read about you and your husband in the paper. Terrible situation. By the looks of you, you have certainly paid the price for any wrongdoings you may have done. What about your husband? Where is he?"

"Mr. Tooley is still in jail. I won't be going with him, however, even when he does get free," Myrtle stated firmly. "I am making an appointment with a lawyer as soon as I can get a job to pay for the services."

"A lawyer?" Grace questioned.

"Yes. I'm going to divorce Mr. Tooley."

Mrs. Hendricks looked surprised at the little woman's statement. "Divorce your husband? You don't have a lover or any other sordid situation like that, do you?" she asked.

"No. It's nothing like that," Myrtle responded.

"What about your lovely children?" Mrs. Hendricks continued.

"That is precisely why I am divorcing Mr. Tooley. He allowed our children to be placed at the state children's home. Now he will not help me get them back. I simply cannot live with or around a person who is that heartless and cruel."

"Oh, you poor dear. You poor dear," Mrs. Hendricks sympathetically responded. "Of course you can stay here and I'll give you work.

You can start tomorrow at seven in the morning. Please understand I can't pay you much. I will offer you board, room, and two dollars a week.''

Myrtle was delighted with the kindness of the lady and thanked her over and over. Two dollars a week wasn't much, but it was a start. Myrtle was grateful for a start.

The sign on the door stated: "W. J. Costello Attorney of Law." Myrtle took a deep breath as she opened it and stepped inside.

"I'm Myrtle Tooley," she announced to the lady behind a desk. "I have an appointment at eleven o'clock with Mr. Costello."

"Yes, Mrs. Tooley. Go right in. Mr. Costello is waiting for you."

She went through another door into a smaller room. It contained a desk and three side chairs.

The man seated behind the desk stood up as she entered the room. He smiled and greeted her very professionally. "Good day, uh . . . Mrs. Tooley I believe?" He was looking at his notebook for confirmation of the name. "What can I assist you with today?"

"I wish to divorce my husband. I need you to help me," Myrtle stated.

"Divorce?" he asked as if the action seemed to shock him.

"Yes. Divorce," she stated again.

"That's a pretty serious step for a woman to take these days, madame. One should be very certain it is the only solution before jumping right into a divorce," the lawyer advised.

"Mr. Costello. This is not an irrational act from an irrational woman. I will give you all of my reasons. You can then tell me if you will help me or not," the determined woman added.

Myrtle explained as much of the situation to the lawyer as she felt necessary for the action she was proposing to take. After she was finished, Mr. Costello agreed she definitely had "grounds to file" her case.

"I know your fee will be high," Myrtle stated. "I will pledge four dollars each month until it is paid in full."

"Under the circumstances, Mrs. Tooley, that arrangement will be fine," Mr. Costello replied. "I wish I could help you with the children. You would be best served by hiring a person who could travel or, better yet, someone who already lives in Lewiston to take on the job for you. I'm afraid there would be a lot of expense to you also."

"I know," she responded as she hung her head.

"I could write a letter or two and get the details of what a good attorney in that area might charge. If it would be helpful," he offered.

"Oh, thank you, sir. If you would do that, I would be most grateful. Thank you again," Myrtle humbly responded and shook the kind lawyer's hand.

She didn't know where life would take her next, but she had started the paperwork to change her current situation. Perhaps when she had her freedom from this awfulness she felt tied to she would have the power to make her own decisions again. It wouldn't be easy by any means, yet Myrtle felt she was going in the right direction.

When Obe got released from jail, the first place he went was back to Lakeview to retrieve his money. He also had the crazy notion he would find Myrtle there waiting to greet him.

The house they had rented was still standing, but everything was in a shambles around the yard. When he went inside, Obe was astonished at what he saw. The inside looked like a tornado had blown through. Everything of value was gone. What was left was scattered all around in every room. Dishes were broken in the kitchen, and all the shelves were empty. The bedrooms were missing all of the furniture. Most of the clothing left were the old raggedly things, items Myrtle had saved to use for patches or rags. The looting of the belongings had obviously been unrestrained. It seemed to Obe that Homer Remer had done his part trying to find the hidden money.

Obe spent the rest of the day sifting through the remaining items. He boxed up the things he thought he could use. There wasn't much left, just a few cooking utensils, some pictures of the family, and a few items of clothing. There was also a couple of blankets that were dirty from being trampled with muddy feet but still usable.

He went to some of his former neighbors and found his wagon and team. He arranged a settlement with the man for their storage and feed and thanked his neighbor for the care his animals had received for the last few months. Then Obe went back to the old house and loaded the remains of this married life in the wagon.

When it got dark and he knew he was not being watched, Obe went to reclaim his money. He cautiously slunk back to the wooded area where he used to sell his liquor. At the edge of a large boulder where he sat to wait for lantern lights, he found the hiding place had been untouched. He brought up the tanned leather pouch that held the precious paper and silver. The filthy lucre he had given up everything else in life for. He sat alone, in the dark, counting out the amount.

It took Obe two days to track down the woman who didn't want to be found. He had already been given the divorce papers to be signed while he was in jail. He wanted to see Myrtle and talk some sense into her before signing anything.

Myrtle agreed to meet in Mr. Costello's office. The lawyer first let the disputing couple talk without him present.

"Woman! What do you think you are doing?" questioned the impatient husband.

"I'm divorcing you, Obe Tooley," Myrtle replied with conviction in her tone.

"Well, just what do you think you'll gain by doing that? A share of my savings?" the rigid, stubborn man retorted.

"You just don't understand anything about me or what I want. You cranky old man!" the frustrated woman responded. "It's not the money I want; it's the children. You have gotten us into this horrible mess, so one way or another, it's going to take some money to get it straightened out. Obe, don't you see? If you would get our family all back together, I would give up this divorce. I would vow to do everything I could to keep us together." Myrtle spoke with firm conviction.

"I told you I would go to Lewiston and get the kids. I've got all our things loaded in the wagon. If you would just listen and come with me, we can leave today," Obe explained.

Myrtle just looked at her misguided husband. She wondered how she would make him realize it was going to take a court battle to reverse the papers they had signed four months ago.

"Obe, I just don't know how to convince you. You will not be able to get the kids by yourself. Talk to Mr. Costello; let him help you understand. The home will never give back our children unless it is done through the courts," Myrtle pleaded.

Obe's face turned red with anger as he spoke. "Courts! Lawyers! Judges! All a bunch of crooks! I'll sign your damn divorce papers. I'll still go down to the place and make them give back the kids. Then you'll be sorry. You won't have your kids or your husband," he spouted.

"OK, Mr. Tooley," Myrtle addressed him. "You do just what you've said. After you have all four children, you write me a letter. I'll find a way to come wherever you are, and we'll get married again. Then we can 'live happily ever after,' " she stated with a smirk.

Obe went to the door and yelled for the clerk to bring in the papers to sign. Mr. Costello entered the room with papers in hand. He instructed Mr. Tooley where he should put his signature.

"You're not getting my money," Obe stubbornly stated. "And I'm not payin' for this divorce either."

"Don't worry, Obe," Myrtle replied. "I am more than happy to pay Mr. Costello for his services."

Obe slammed down the pen and stomped out the doorway.

It was a year before the Tooley divorce was final. In the meantime Myrtle stayed on at the hotel. She worked hard to pay off the lawyer and save as much as she could. She lived a pretty meager life that year, with very little money to spend on herself. She never lost her desire to be back with her children. She had written several more letters to the children's home but each time was informed that the children were no longer there. They had all been placed elsewhere. She didn't hear anything from Obe during that time period. She knew his "I'll just go down and get the kids" idea had not worked as he thought it would.

In the spring of 1916, a letter found its way to Myrtle at the hotel. It had been addressed to Mr. and Mrs. O. A. Tooley. The postal carrier knew of Myrtle's circumstances and routed it to her:

Calgary, Alberta Feb. 16, 1916

Dear Friends,

It has been over two years since we have communicated. I had heard from a former acquaintance the Tooleys might be in Sandpoint again. If so, please let me know. I'm preparing to take a holiday trip down that way again next summer. I would most like to drop by and see you.

Your friend,
Nat Broughton

Myrtle was so glad to hear from a friendly person. She felt she needed to write and let Nat know Obe had left the area. She didn't want Nat to expect to find Obe in Sandpoint. Of course she had no idea where her former husband now resided and was not be able to give Mr. Broughton any forwarding place to look.

She penned her letter before bed that evening. She tried to briefly tell Nat Broughton of the divorce and of not knowing Obe's whereabouts.

It wasn't too long after Mr. Broughton received Myrtle's letter that he wrote back wanting more details. He was especially interested in her personal plans.

Nat and Myrtle corresponded a few more times between February and June. At that time, he traveled to Sandpoint to see her.

Myrtle wasn't sure of her feelings toward Mr. Broughton at first. She was still more concerned about her children than anything else. She felt so helpless in not being able to do anything and so alone in her grief. The warm, comforting arms of a good friend made Myrtle feel more secure than anything or anybody had in the last two years. She was so vulnerable to his charms and promises. The weary woman could see this man as a way out of the "doldrum" existence she was presently living.

Nat, on the other hand, had been infatuated with Myrtle for several years. At one time he had even suggested she leave her husband and go to Canada with him. He knew, however, that because she was a woman of integrity she would refuse his offer, as she did. But now here they were both single and both needing someone. The timing was perfect for a new romance.

After a few weeks of courting, Nat proposed marriage. Myrtle got "cold feet" about the possibility of being with Nat and losing sight of her goal concerning her children. She explained her concerns to him. She wanted him to understand that marriage to him might delay her quest, but retrieving the children was the main focus of her life. She had wanted to accomplish that task for the last two years. But Nat was a fairly patient man. He felt if he could get her away from this town and its memories, he would have a better chance of matrimony.

Nat asked Myrtle to take a trip with him to Calgary, where he was currently living. He offered her a chance to see the beautiful country and even have a little fun. The offer was very tempting to a person who had not had any joyful times in the past two years. She jumped at the opportunity to have a little happiness back in her life. As long as he promised there would be "no strings attached" or other expectations along with the offer.

Nat was right. The weather was beautiful, the scenery magnificent, and romance bloomed brighter every day. By the time they had reached Calgary, Nat had convinced Myrtle to marry him. He promised her if she would stay with him in Canada for one year, they would go and fight for the children the following year. They would then have enough money saved to go back to Idaho and fight through the courts. The offer was the most positive hope she had heard in two years. With renewed energy, she agreed to become Mrs. Nat Broughton.

Myrtle and Nat were married in the fall of 1916. They stayed in Calgary until the next spring. At that time, they went farther north to Evansburg, Canada. Nat had heard Evansburg was the newest coal-mining bonanza spot. The men up in those parts needed somewhere to spend their money on the off hours. He opened a recreation center there, where the men could play cards, shoot pool, and basically just relax. The business thrived about two days a week, but the rest of the time the place was empty. The big fortune he had anticipated came slower than he had planned.

In the early summer of 1917, Myrtle realized she was going to have another baby. She was so full of joy at the prospects of again holding a small infant in her arms. She resolved that this time no one was going to take the child away from her.

She busied herself with making baby clothing and blankets. The same feelings encompassed her soul that had come to her when she was pregnant with Pearl. It was like a new beginning all over again. Myrtle wished this child could be raised with its sisters and brothers someday soon. She prayed God would watch over Pearl, Helen, Roy, and Earl until they could all be together again.

Myrtle had written to her friend Grace Hendricks at Christmastime about the expected arrival of another child. She received a letter back that included a message from Obe.

Obe had sent a short letter to ask Myrtle to go with him to the children's home for the children. He was in Alaska but planned to come back to Sandpoint to get her.

Myrtle quickly penned a letter back to Obe to explain her current circumstances.

Mr. O. A. Tooley   December 20, 1917 Canada

Dear Mr. Tooley,

I am answering the letter you sent to Mrs. Hendricks, in order to inform you of my current whereabouts. I am now living in Canada and have remarried.

306

Last year Nat Broughton and I married in Calgary, and I am now expecting a child.

Mr. Tooley, you had your chance to have a life with your wife and family, three years ago. You chose not to do it, and now it is too late. If you would have paid the fines the court demanded for our misconduct, our lives and our children's lives would have been much different.

Next year my current husband and I plan to go to Lewiston and fight to get the children. He and I will then make a home for them, and try to undo the injustice you have caused. You had the money, but you refused to part with it to pay the fines. You also could have paid for a lawyer when you had the chance. Because you refused to part with the money you had, you are going to have to live with those decisions the rest of your life.

I now have a new life and will be much happier when I am reunited with my children once more.

Please do not write to me again as it may make trouble with my husband.

Sincerely,
Myrtle Broughton

On January 17, 1918, Myrtle gave birth to her fifth child, her third son. He was strong and had the looks of his father. Some red tints of his mother's hair adorned his sweet little head.

Myrtle tried hard not to spoil the little guy. She had trouble, however, putting him down or letting him out of her sight. She found herself spending hours of time holding and rocking this new infant. A luxury she hadn't had time to indulge in with her last three babies.

Nat named the boy Harry Duncan Broughton. Like most men of his day, Nat didn't spend much time with the small baby but depended on his wife to give the child all the love and attention he needed.

The town of Evansburg planned a big May Festival that year. The people wanted to honor the heroes who had already returned from the war in Europe.

It had been a long, cold winter. The snow in Hawkin Valley, however, had melted where the Maypole and tables were arranged for the celebration.

Myrtle had baked two of her special "chase the blues away" cakes to add to the dessert table.

307

The sheep had been slaughtered and prepared on the spits. The spicy aroma was spreading through the valley, welcoming the folk who had traveled here from miles away to attend the event.

Nat descended from the wagon and carefully took from Myrtle's arms the basket that held the precious three-month-old infant. The boy had been bundled oh, so meticulously to prevent any chilling breeze from touching any part of his delicate skin. Harry had slept the whole two miles as the family traveled to the party.

Just after they arrived, a small marching band paraded onto the newly erected stage. They began to play "Oh Canada" as the flag was presented by the men who were being honored that day. Each man was clad in his military uniform and appeared proud to be wearing it.

Everyone stopped where they were standing to salute the waving colors. A great feeling of patriotism filled the air. Everyone was proud of their country and the soldiers who had sacrificed and fought to keep Canada out from under Prussian rule.

After the speeches and braiding the Maypole, everyone present was invited to share the food that had been prepared for the occasion.

Nat took his place with the men slicing the roasted meat and placing it on trays.

Myrtle went to help at the table supporting the cakes. She sliced and served the selected pieces to each guest who wanted the tasty treats. She was extra proud when a compliment was sent her way about one of her homemade delights.

When everyone had been served, Myrtle noticed the lonesome-looking man. He was seated under a small pine tree with a paper and pen in hand. The blank stare in his eyes and motionless hand gave Myrtle the impression that the soldier was trying to think of what to write. He looked so alone and sad as he sat by himself with the writing material.

"Excuse me, sir; could I get you a piece of cake?" Myrtle asked as she approached the man. It seemed he hadn't heard her offer as he sat almost in a trance, looking off into his own thoughts.

"Sir," Myrtle asked again, "could I get you something?"

The man blinked his eyes and shook his head as he came out of the daze and looked at the lovely woman who stood before him. "Oh, were you speaking to me?" he asked almost apologetically.

"I was just wondering if I could get you something."

"Well, thank you, madame; that's very hospitable of you," the soldier replied as he studied Myrtle's face intently.

She waited patiently for the man to make his request, but he just stared at her and said nothing.

Myrtle became slightly uncomfortable with the silence. "There is still some cake on the table, sir; would you care for a slice?" she asked, breaking the stillness.

"Oh, yes, cake," the doughboy responded as he turned his head from Myrtle and faced the direction of the table she was pointing to.

"What kind would you prefer?"

"Did you make the cakes?" he questioned.

"Not all of them, just the two at the far end of the table."

"I'll take a piece of one of yours, if you don't mind." He gave her a nice smile as she turned to fetch a slice. Upon her return the soldier continued to watch her.

"Madame, could you spare a moment to sit down to answer a question?" he requested.

Myrtle politely smiled, handed the man the cake, and sat down near him.

"Please don't get the wrong idea. I can see by the band on your finger that you're already spoken for, and I'm not trying to be fresh. But don't I know you from somewhere?"

Myrtle opened her eyes wide in a gesture of surprise at the soldier's question. She looked at him hard but saw no features about him she recognized. "I don't think so," she responded. "Perhaps I simply look like someone else you've known."

"Perhaps," he commented, but was not willing to give up so easily. "Have you lived here your whole life?"

"No," she answered. "I was born in Wisconsin but lived in Montana and Idaho before coming to Canada."

He wrinkled his mouth and gestured in a negative manner. "No, I've never been to the lower States, just Canada and France, where I served in the war," he remarked.

"France!" she blurted out. "I have a brother in the Canadian army serving in France." She hadn't meant to change the subject but couldn't resist expressing the information when he mentioned France.

"Is that so?" the interested soldier replied. "Where in France?"

"I don't know," Myrtle responded sadly. "I just know he's in France somewhere. I've tried several times to find out, but so far all the letters I've written have been returned. When I first wrote to his last known address, the woman he had rented a room from informed me

309

that he went into the military two years ago and had been shipped over to France.''

"What's your brother's name?'' the man asked, trying to simply be polite.

"John,'' she forlornly answered. "John Knowles.''

The demeanor of the soldier quickly changed, and his whole countenance magically came alive. "Johnny Knowles!'' he sang out. "That's it. That's who you remind me of. You look like my friend Johnny.''

Myrtle gazed at the man in amazement. It couldn't possibly be her John he was so joyfully speaking about.

"Wait a minute,'' he continued. "If you tell me your name is Myrtle I think I will faint right here on the spot.''

The woman was stunned when the soldier spoke her name right out of the blue. She knew he didn't find it out from any of the local folk. Nearly everyone addressed her as Mrs. Broughton, never Myrtle. She was speechless.

"Is your name Myrtle? My friend Johnny said his sister's name was Myrtle and his brother's name was . . . ah . . . Alfred, no, Al—''

"Albert,'' Myrtle spoke up to complete the name the soldier was racking his brain for.

"Albert, that's it. I knew it started with an 'al' sound.'' The man in uniform stared at the woman again. "O sweet mother of angels, who would have ever imagined that in this whole wide world I would be in the same town as my buddy's sister? It almost seems impossible.''

"This is probably just a coincidence. I'm sure there are a lot of John Knowles in France right now,'' she remarked, trying to explain away this man's claims.

"Hold on,'' he stated. "I think I have a picture on me.'' He felt through his clothing before finding the leather billfold in his jacket pocket. He opened it up and pulled out a section where three photographs were stored. He took one out of the holder and handed it to Myrtle.

The snapshot showed the close-up faces of two men in military uniforms on either side of a pretty blond woman. All three were smiling for the camera.

Myrtle made a gasping, "Ah,'' as she identified one of the male faces as that of a mature-looking John and the other as that of the soldier who sat near her. She began to laugh out loud as she lunged for the soldier and wrapped her arms around his neck for a big hug. The response was a surprise to the man in uniform as well as to Myrtle herself. She had been so excited at seeing a recent picture of this lost sibling that all the proper protocol had momentarily been forgotten.

"Oh, thank you, thank you!" Myrtle cried out. "Please tell me all about your friendship with John."

The soldier spent the next hour conversing with his friend's sister about when and how the two men had met and became such good pals. He told of John's marksmanship and the heroics the two had experienced together.

Myrtle was so intent on listening and getting answers to her questions that the time flew by quickly. It was only the shrill cries of her hungry infant that released the mother's mind from the foxholes in France back to the celebration in Canada.

"Please, sir, stay here. I'll be right back," she pleaded with the soldier.

While Myrtle went to retrieve the infant from his basket, the man wrote something down on a sheet of the paper he had near his side.

"I bet you would like to have this." When Myrtle returned the soldier offered her the paper with the address she so desperately wanted written on it. "It's Johnny's address. I know he'll be stationed in this place for a few more months, if you want to write him."

"Again, thank you. This means so much to me. You must have been sent by a divine messenger. I have been praying for the last several years to find my brother again. There is so much I want to tell him. A person doesn't realize how much a family means until she's separated from them," Myrtle uttered.

"Maybe so, madame. Maybe so," the soldier acknowledged.

"I don't even know your name or where you're from!" the excited woman exclaimed. "I was so caught up in my own excitement, I failed to ask. Please forgive my rudeness."

"No worry, madame. My name is Cal Olsen. I have a little place just north of Entwistle."

"OK, Cal, perhaps our paths will cross again someday. John will sure be surprised when I write and tell him about this meeting. You'll never know how much this address means to me."

Myrtle smiled and waved good-bye as the wagon took her back home.

FRANCE, 1914

"Mail call!" the sergeant yelled. The weary men struggled to rise from their rest positions to receive the long-awaited letters.

John Knowles however, didn't bother to get off his cot. He hadn't received any mail for the last several months. Even his so-called sweetheart had found someone else and stopped sending letters.

"John Knowles!" the sergeant called out.

The man lying on the bunk didn't respond but stayed on his bed with his eyes closed.

"Hey, Johnny!" the sergeant called louder. "Get over here and get your mail."

John sat up so quickly he almost hit his head on the ceiling. "A letter for me?" he questioned.

"Yeah. By the flowers on the stationery, I bet it's not from a man!" the sergeant yelled out. The catcalls and whistles were started up by the other soldiers in the barracks.

John took the letter and examined it quickly. *Who is Mrs. N. Broughton?* he thought to himself. *I remember Nat from years back, but how did he get my address, and why would his wife be writing me a letter?* It was only when he opened the letter and started reading that the mystery was revealed.

"Great!" he exclaimed out loud. "It's from my sister, Myrtle."

"Sure it is!" one of the men called out. "I've never seen anyone get that excited about a letter from a sister." The fellows laughed and teased as was tradition at mail time.

"I've been trying to track her down for the last five years. How in the world did she find me?"

John shut the surrounding noise of the other men out of his mind as he devoured every word his sister had written. He was shocked, amazed, and deeply saddened at the tragic events she wrote about. He could tell by her words and phrases that she was devastated and heartbroken about her first four children. John wished he could find a way to be with her and help. Never in his wildest dreams had he imagined Obe would turn on Myrtle and the kids the way she explained.

After reading and rereading the letter, John lay on his bunk and pondered his sister's situation. By the time morning came, he had formulated a plan and was ready to set it in motion. One way or another he would ensure a means by which Myrtle could get the children back.

He knew he would be going back to the front lines in a few days and his future was unknown. He hoped this war would be over soon and he could go back to Canada and personally get the legal process to reunite Myrtle with her children started. He would use his army pay to get a good lawyer for the task. If for some reason he didn't make it through this war alive, the plan he had in mind would still give Myrtle plenty to do the job herself.

John got permission to go to the main headquarters building to fill out the necessary paperwork for the military insurance plan.

"Yes, sir, that is correct. If I get killed, I want the beneficiary of this policy to be my sister, Myrtle." John went on to give all the other necessary information to the clerk to finish the papers.

"OK soldier, everything is in order. Let's hope this policy never has to be cashed by your sister," the clerk commented.

"Thank you, sir. That is my hope also. I know if something does happen to me, however, the money will be used for a very good cause." John saluted and left the office. He then found a quiet place to answer his sister's letter.

EVANSBURG, MAY 1918

Two weeks after the festival the first case of Spanish influenza broke out in the town. This virus was somewhat picky about whom it attacked. The rich, the poor, the large, and the small were chosen as victims, but it particularly liked people in their teens, twenties, and thirties. The very young and the older folk seemed more resilient to this killer. Not as many people in the young and old age brackets were affected.

No one knew who would be this plague's next victim. The symptoms started with a headache, a sore throat, and fever. Weakness in the body could quickly progress into pneumonia. Each body's ability to fight this disease determined whether the person lived or died.

The flu struck the Broughtons' home like a thief in the night. She tried to open her eyes but the throbbing in her head reminded Myrtle of years back when too much champagne had resulted in a similar feeling. But this time it was different. Along with the pounding in her temples, her eyes were hot and the lids resisted lifting.

She struggled to get out of bed. Breakfast needed to be prepared and served to her husband, and the baby would be up soon also. Again she tried to sit up, but her head and shoulders seemed to be extra heavy this morning.

"Oh-h--h-h . . . ," she moaned before preparing for another try.

"What's wrong?" the groggy-voiced man inquired as he peeped through his sleep-laden eyes.

"I don't know," Myrtle slurred out and moaned again. "I'm sick, I guess." She lay in silence until Nat had woken up completely. "I don't think I can get up right now. Maybe if I just stay here for a while I'll feel better. My body seems so heavy I can't get it to move."

Just then the four-month-old infant began to stir in his cradle. Myrtle knew he would be expecting breakfast shortly.

"I guess I can get my own breakfast, but you're still going to have to feed the baby," Nat grumbled a little. He didn't like disruptions in his normal routine.

Baby Harry was now in full cry as Nat got out of bed and started dressing.

"Whoa, little fellow," Nat comforted the child as he picked him up and carried him to his mother. "You have a healthy set of lungs. You take care of your momma today; she's not feeling good. Daddy has to go to work, but I'll send someone by later to check on you two."

Nat kissed his son on the forehead as he handed the bundle to Myrtle. "Don't try to get up until you feel better," Nat instructed and bent down and likewise kissed her forehead.

It was almost noon before she was able to muster enough strength to get out of bed and move around a little. She put on her robe and sat at the dressing table. She tried to get a brush through her auburn locks, but every stroke and movement was an effort. Looking at herself in the mirror was unpleasant, as her now-red eyes squinted to keep the brightness of the afternoon sun out. Her throat was now sore and hurt when she tried to swallow. As she sat there, goose bumps began to form on her body and she became cold all of a sudden. Now that she had finally been able to get out of bed, she wished she had the strength to get back in and wrap in the warm covers.

She laid her head across her own folded arms and slumped on the table *shivering*. In her nearly unconscious state she lost all track of time. The sound of knocking at the door roused her back to the present.

"Mrs. Broughton!" the man spoke loudly and knocked for the fourth time. "Mrs. Broughton, are you all right? It's Newly. Your husband sent me out to check on you."

Myrtle recognized the voice of Nat's helper from the business. Her throat was swollen and her tone sounded deeper than normal as she cried out to him, "Newly! Come in please. . . . I need your help."

The man opened the unlocked door and hurried through the living room to find his employer's wife.

"I'm in here, Newly!" she called from the bedroom.

Newly was shocked to see Myrtle slumped over the dressing table yet did not hesitate to rush to her aid.

"Newly, I'm *freezing*." The shaky words were hard to interpret due to the trembling jaw and chattering teeth of the woman.

"Mrs. Broughton, you need to be in bed," Newly stated as he grabbed ahold of the shaking body. "Oh, dear Lord. You're burning up. Let me help you get in bed." He put his right arm around her back and under her right arm. With his left hand on her lower left hip he was able to pull and push at the same time.

Myrtle was soon upright, but her own legs refused to hold the weight. She started to buckle under the pressure. Newly felt her slipping and quickly slid his left arm under her legs to cradle her entire weight in his arms.

"OK Mrs. Broughton, I'll put you in bed." He went to the kitchen and brought back some refreshing water and gave the feverish woman a drink.

"You stay in bed now, you hear," Newly instructed the sick woman. "I'm going to tell your husband he had better get the doc out here to see you."

As he turned to leave the house, Myrtle called him back. "The baby," she managed to choke out in another plea for assistance.

"Oh, my. I forgot about the baby. Well, you're in no condition to take care of him right now, little momma." He looked in the direction in which the mother's limp hand was pointing and went to retrieve the infant from his cradle. "Mrs. Broughton, I don't want you to worry none right now. I'll take the boy down to Mrs. Perkins. She's nursing her own baby and I'm sure she'll help out for a few days." He didn't wait for any argument from the mother but wrapped little Harry in a blanket to take him to the neighbors.

"Newly!" the mother whispered in a weak but pleading voice. "Please, I need to hold him for just a minute."

The kind helper placed the boy in his mother's arms while he gathered clothing and diapers from a nearby chest. He loaded everything into his wagon before going back inside for the baby.

Using all her strength, she lifted her infant in her arms and placed her burning lips against his cool, sweet cheek. "I love you, my child. If I could care for you myself right now I would never let you go. It's killing me inside to have you away from my presence for even a short time. When I'm well enough, Daddy will bring you home again."

Newly tugged softly to take the baby from his mother. He knew he would have to move quickly. Mrs. Broughton was terribly ill and needed the doctor out here as soon as possible.

Myrtle fought hard against the virus for the first few days. Her frail body was still in a weakened condition from her pregnancy and delivery of the baby. Her soul had been through so many emotional hardships the last several years, it seemed unwilling to keep fighting.

As the torrents of disease continued to sweep through her, Myrtle knew she was losing the battle for her life. She opened her eyes with difficulty and looked at Nat. He leaned over her face and kissed her lips gently. She closed her eyes again as Nat sat by her bedside holding her limp, delicate hand. It had been five days of trying to shed the killing virus that was running rampant in her body. Nat had been by her side most of the time trying to perform the treatments the doctor had prescribed and was extremely tired and yearned for his wife to rally from his efforts.

She fell into a deep sleep of relieving comfort as her breathing became more and more shallow.

"Momma-a-a-a . . . Momma-a-a . . . I need you. Where are you?" the little voice called out from a distance. Myrtle had to strain her ears to make out the words.

She looked around and found she was at the top of a very high mountain. The grass was tall and green, and a cooling breeze made it rustle softly around her legs.

"Momma-a! Come and get me," she heard the voice again. She couldn't see him because of the surrounding clouds, yet she recognized the voice of young Roy.

"Momma, you promised. Where are you?" a girl's voice joined in off to Myrtle's left side.

"Helen!" she called back. "I can't see you. Where are you?"

"I'm trying hard to be brave, Momma, but it's hard out here alone," the third voice spoke out.

Myrtle turned to her right side and saw the clouds breaking apart. Pearl was standing on a steep ledge with hundreds of feet of sheer cliffs below her. She was holding onto a small limb of a plant growing from the outcropping.

"Hurry, Momma. It's hard to stay out here alone," Pearl whimpered.

"Momma!" "Momma!" "Momma!" the cries continued to come from all directions.

As the clouds lifted, Myrtle focused in on each of her children as they clung onto the jagged rocks.

"Hold on!" she called out in panic. "Don't move. Mother will come for you."

Each little one needed her, and yet they were so far away. Each one was so far apart from the others, Myrtle didn't know which way to go after first. As she began to descend the mountain, she became confused. Which one should she rescue first? What would be the best direction? Myrtle's mind began to whirl, and she became dizzy in her confusion. She put her hands to her head to stop the spinning.

"Help me! Somebody help me!" she cried out.

317

The spinning stopped and she again opened her eyes. This time she was at the bottom of a large marble staircase with a golden handrail. She reached out and took hold of the rail to balanced herself.

"Myrtle," a voice whispered magnificently from the top.

"Myrtle. It is time to come home," another one added.

She paused and gazed longingly toward the new but familiar voices. There was a group of glowing figures all extending welcoming hands. Her father and mother and Mabel were the three nearest her. They were beckoning her to climb the stairs.

She took two steps up toward the people she had loved so dearly. She desired to be close and embrace them once again.

"Momma! Momma" the children desperately called out. "Wait! Don't go!"

"It's all right Myrtle," her father's comforting tones whispered, enticing her to take another step upward.

"But my children," she spoke up to the waiting angels. "I need to save my babies."

"You can't save them, Myrtle. Your time on earth is finished."

"How will they survive without me? How will they know I love them?"

Her angel father pointed out to the cliffs. "Look at them, Myrtle. See how strong they are. They have generations of strong spirits pulling for them. Their climb won't be easy, but they will have to reach safety on their own."

Myrtle looked and saw each child starting to climb. It looked slow and painful, but each seemed to have the will and determination to get to a safe haven.

"Daughter," Myrtle's mother spoke compassionately, "how did you know your family loved you? We never spoke the words very often on earth."

"You didn't have to say the words, Mother; somehow I just knew who loved me and who didn't" Myrtle responded.

Her sister, Mabel, explained the reason. "Love is not just an earthly expression, Myrtle. Love can pass through the barrier between earth life and heaven. Your children will be able to share love with you as you did with us when we left earth. They will know in their hearts that you love them."

Myrtle embraced the words and knew they were true. With the next two steps upward her life journey came to an end.

318

Claramead Myrtle Knowles Tooley Broughton died June 2, 1918, at the young age of thirty-three. She was buried a few miles north of Evansburg in Entwhistle, Canada.

Nat was a broken man. He had loved Myrtle and was not prepared for her sudden death. At age fifty, he had no idea what to do with a four-month-old infant, now that his wife was no longer around to care for the baby.

With Myrtle gone, all their hopes and dreams for the future went with her. Everything changed for Nat. Their plan of going back to the States in August to fight for her other children were also gone. He was grieving and lonely for his beloved but did not see how he could raise a small baby by himself. After a few weeks of trying to be a single father, he gave up in frustration. He took his son Harry, back to the neighbor woman who had cared for him before and asked her to take the child and raise him as her own. Nat would send money from time to time as he was able but knew he could not care for the boy by himself.

Nat Broughton then left Canada to escape the memories of Myrtle and the child. He went back to the States to start over again.

INSURANCE

Obe Tooley had spent six years in Alaska after being divorced from Myrtle. He was shocked when he received a letter from Mrs. Hendricks, who informed him Myrtle had passed away. A few years later, Mrs. Hendricks also sent him a newspaper clipping in hopes it would help him locate his children someday.

Children Get Insurance

Five to Receive $5000 from John Knowles Killed in France

SANDPOINT, Idaho Jan. 12, 1923—The Rev. M. A. Covington, Superintendent of the Lewiston Children's Home, was here today to obtain affidavits of Sandpoint and Ponderay people regarding the birth of children to Mr. and Mrs. Obe Tooley, that the children may qualify for a share of a $10,000 war risk insurance of an uncle John Knowles, who died in France during the World war. The probate matters are being handled in Montana courts, where five children will receive $5000 of the legacy.

When Knowles took the insurance, he made his sister Mrs. Myrtle Tooley wife of Obe Tooley his beneficiary. Mrs. Tooley died in Canada before the death of her brother. The Tooley's lived at Thompson Falls, Mont, and at Ponderay.

While at Ponderay, two sons and two daughters were committed to the children's home. Mrs. Tooley later divorced Tooley and married a man named Broughton, with whom she moved to Canada, and to which union one child was born. This child is with relatives in Canada.

The Rev. Mr. Covington has found that Mrs. Broughton's second brother, who served with the Canadian army in France, died in Nevada, that her sister died many years ago in Minnesota, and that but one brother survives, Clarence Knowles, Thompson Falls, Mont.

Under the probate laws of Montana, Knowles' will divided the estate of John Knowles with Mrs. Broughton's children, none other of the Knowles family being survived by children. The brother at Thompson Falls is receiving a share in monthly payments from the federal government, and has waived any rights to further participation in the money, the Rev. Covington states.

May 1928

As Pearl read the letters and news article their message lashed out at her like the claws of an angry cat. They left a lingering sharp sting as

320

she contemplated the meanings and implications. *Her mother was dead!* That message brought tears to Pearl's eyes.

"Oh, Momma! Poor Momma!" Pearl said out loud even though no ears were near enough to hear. After the sorrow came anger. Her father had known all along her mother was dead. Why had he led her to believe otherwise?

Next was the other part. Her father *had* the money to pay the fines for the arrests, but he wouldn't do it. That was just too hard to believe. She had been led to believe the fines were too high. That her father couldn't pay them. If he had the money and still put his own kids through the hell they had suffered, the act was just *unforgivable,* at least for right now.

And the third thing: Daddy knew all about the insurance money. Was he really interested in their welfare or the insurance money they would inherit? Pearl figured she would probably never know the real truth about her father's thinking. She was sure of one thing: she was not going to stay around Sigurd long enough to find out about his motives.

She held up the pictures and studied them again. She stared into the face of her mother and could feel a special love as the eyes in the picture looked back at her. Pearl had known in her heart all along that her mother really had loved her and the others and wondered how she had ever doubted. Pearl knew for a surety that her mother would have kept her promise if she had not died at such a young age. All this new knowledge was very overwhelming, and Pearl buried her face in the pillow and cried for a long time.

Pearl heard the men coming in the front door. She gathered up the box and its contents and stormed into the kitchen to confront her father. She was so angry her normally calm nature had disappeared. The young woman struck out like a tiger at the unsuspecting man.

"Why did you lie to us about our mother?" was the first question out of her mouth.

Obe looked surprised, as did Roy. Pearl continued without giving her father time to think of the answer.

"I found these pictures and letters," she stated. "And I know my mother is dead. You knew it all along. Why did you lie to us about it?"

"Have you been snooping into my private things?" Obe questioned defensively. "Give me that box. It's mine," he demanded.

"OK. First I want you to tell Roy why we were really taken to the home in Lewiston," Pearl demanded as she looked her dad straight in the eye.

321

"What do you mean?" he yelled back. "I told you those guys were crooks. They wanted too much money."

"No, Daddy. You were the crook. You robbed us children of our mother," the angry girl accused. "Was everything about money? Go on, Dad. Tell Roy you had the money to pay the jail fines. But you, dear old dad, wouldn't do it."

Roy, who up to this point seemed dazed about the accusations, looked at his father with a new hate and disgust. "Is what Pearl is saying the truth?" Roy asked with anger in his tone. He waited for an answer. When the old man stammered on his words, the young man knew the answer must be "yes." "Do you have any idea what kind of misery you willed to me by not paying that money? I was treated like a slave most of those years. The family I lived with never made me feel like anything but a poor second-class citizen. They told me they were doing me a big favor to let me work for them. Oh, I didn't mind the work most of the time; everyone is expected to work. No one, however, should have to endure the way those people made me feel when I was only five years old. I remember one Christmas the boy who was their real son and I both asked for a bicycle. Well, when Christmas rolled around, there was one bicycle for him, but not one for me. I asked Mrs. Sleighter why I didn't get a bike, too. I was told it was because I was just the house worker, not a real son. Those kind of things happened to me for nine years."

"Life has been tough for all of us." Obe retorted. "You just don't understand how it was back then," he added, trying to make excuses for his actions. "And anyway, if you don't like it, you can leave. No one is twisting your arm to stay."

"Daddy. You're the one who doesn't understand," Pearl stated, now trying to calm everyone down before fists began to fly. "The money you didn't pay to keep our mother from going to jail was such a small amount, compared to *the price* all of us paid, for one bad choice. Our lives could have been so different if you had only paid that fine."

Pearl was still holding onto the box as she walked out of the house to be alone. She needed time to think about everything and plan what to do next.

FLY AWAY, LITTLE BIRD

Roy found Pearl at the top of the hill behind the house. She was sitting at the edge of a stand of quaking aspens. The sun was hanging low in the western sky as Pearl sat grieving for what could have been.

"I thought this might be where I could find you," Roy remarked.

"I thought you had to work tonight," was Pearl's return comment.

"I informed our so-called daddy he would have to tend his own business tonight. I needed to be with my sis."

"Bet he didn't like that." Pearl snickered through her sniffles and teary eyes.

"He actually didn't dare say a word back to me," Roy stated. "He knew I was looking for a reason to punch it out with him."

"Don't do that, Roy," Pearl advised. "Fighting is what stupid folks do when they try to solve problems. It only makes the situation worse. Sometimes you just have to keep quiet so time can heal the angry soul."

They sat there together and watched a flock of birds flying low in the evening sky.

"If I were a bird, I'd fly away from this place," Pearl remarked.

"What are you going to do, Pearl?"

"Well, I'm not going to stay here much longer. Not just because of all this stuff that happened today. I thought I might go back to Moscow, but I got a letter last week from Aunt Lillie. She said she and Uncle Charley were going to California to be near their oldest son. I guess there is nothing left for me there. I was thinking of going to the city," Pearl commented. "There are more opportunities for me in a more populated area. I still have a little money. Enough to pay for myself until I get work," she continued. "There is really nothing for me here except you and Helen. Helen has her husband to think of now, and I don't suppose you'll stay here very much longer."

"What about that beau of yours?" Roy questioned.

"I don't know. We haven't said much about a future together. Herb is still young and probably isn't ready to settle down yet." She paused and stared at the hills around her before speaking again. "I will say this, however: he better decide right away if he wants me or not, because I'm leaving here in a few days." They listened to the birds calling to each other before she added, "What about you, little brother?"

"Well, I really want to do a little more ranching. I'll have to go away somewhere to hire on," Roy answered. "If the old man and I can keep from killing each other for a few more months, I'll save as much money as I can. I'll need a little more cash than I have right now to be able to live on for a while. I'll just have to see how it goes.''

"I hate to leave you here by yourself. I—''

Roy stopped Pearl from saying more. "Pearl. Look at me,'' Roy demanded of his sister. "I know you feel a responsibility for all us kids, but you don't need to anymore. We are all grown-up and especially me. I have been on my own for several years now, and so far I have survived.''

"I know you can survive physically, Roy; I can, too. But it's just this family bond I want to hold onto.'' Pearl began to cry again.

Roy handed his sister a handkerchief to dry her eyes. "Pearl. You were just a little girl when we were separated. Somehow you managed to keep us a family by your diligence in letter writing. When times got tough for me, I always knew I had sisters out there somewhere I could depend on getting letters from. And even when I didn't write back very often, I could still depend on you. You didn't give up on me. You kept writing anyway. It's going to be that way our whole lives. We're just going to have to keep close through letters.''

"I know,'' Pearl agreed. "I just wish we hadn't been robbed of growing up together. It's just hard to leave you after only a few months of being together again.''

They sat on the hill together as the sun started to get closer to the horizon. Pearl opened the box she was still holding. She shared the contents with her brother. Together they read the letters and studied the pictures.

"Do you remember when these pictures were taken?'' Pearl asked as she held the ones of the three oldest children. "That's you in the middle, you know.''

He studied the young innocent faces carefully before answering. "How old was I then?'' he questioned.

"You were only about three and a half years old. You probably don't remember that day like I do,'' she remarked. "I remember Momma was so excited about getting us all dressed up. She made sure every hair on our heads was in place before she would let the man take the pictures. She was so proud of how nice we looked.''

They paused to study the photographs together.

"It seems like another lifetime ago. I'm going to stop wishing for what never was and concentrate on the future from now on,'' Pearl resolved.

They promised each other that evening that they would put their former life behind them and speak of it no more. At least until all the wounds of the past had time to heal.

Pearl went to visit her sister, Helen, that same night to tell her of the new discoveries. Helen was just as shocked and saddened as Pearl. This new discloser just tightened the disgust and contempt the married sister felt for her father. She never was thrilled about getting back with him anyway. The only reason she had agreed to leave Idaho was because of Pearl and Roy. When Pearl reminded her if it hadn't been for coming to Utah she would never have met Merlin, then Helen agreed at least some good had come out of this otherwise-bad situation.

Pearl confessed to her sister that she was planning to go up north to the Provo area. Helen was both happy and sad. She wanted Pearl to be happy, but she would also miss her company.

Helen did tell her sister that she and Merlin had also talked about moving up north. Maybe Provo would be a good place for them, too.

The next couple of days were difficult, as Pearl and her father tried to resolve their differences in silence. Neither one wanted to be the first to speak to the other. Obe was just being stubborn as usual, and Pearl was just afraid.

On Saturday Herb came for his weekly visit and wanted to go out by the lake to do some fishing and have a picnic. Pearl agreed to go. It would give them a good opportunity to talk.

As Herb concentrated on his fishing skills, Pearl took out a notebook and penned a poem. She needed some cheerful thoughts to go through her mind for a while. She desired good feeling to help get rid of the gloom she had been through the past few days. While looking at the beauties all around she wrote a few lines.

The Voice of Spring

The breezes waft to me the fragrance of the flowers,
The birds accent the voice of Merry spring time.
Fair mother moon sheds out her silvery light,
The orange spray is budding on its leafy bough.
'Tis the time for mating and for wooing,
The bluebird sweetly calls unto his love,

The Oriole's softly singing in the woodland,
On the belfry you can hear the cooing of the dove.

P.E.T.

Before they finished their picnic Herb insisted on hearing the poem Pearl had written. Of course, like all shy writers, she tried to hide if from him. He was stronger than she, however, and was able to get the paper away from her grasp. He teased and tickled her until she let go.

As he read the lines out loud he especially liked the part about the "time for mating and wooing." He read that part over and over, making Pearl blush each time he said it.

On the ride home from the lake, Pearl finally got up enough courage to tell Herb about her plans. "I had an awful run-in with my dad the other day. I think it's time for me to leave and move to the city, where there's more things for me to do," Pearl stated.

"Hey, wait a minute," Herb replied. "What did your dad do? Did he hit you?"

"No," Pearl quickly responded.

"Well, he better not or I'll . . . ," Herb spouted.

"No, he didn't touch me. I just found out some things he had been lying about and . . ." She paused. "I have some 'mad spots' that need scratchin'. I just can't do it here," Pearl calmly stated.

"Why don't you go and move in with Helen and Merlin? If you did, you would get away from your dad," he suggested.

"No, Herb. I did the same kind of thing once before. It just didn't work out the way I thought it would. The best thing for me is to go away from this area. I like living in the city, and I'm sure I could get work there," the determined young woman reported.

"Well, what about me? I mean us?" Herb asked seriously. "If you leave, I guess that means you don't care about me," he pouted.

"No, that's not true. I do care about you. But what *about* us?" Pearl questioned him back. "You have never said how you feel about me. If you just want to be friends, we can do that by mail. If you want something more, you will need to decide soon. I plan on leaving this next week," she declared.

With that declaration Herb turned all sweet and mushy. He begged the nice young lady to stay. "Oh, Pearl sweetie, please don't leave. I'll be so lonesome without you. You'll miss me, too, won't you?"

"Yes, of course I'll miss you," she shyly stated as she felt the blush rise in her cheeks. "What girl wouldn't miss a great fellow like you?"

"Do you like me enough to get married to me?" the young man asked.

"Well," she bashfully replied, "I guess I do. Anyway, if we were married we could go away to the city together."

"Wouldn't you want to stay here if we were married?" he inquired.

"No, Herb. Married or single, I need to get away from my father. And I'm going to do it soon. You need to go home and think about what you want. Nobody can make a big decision like this one for you. You have to make the choice yourself," Pearl firmly stated.

"Don't you dare leave Sigurd, Pearl Tooley, until I can talk to you again. I'm coming back here tomorrow. I just need to think about some things first." He gave her a long romantic kiss good night, then walked her to the door in a gentlemanly fashion. "Remember, I'll be here tomorrow and we'll talk more about this," he promised.

Pearl waited all day Sunday for Herb to keep his promise, but he never showed up. She figured she had his answer by his absence. It was just another crushing blow, one more thing to add to the "Why I feel sorry for myself" list.

She was in the kitchen when her father came in and spoke to her for the first time since the controversy. "You can have all that stuff in the box, if you want it," Obe said in a gruff voice. "I suppose I should have told you right at first about your mother."

Pearl was surprised at her dad's willingness to say he was wrong. All the angry words she had rehearsed seemed to fade from her lips. "Yes," she agreed. "You were wrong about keeping Mother's death from us. Why did you want to do that?" she questioned.

"I don't know. Why do people do a lot of foolish things?" He questioned his own motives. "I guess I didn't want you to think your mother would probably still be around if I would have been a better husband."

Pearl was quiet for a few minutes. She wasn't sure just what to say to her dad.

"You know, I'm still so sad about so many things. I don't know what I really want to say right now. I suppose it will take time for all these scars to go away," Pearl confessed.

She poured her dad a cup of coffee and offered to fix him breakfast. She needed some stalling time before she could tell him of her plans to leave.

"Thank you for the box. Having all that information and the pictures means a lot to me. I'm grateful you're willing to part with them. You can keep them longer if you want to," Pearl offered.

"No, Pearly, you take them. I've just had them hidden away in that dresser drawer way too long. The pictures need to be out where they can be looked at and enjoyed. And those papers and letters, well, they are as much for you as they are for me. Your mother must have been prompting me from her grave to save these things for you. They won't do me any good anymore," the slightly repentant man confessed.

Obe sipped his coffee and waited a few moments before asking his oldest girl the next question. "So where are you going?" he asked her out of the blue. "I saw you getting your trunk out of the shed yesterday."

"I'm going up to Provo, I guess," Pearl answered without the fear that she thought would go along with the answer.

"Provo, huh? Well, that's OK I guess. At least you'll be away from that Creviston clan up there," Obe growled out.

Pearl didn't make any comments. She didn't want her father to detect her broken heart.

"I never did like that group of roughnecks. I'm always hearing stories about one or the other of them getting into fights and causing trouble," Obe continued. "No-good bunch of 'Arkies' is what they are."

Pearl finished her cooking and excused herself while her dad ate the rest of his breakfast. She shut the door of her bedroom and started her packing. The tears of a lovesick heart rolled down her face.

Why? she questioned to herself. *Why do I have such bad luck with keeping a boyfriend? Maybe I'm just not pretty enough. I must be too short or too fat. I know my hair is ugly.* Pearl tried to reason with herself. She thought of all the possible reasons she was twenty-three and still single. Why, she was almost an "old maid" by modern-day standards. All she had ever really wanted in life was to have her own family. She had been torn away from being part of one for so many years. She had always dreamed of having children and making a better situation for them than had been thrown at her. Somehow she thought it would be a way of restitution for the kind of life she had experienced.

It was late afternoon the following day. Pearl was starting supper for the last time in Sigurd when she saw him coming down the street. He was dirty and had a bedroll bundle under his arm. It took Pearl a few minutes to realize the man she was staring at was Herb. He looked so different somehow. When he turned up the walkway, she went to the front door and opened it before he knocked. His face was bruised and there was a cut over his right eye with a new scab just starting to form.

"Whew! Are you a sight for sore eyes!" he said to the concerned girl at the door. "I could sure use a cold drink of water."

"What in the world?" she gasped as she held the door open for the battered young man. She quickly fixed him the water.

He dropped his tired body onto the kitchen chair and drank the cooling liquid.

"What has happened to you?" Pearl questioned the tired-looking warrior.

"I'd have been here yesterday, but my old man told me if I was going to leave and get married, I could just walk the whole way," Herb reported. "When I tried to persuade him to let Abe drive me he just . . . , well . . . , kicked my butt out, you might say."

He tried to be brave and talk big about his trouble, yet Pearl knew he felt bad. The damage of rejection hurt on the inside just as much as the bruises did on the outside.

"How did you get here, if you didn't get a ride from your family?" she asked, suspecting all along what the answer was going to be.

"I walked," he replied. "It's only about twenty miles. I would have come yesterday like I promised, but I had to hide out until my pa went to sleep. I had to sneak back in the house to get my things. I don't have much, but I did want my good clothes to get hitched in. That is, if you still want to do it?" he inquired of the sweet young woman.

Pearl looked at the normally handsome young man almost in disbelief. "Sure I do if you want to," she replied.

"What about your dad?" Herb questioned, hoping he wouldn't have to go to battle with Pearl's father also.

"Oh, he won't like it, that's for sure. But it really doesn't matter much what he likes or wants right now," Pearl commented. "He hasn't earned the right to tell me what I can or can't do, not at this point of my life anyway, and he knows it. He knows I'm leaving tomorrow and he won't try to stop me."

"Good," Herb remarked with a bit of relief in his voice. "When should we get married, today or later?"

"Well, if we're going to be traveling together . . . ," she started in her most proper voice, "then we ought to be married. We don't want to give people cause for gossip; there will be enough of that anyway. We

329

could get married tomorrow morning. Roy would drive us to Manti, where we can board the train that goes to Provo," Pearl suggested.

"Then it's set," Herb agreed. "We'll get married tomorrow."

They were so deliberate in their planning it was as if they were deciding on where to go for a picnic or what pair of shoes to buy, something other than planning a marriage. Yet each was terribly excited about the idea of a new life together.

"Are you hungry?" she asked her new fiancé. It was a way of changing the subject as she felt the red blush coming to her face.

"Starved!" he replied. "I haven't eaten since yesterday afternoon."

"You get washed up," she instructed. "I'll have you some supper ready by the time you come back. I can't have my future husband going hungry," Pearl remarked as she stirred the pot of beef stew that was bubbling on the stove.

SOMETIMES HAPPILY EVER AFTER

It was a quiet ceremony held at the courthouse and performed by the justice of the peace. It was legal, however, and Pearl became Mrs. Herbert E. Creviston. It took place on May 29, 1928. Even though Obe thought the Crevistons as a whole were "no good," he knew he had no room to judge someone else. He did care about Pearl; she seemed to bring out his good side once in a while. So he swallowed his pride just a little and attended the ceremony along with Roy, Helen, and Merlin. Obe wanted his daughter to be happy, even if he didn't think she was on the right path to get there. He tried at least for one day to be supportive and wish the newlyweds "good luck" on their journey through marriage. Obe even gave them twenty dollars as a gift, something neither Herb nor Pearl expected.

After the ceremony and congratulations were over, Roy drove the couple to Manti. The drive took about an hour. The newlyweds were so much into their own anticipation of married life, the journey was over before they realized it. They said their thank-yous and good-byes to Roy, then got a room at the local inn. The newlyweds spent the next two days on a honeymoon.

On Friday, they caught the morning train and headed north to Provo. With great expectations, they were ready to start their life together. It would be hard for them, being in a new place with no job and not much money. But the couple were in love, and each was willing to do his or her share to make a go of it.

Life for the couple was not easy at first; they struggled just to make ends meet. Herb worked at every kind of job he could find during the depression years, everything from digging ditches to building fences. Pearl got a job as a housekeeper for a university professor, an occupation she had lots of experience doing.

Helen and Pearl both got pregnant that year. By the spring of 1929, they each had baby girls.

Pearl's new happiness reached deeper into her soul than she ever imagined possible as she held her firstborn child in her arms. She could now understand the immeasurable sorrow her own mother must have felt the day her children were ripped from her arms. Pearl never wanted to experience such terrible grief with her own offspring. As she held the little girl in her loving arms she sang her a song from the heart:

"Dream Girl, little flower, sweetheart of mine,

As the sun after the shower softly does shine
Your smile will cheer me when days are gray.
Oh, please stay near me; don't go away.
Because I love you, dear, and need you all the time
Smile now and whisper you will stay mine.
We will build a cottage out of dreams so true
Where the sun is shining and skies always blue.
As a little garden our love will grow,
Blossom into brightness, 'cause I need you so.
Dream Girl, little flower, I will care for you,
Love you every hour; won't you love me, too?
Smile just at me, dear; tell me you'll be true.
Whisper that you love me; you know I love you.''

Not too long after Helen and Merlin had their baby, they, too, moved to Provo. Merlin was able to get work at a pipe plant just south of town.

Roy left Sigurd by March of the same year. He took a train and headed east to a place where he could hire on as a cowboy again. Pearl got letters that summer from Green River, Utah, where Roy was working.

May 23, 1929, Green River, Utah

Dear Sister,

Sure was glad to hear from you. Didn't get to read your last letter very good tho as we drove some wild ponies into Green River to the stock yards, and coming out I rode one of them and had your letter in my pocket and it evidently shook out because the ponies will buck.

You will need to give me Helen's address because of the lost letter.

Green River is about 300 miles from Sigurd by rail, and about 160 miles straight west.

Went out riding Sunday and roped a wild burro or jack ass about the size of a police dog. Sure is some animal, but will make a good pack animal some day if it lives long enough.

There is no news here at all so will have to close.

With love to the family and yourself,
Roy

July 11, 1929 Green River, Utah

Dear Pearl,

How does it with you. I am having quite a time down here and am quitting my job. Is there any work around Provo, as I will be out of work and foot loose pretty soon.

As ever with love,
Roy

Aug 9, 1929 Green River, Utah

Dear Pearl,

Read your most welcomed letter the other day and was very glad to hear from you. I am still punching cows and don't know just when I'll be through but I think I will quit when my month is up.

I am bunking in a little cabin and the other morning I went to build my fire and found a scorpion about eight inches long in my wood pile, and they are not very good to look at and are also very poison.

We killed twelve rattle snakes all toll this summer and some were pretty big, but such is life on the desert.

Tell Helen she had better write to me pretty soon or I will forget what her writing looks like.

I may be up there pretty soon and I may stay here all winter, I don't know just yet. I don't know just what kind of a mine the boss has, but heard he was pretty excited about it. I haven't heard from Bob since he left Sigurd.

Well hoping both babies are well, also their mothers, and give my best regards to the husbands.

With love, your brother
Roy

The 1930s were hard for most Americans, but especially the common laborers.

Herb finally got work with Merlin at the pipe plant in Provo. The work was hard and the pay was low, but they were both glad to at least have jobs.

By 1936, Pearl had two more children, making three in all. By saving and scrimping the Crevistons were able to make a small down payment on a house in south Provo. The property had enough space for a few animals and a garden.

Herb struggled with his temper. He sometimes reigned with terror over his little domain. Pearl had to work hard to keep her little family together.

In that same year, Pearl received a letter from a lady in Sigurd. She reported that Obe was quite ill. He was in his midsixties and becoming unable to care for himself.

There was no answer to the father problem but one. Roy had joined the military and was unable to help. Helen was so negative about her father she told Pearl he could rot in "you know where" for all she cared. And anyway, she was working part-time and didn't want to quit work to tend the old man. Robert was off to "who know's where." Each time a letter came, he was living someplace different.

Pearl might have said, "forget him," like Obe had done to her as a child. But she couldn't. She wanted to be a better person than he had been. Time had helped to heal the wounds on her heart from long ago, and now the scars were hardly noticeable in her mind. Maybe with service to the man she could rid herself of them completely.

The little Creviston family drove down to Sigurd to pick up the aging grandfather. He was still a grumpy man and gave off the attitude that he expected his children to take care of him. It was difficult to feel good about service to a man like her father had turned out to be, but Pearl resisted her feelings of wanting to leave him alone to die. They took him back to Provo so that they could care for him.

In December of 1940 tragedy happened. An accident at the pipe plant took the life of Helen's husband, Merlin Taylor. Everyone was devastated and full of grief. The two couples had been so close for over twelve years. The loss of Merlin hit Herb and Pearl nearly as hard as it did Helen and her daughter. All the comforting and well-wishers couldn't make up for the loss of Helen's husband and a good friend.

Pearl only knew one way to express her feeling, the method she had been using for so many years. She sat down alone in a quiet place and wrote a poem for her sister about the tragedy.

The Glorious By and By

In the west the sun is setting underneath the clouds
Where none but God who made it can see the beauty of its
Day's reign, now drawing to a close.

334

And tho this world be full of sorrow,
And Grief seems to be your lot
Tho the clouds are hanging heavy in the sky
Our God is watching up above
And the sun light of his never failing love
Will break upon you bright and glorious by and by.

P.E.T.C.

In March of 1941 Pearl had her fourth child, another girl. The family was quite poor at the time, so Helen helped her sister deliver the child at home.

Obe was still living with Pearl's family and was now almost fully dependent on Pearl and Herb for his needs. Between caring for a new baby and an old baby Pearl had her hands full. Herb was good and kind to the aged man and helped Pearl a lot with Obe's physical hygiene.

Obe was still as grumpy as ever, but he did appreciate the tenderness of his eldest daughter and his grandchildren.

"Pearl. Come closer," the weakened man asked. "I need to tell you something."

She sat on the edge of the dying man's bed and leaned her ear near him to hear the strained words. "I don't want to die, Pearl. How am I ever going to face your mother? She was right, you know. I'm going to have to pay." Obe coughed and almost choked on the words. He could somehow anticipate the fate that awaited him.

"Well, maybe you won't have to face her," Pearl tried to make a subtle joke. "I don't think you will go to the same place she's at."

Obe smiled slightly at his daughter's humor in this tense time. "You're probably right." He started to laugh but ended up coughing even harder.

"Take it easy, Daddy, don't try to talk anymore. Maybe you should get some more rest."

"Wait," he pleaded as he grabbed for her hand. "I'm sorry." He started the coughing again but wouldn't let Pearl's hand go. "Can you forgive me?"

She just looked into the aged and sick man's face. She had once had so much hate and disgust for him. But here he was weak and dying before her very eyes. How could she say she could never forgive him?

"Daddy, I'll really try," was all she could promise.

On November 12, 1941, Obe Tooley died in Provo. He was taken down to Richfield, Utah, to be buried.

Pearl sat alone by his grave on that crisp November day. He had passed away quietly in his sleep, but the impact of this man's life would be hard to sort out. She pondered what it would be like for him on Judgment Day. Pearl wondered what kind of *hell* he would have to suffer. What price would he have to pay for the deeds he committed and the ones he omitted in regards to his family?

She looked back and tried to think how this *one man* had caused each member of his family a different grief. Her mother, Myrtle, had just plain given up on him and chosen to leave. Helen chose to ignore him and the whole situation. She pretended it never happened to her, at least. The subject was never discussed at any length with her children. Roy could talk about the old man but never forgave him for his actions. And Pearl herself, she tried to do some real soul-searching as she sat next to the box holding the lifeless remains. This man had caused her so much heartache and pain in her younger years. Yet she knew because she was a good Christian she would have to forgive him. She prayed she would be able to complete that quest someday. Pearl had come a long way from hate to service. However, she still had to get rid of the small amount of resentment that managed to hold on inside her.

Standing by the River at Twilight

Standing by the river at twilight a voice comes over the water to me,
And speaks in those calling melodious tones, that tell of Jesus of Galilee,
Saying with sweet gentle compassion,
Prepare, prepare to meet me in Heaven for 'tis the even tide of life,
Prepare to share with me my kingdom, before the night closes round
And shuts out Eternal Life.
Jesus that kind loving Savior's entreating us to prepare,
That we in heaven's glory His blessed kingdom may share,
And the voice steals over the river sweetly calling that loving plea,
Prepare, prepare to meet me in Heaven for 'tis the even tide of life,
Prepare to share with me my kingdom, before the night closes round
And shuts out Eternal Life.

P.E.T.C.

LIFE MUST GO ON

After Merlin's death, Helen started dating another man. His name was Frederick Hoffman, and they liked each other a lot. They wanted to get married right away, but because the insurance was not settled after Merlin's death Helen's lawyer advised them to wait.

Fritz, as he was nicknamed, lived out of town. Helen would go with him to visit his family. She had injured her leg, and it wasn't healing properly. She went to see a doctor on one of the visits to have it looked at. While she was recuperating, she wrote Pearl a surprising letter.

Jan. 28, 1942

Dear Pearl,

Don't be too surprised when you receive this letter. I meant to write sooner but just didn't.

I came up here a week ago Monday to have my leg treated—the doctor decided I had to be operated on immediately instead, so here I am. Fritz brought me up and stayed until I was O.K. and said he would stop by and tell you on his way back, but I told him I would rather write to you instead, but it has taken me much longer to get around to it than I planned so forgive me for the delay.

I am feeling fine now and will be home about Sunday, I think I'll tell you more about everything when I see you.

We haven't said anything to anyone on account of that darn court and everything, but Fritz and I were married last year. My daughter knows it now and so do his folks, but my lawyer advised me not to say anything about it until after things were settled. He told me as you know, things would be settled last June and we thought we could tell you then, but it isn't finished yet but we decided we would let people know anyway as we are tired of pretending and living apart. I may have been stupid but I refused to let him help me until we were living together and I could do my part too, but we feel we have waited too long now and there will undoubtedly be a lot of talk, but I guess we should expect that.

Fritz is here again today. He had been called up for promotion to engineer with the railroad, and will have to be up here next week taking examinations. But I will go home Sunday anyway as I can relax more at home than with his folks I believe.

337

I'll be seeing you soon. Come over as I won't be able to drive for a while.

Love,
Helen

The secret-marriage confession was surprising to Pearl. But she had been suspicious of the couple for some time. She now was able to understand some of her sister's strange behavior over the last few months.

A short period of time after the announcement of marriage, Helen gave birth to another baby girl. The newly formed family now had a new bond and a special child to love.

The letters from Roy were few during the thirties. He stopped writing when the price of stamps became too high for his budget. Pearl only received a couple of letters from her brother Robert during this time also.

Roy became so busy traveling in the military when World War II was in full swing, he had a hard time keeping in touch. Pearl finally tracked him down at Christmastime 1942 and received a letter back the following month.

U.S. Army Camp White Oregon   Camp White Jan. 7, 1943

Dear Pearl,

Received your awfully nice Christmas card today. Sure was awfully happy to get if after all these years.

How are you and Herb getting on and all of the children, it seems only like yesterday that we were all together in Sigurd, and then again when I count the things that have happened since then it is a very long time. I have been in the army almost 12 years, quite the old soldier.

I hear from Helen, and tried to get your address from her after you moved. I took a furlough this Christmas, the first I have taken since I joined the Army. Went to San Antonio, Texas. Tried to get routed by Salt Lake, but the railroads have so much traffic that you almost have to beg to get on a train.

Would sure like to see all of you again, I am going to try and make it some time next summer if I am still in the Country. The way things are now a soldier can't plan very far ahead.

I had a letter from Bob about the middle of December. His address is General Delivery Vancouver, Washington.

Well Pearl will close for now, please write and tell me how you have been getting along these many years.

With love,
Roy

Just after Christmas of 1944, she received another letter from her brother Roy, only this one came from another country.

Dec. 26, 1944 Italy

Dear Pearl, and all the family,

I want to thank all of you for the lovely Christmas package. I just opened it yesterday, it was quite a temptation not to open it before Christmas, as I received it around the 15th of the month, but I exerted my will power and it was certainly grand when I did get it.

I also received two letters yesterday that were written around Thanksgiving, and Pearl you must be a very energetic girl to work and raise your family too. I guess though everyone is kept very busy in the States now.

I sure wish this War would end so life would get back to normal again. Do you know Pearl, this is the first time in my adult life that I have ever been homesick. I can't hardly explain it but the U.S. would sure look good to me, any part of it. I have seen enough of Africa and Italy now and I have no desire to see any more of Europe or Asia, it would please me to no end if I could spend the rest of my life in the States when this job is done over here. But it isn't finished yet, so I can't make any plans, but when it is over I know one thing, we are going to do, Marie and I, that is see you and Helen and the family. And I hope I will be in the coming year.

I have been married almost a year, and 21 days of that Marie and I had together. As you know, she is in India now and the country is not a very pleasant place to have to stay. I wish she could be back in the States, I would feel a lot better about this war if she were, but enough of my wishful thinking for the present.

Did you folks have a good Christmas, I hope you did. We had a very white one here. The snow in the mountains is several inches deep and plenty cold. It is clear and cold today, good "observation" for us, and also the other guys too, and by the noise, they are not wasting any clear day in Italy. But that is what we are over here for, so why complain. The sooner it is over, the sooner we will either go home or somewhere else.

339

I must close for now, hoping to hear from you again soon, also hoping to see you next year.

> With love to all,
> Roy

Dear Pearl, and family,

I received your last letter a few days ago and I have intended to answer it before now. But straightening everything out after a War has kept me very busy and I have neglected my letter writing terribly.

I had been in the hospital about a month just after the war finished until recently, I had a mild case of ''Yellow Jaundice,'' but I am all over it now.

I may be back in the States before long and take a 30 day leave before reporting for a new assignment, I surely intend to visit you folks if I do, but I can't bring Marie (my wife) with me as she is still in India and I don't know when she will be able to come home.

I am near Trieste Italy near the Austrian and Yugoslavian border, and it is a very nice country and hardly touched by War. It certainly is different than the country along Highway 65 in the Apennine Mountains south of Bologna. That part of Italy was pretty badly torn up by War. We stayed in one place for almost 6 months there and we were not the only ones shooting either. ''Jerry'' was quite active, that is one winter I don't believe I will ever forget, and I feel that I am quite a lucky person to come out of it, as ''Jerry'' never missed a day all winter, shelling Highway 65. And there was plenty of artillery against us too. Oh well, that is history now for the ones that made it O.K., and the ones that didn't know that they died for what was right. There cannot be too much praise for the Infantry Man in this War that has finished here, as they had it plenty tough all the time. The artillery had some tough going once in a while too, but nothing to compare with the guys sitting in a foxhole just waiting for ''Jerry'' to slow up.

When we made a drive to the Po Valley, ''Jerry'' was ready to quit, and it turned into a race. There wasn't any front line left and the ''krauts'' were surrendering by the thousands. There was an awful lot of destruction on the south bank of the Po River. Horses running loose by the hundreds, burned out vehicles, and guns everywhere, and it wasn't a pretty sight. But I am glad it was all ''Jerry'' equipment, but it wasn't very nice at best.

I guess there will be a lot of us go to the Pacific from here. I sure wish that those "Japs" could realize they haven't a chance and quit fighting so we could all go home.

Will close now, hoping all of you are well and in the best of health. I also hope I will be seeing you soon.

With love,
Roy

It wasn't until the war was over that Roy was able to again see his two sisters. On a trip from Fort Bragg, North Carolina, to California and back, Roy and his wife, Marie, stopped by Provo and met all his nieces and one nephew. They also met Helen's second husband, Fritz Hoffman.

Pearl spent the first part of her married life scraping to make ends meet. In 1944 she felt she needed to help her husband to make a living again. Herb was sick a lot of the time with one thing after another. In 1940 he had contracted the mumps. A simple affliction for a child, but terrible for a grown man. The disease moved from the glands of his throat down to his groin. This caused him to suffer awful pain. His thyroid gland was next. In the mid-1940s he developed a large goiter that had to be surgically removed.

Work at the production plants in Utah was sometimes unstable, being under union rule. When the workers were forced to go strike against management for benefits, the paychecks stopped. With both of these problems occurring at the same time, illness and a strike, Pearl felt she needed to get a job herself.

She acquired work as a cook at a little café close to their house. She could walk to work and back, and save the gasoline in the car for other things. She continued as a cook for many years and was considered one of the best in Provo. Pearl intended to quit when Herb got better and back to work, but his health continued to go downhill. Illness next affected his insulin gland and he developed diabetes. After that, another goiter in his thyroid glands had to be removed.

After working for other people for ten years, Pearl decided to open her own café. She and Herb wanted to try their skills at management also. The café became the center point for the family, with almost everyone involved. Pearl and Herb's daughters were able to work as waitresses there and make enough money to help support themselves. Everyone seemed to have a niche in the business. Pearl worked at and ran this café for about eight years before getting tired of so much work for so little profit.

Helen worked as a nurse at the hospital in Provo. Her two daughters followed in her footsteps, also becoming nurses. Helen's husband worked for the Union Pacific Railroad as an engineer for many years.

Roy made a career of the military. He and Marie were able to live in Sacramento, California, after the war years.

The letters from Robert Earl quit coming to anyone in about 1945. The family never heard from him again. They feared he had lost his life in the war but could never find out any more about him.

ALL ARE SAFELY GATHERED IN

In 1961, Pearl and Herb took a trip back to Idaho. All of their own children were married or living on their own. Pearl and Herb no longer had the full responsibilities of the café, so they took the time to do a little traveling.

Pearl still had an empty place in her heart that needed filling. She wanted to do something about it. The message she had read long ago about a half brother continually remained in the back of her thoughts. She was haunted and wanted to know more about him.

Pearl and Herb stopped in at the children's home in Lewiston and were allowed to have copies of the letter written back in 1914. It was explained to her by the kind woman who currently ran the home that at the time Mr. Chase was superintendent many people suffered because of his financial greed. Children awarded to the home were treated as merchandise. For each child the state of Idaho gave the home a certain sum of money for his or her care. Each youngster became a valuable asset the superintendent did not want to lose. Consequently, he discouraged any parents from regaining custody of their children.

The woman admitted Mr. Chase was wrong in denying Mrs. Tooley the right to correspond with her children. After he was gone, things got much better for home-and-parent relationships. It was a bad time at the home when Mr. Chase was in charge, the woman noted.

Pearl was also able to find out a little more about her half brother, Harry Broughton. She found the name of the woman who took him when his father left. That little bit of information would nag at Pearl for the next two years.

When she returned home from Idaho, she shared the information with Helen and Roy. Roy also became interested in knowing more about his half brother. Helen was satisfied to let well enough alone, fearing this third brother might be of unsavory character. She was satisfied to forget the past and only dwell on the future. But not Pearl; she needed to fill in that last piece of her puzzle.

In August of 1963, Pearl and Herb met Roy and Marie in Lewiston, Idaho. Pearl and Roy wanted to visit their old stomping grounds and also see if they could locate their mother's grave site and other records. Besides having a good time seeing all the sights of northern Idaho and Canada, the trip became a real search for their half brother. The four folks searched the telephone books of every town. They were looking for any Broughtons that might be listed. If they happened on any with *H.* initials or "Harry," they would call, trying to find the right one.

When they arrived in Calgary, Canada, on their way back from Entwhistle, they found the name Harry Broughton listed in the telephone book.

Marie, Roy's wife, being the bravest of the bunch, called the number. When no one answered, they acquired a street map of the town. It didn't take them long to figure out how to get to the address in the phone book.

When they arrived at the Broughtons' address, they could tell no one was home. The grass was long around the house and looked like it hadn't been mowed for about two weeks. There were several days' worth of newspapers on the front porch, another indication of absence.

The lady who lived next door was outside watering her flowers. Marie went to the woman to inquire about the Broughtons who lived there. The neighbor was very nice and explained that the people who lived next door were on holiday. She didn't expected them back for a week or more.

Marie explained why the four of them had come to this address and why they were inquiring about the family. She asked the woman if she would give the vacationing family a letter they would write. It would explain to the people who they were and what they wanted. When the neighbor agreed to do it, Pearl got out her pad and pen. She wrote a short letter with some simple information.

Aug. 10, 1963

Harry Broughton,

We are looking for our half-brother. Here is the information we have. His name is Harry Duncan Broughton, son of Nat Broughton and Myrtle Knowles. He was born about April of 1918, and his mother Myrtle died June 1918. She is buried in Entwhistle, Canada. If you are this person, then I am your sister. We had the same mother, but different fathers. You also have two other brothers and another sister. If you are this brother we are looking for, please write and tell us.

Sincerely,
Pearl Creviston (Addresses enclosed)

By the end of August, Pearl received the answer she was praying for, one more of the missing pieces to the "puzzle" she was trying to complete.

Dear Pearl,

It was really a surprise to get your letter from our neighbors when we returned from our holiday.

Yes I am the Broughton you are looking for. I am sure sorry that we were away when you came. I would sure like to have met you people. We will sure have to make some arrangements to meet on the next holiday season or sooner if possible.

I don't know whether you know or not, but mother passed away about three months after I was born. I never knew her at all or any about her side of our family. I was placed with foster parents and my father went back to the States. I can only remember seeing my father three times before 1945, which was after the war.

My wife and I spent a few holidays with my father after the war, in Spokane. I tried to get information from him regarding my mother, but he didn't seem to know much or at least didn't tell me anything by which I could find anything out.

My father died in Spokane in 1952 at age 84.

My family and I were going to immigrate to Hawaii in 1961, and in the course of getting my papers I wrote several places in the States to find out information about my mother. Every letter I wrote drew a blank, so I finally gave up.

You can see what a surprise it is now when you people come along. How did you happen to come up this way and start looking for me?

Have you any pictures of mother, I would sure like to see them if so. My father said most of his stuff got burnt in a fire years ago and also some pictures of mother.

I have written your brother in Sacramento, but did not send my pictures of our family.

From the end of the war until a year ago, I worked at the carpentry trade. I have a job now with a firm of architects as a building inspector.

Well I don't know much more to say, just now, but will sure be glad to hear from you and find out about mother's side of the family

Sure hope you write soon.

Your truly,
Harry Broughton*

---

*Letters in this book from Harry to Pearl are actual letters, published here compliments of Harry Broughton.

Oct. 3, 1963 Calgary Alberta

Dear Pearl,

Thank you very much for your letter. We are really pleased to hear from you. I don't know how you feel, but it was sure some welcome surprise to me to find that I had brothers and sisters after all these years.

It sure seems a shame that my father did not tell me about you people. I sure asked him enough times about my mother but never did get any straight answers.

Have you any information on our mother's side of the family? Do you know if she had any brothers or sisters or where her parents came from? I would sure be glad to find out.

I have written away for the correct information regarding mother's death and when it arrives I will forward it to you.

My birth certificate has my date of birth as Jan. 17, 1918 so I am sure that part is correct. About 3 years ago we were going to go to Hawaii to live. I tried then to find out about mother and wrote several places in the States but all drew blanks. It took me so long to get my information for my passport, that the job I was going to fell through. We then gave up the idea of moving. It seems queer that I should start hunting for information of mother and give up, then along comes you and Roy with all the answers.

I had a letter from Roy shortly after you wrote. His holiday suggestion for next summer sounds O.K. to me. I will know in Jan. when I can get my holiday, and I hope Roy can arrange them at the same time. I sure wish there was some way that we could get together sooner.

I will sure be glad to hear from Helen. I told Roy I would write to her but I have not done so yet. Letter writing is quite a job for me.

Did you get any information of mother at Evansburg when you were up there?

I sure would be glad to have pictures of your family, and also of mother. I will be waiting for them.

Well Pearl, my wife and children are sure excited about our next summer holiday and meeting new relatives. It is quite a thing for them too as I was married in England and my wife has no one in this country on her side of the family. Well, this will be all for now and I hope to hear from you again soon.

Sincerely,
Harry and family

Oct. 7, 1963 Calgary Alberta

Dear Pearl,

Just a few lines to thank you very much for the pictures. I was sure glad to get them Pearl. This is the only picture I have ever seen of my mother so you can see how I looked forward to it.

I now have a date of mother's death as registered with the Dept. Of Public Health. It is June 2, 1918. Hope to hear from you again soon.

Sincerely,
Harry and family

Dec. 2, 1963 Calgary Alberta

Dear Pearl,

Thanks ever so much for the enlarged picture of mother. It was really good of you to get it for me. . . . I wrote a letter to the Children's Home in Lewiston, Idaho inquiring about the trustee of mother's estate as Roy suggested but have had no answer. Did Roy tell you I had never received any thing from it. I gave up trying to get information about it at the start of the war. I suppose if I had pushed my father a little harder after the war for information about mother we would probably have known each other much sooner.

I can't understand my father not telling me about all of you but I guess it's too late to worry about it now. . . .

Well we are sure looking forward to next summer and to meeting all of you. . . .

With Love,
Harry and family

Finally, in August of 1964, the Broughtons traveled to Provo. The Tooleys came from California, and the two sisters and one brother met the half brother they had been searching for.

Some of the relatives in the States were skeptical about this half brother. They thought he might be some sort of a scalawag. All were pleasantly relieved to find him a wonderful, gracious man, with a fine wife and children.

Dear Pearl and Family,

Well folks guess you are wondering how we are. Everything is fine and we sure have not forgotten you all and how welcome you made us and how wonderful you treated us.

We really enjoyed ourselves in Provo Pearl what with the lovely meals and side trips.

It's sure wonderful to know I have brothers and sisters and could take part in a family get together after all these years. I just hope it is not too long between these get togethers.

On the way to Roy and Marie's we spent the night at Winnemucca. Made some small investment but didn't get any returns.

Stancy didn't care too much for Donner Pass. She was all ready to get out and walk when she saw that bridge up in the clouds.

Roy and Marie took us into San Francisco on Sunday. We went to Seal Rock, the Zoo, and Fisherman's Wharf and also had a ride on the cable car. . . .

We left Roy's on the Wed. And intended to stay over one day in Sandpoint, Idaho. I was in the court house there but could not find any new information concerning my father.

The Tooley divorce papers had the same Lawyer's name (W. J. Costello) that had signed the letters I had about the insurance money. Our mother had hired the same man.

I also went to the court house in Bonner's Ferry, but there was nothing there concerning my father either.

I am going to write to the Bureau of Vital Statistics at Edmonton, to see if I can find out where and when my father was married.

Well Pearl we want to thank you and Herb and everyone for the wonderful time we had and it's a great joy to know that we have found one another or should I say you have found us.

We sure hope you will be able to come and see us. If any of the children want to come up we will sure make them welcome.

Give our love to everyone and thanks again.

With all our Love,
Harry and Family

NOW THE DAY IS OVER

Harry fit into the family from that time on. Pearl never got to Canada again, but Roy did. Harry made several trips to visit his newly found family in the States.

Harry and Roy were just the brothers each one needed. Pearl and Helen were close all their lives and died within three months of each other.

Upon Pearl's death in July 1992, the obituary in the newspaper was short and sweet. It briefly described the life of the eighty-seven-year-old woman. For those who only knew her as a friend or acquaintance it stated the simple life of a quiet, unpretentious, patient woman of service. Yes, she was that. Yet for those who really knew her, and very few did, she was a "giant" of a person, in her small five-two body. She had diligently kept a torn-apart family together and was the main drive in finding her half brother. She tried to be the kind of mother hers had been the few short years she was with her children, and Pearl's own children loved her for her efforts.

Pearl struggled with her husband's mood swings and illnesses and with her own children's problems. However, she never gave anything but positive, uplifting encouragement to help them get through their trials.

She was loved and revered by each family member in his or her own way, as each related to her with his or her own personality.

Pearl was never rich by the world's standards and never had a lot of worldly possessions, but she left the people she touched better for having known her.

Pearl was a woman anyone could emulate and be proud to have her qualities.

A woman who had been a neighbor and friend for over forty years remarked about Pearl at her funeral, to one of her daughters, "Your mother was a 'real lady.' One of the very few I have ever known."

For every deed there is a *price*. The circle of people whom Pearl touched were richer for having known her.